CONTEMPORARY

PSYCHOTHERAPIES

CONTEMPORARY

PSYCHOTHERAPIES

EDITED BY

MORRIS I. STEIN, Ph.D.

PROFESSOR OF PSYCHOLOGY,
DIRECTOR OF THE RESEARCH CENTER FOR HUMAN RELATIONS,
NEW YORK UNIVERSITY

THE FREE PRESS, *New York*
COLLIER-MACMILLAN LIMITED, *London*

Collier-Macmillan Canada, Ltd., Toronto, Ontario

Library of Congress Catalog Card Number: 61-13969

printing number
5   6   7   8   9   10

CONTRIBUTORS

NATHAN W. ACKERMAN, M.D., Associate Clinical Professor of Psychiatry, Columbia University, New York, New York; Lecturer, New York School of Social Work; Clinical Director, Family Mental Health Clinic, Jewish Family Service, New York, New York.

RUDOLF DREIKURS, M.D., Professor of Psychiatry, Chicago Medical School, Chicago, Illinois; Director of Alfred Adler Institute of Chicago, Illinois.

JEROME D. FRANK, M.D., Ph.D., Professor of Psychiatry, Johns Hopkins University Medical School, Baltimore, Maryland.

ROY R. GRINKER, M.D., Director of Institute for Psychosomatic and Psychiatric Research and Training, Michael Reese Hospital, Chicago, Illinois.

DON D. JACKSON, M.D., Director of Mental Research Institute, Palo Alto Medical Research Foundation; Head, Department of Psychiatry, Palo Alto Medical Clinic, Palo Alto, California.

AARON KARUSH, M.D., Associate Clinical Professor of Psychiatry, the Psychoanalytic Clinic for Training and Research, Department of Psychiatry, College of Physicians and Surgeons, Columbia University, New York, New York.

ARTHUR A. MILLER, M.D., Clinical Associate Professor of Psychiatry, University of Illinois College of Medicine, Chicago, Illinois; Faculty, Child Care Program, Chicago Institute for Psychoanalysis; Attending Psychiatrist, Division of Neuropsychiatry, Michael Reese Hospital, Chicago, Illinois.

ROLLO MAY, Ph.D., William Alanson White Institute of Psychiatry, Psychoanalysis and Psychology, New York, New York.

CARL R. ROGERS, Ph.D., Professor of Psychology, Departments of Psychology and Psychiatry, University of Wisconsin, Madison, Wisconsin.

MORRIS I. STEIN, Ph.D., Professor of Psychology and Director of Research Center for Human Relations, New York University, New York, New York. Formerly, Associate Professor of Psychology, Department of Psychology, and Co-ordinator of the Inter-departmental Committee on Clinical and Counseling Psychology, University of Chicago, Chicago, Illinois.

OTTO ALLEN WILL, Jr., M.D., Director of Psychotherapy, Chestnut Lodge, Rockville, Maryland; Associate Clinical Professor of Psychiatry, School of Medicine, University of Maryland, Baltimore, Maryland; Training Analyst, Washington Psychoanalytic Institute.

Preface

THIS BOOK contains a series of lectures on psychotherapy that was sponsored by the Department of Psychology at the University of Chicago during 1958 and 1959 while the editor was Co-ordinator of the Interdepartmental Committee on Clinical and Counseling Psychology there. Ten therapists were invited to present their approaches to psychotherapy and to discuss their current thinking about significant issues in the therapeutic process. The major theoretical orientations represented were: Adlerian, Client-Centered, Existential, Interactional, Interpersonal, Psychoanalytic, Reparative-Adaptational and Transactional. In addition to these orientations, which focussed on individual psychotherapy, papers were also presented on group therapy and family therapy.

The papers were presented informally. They have been prepared for publication by editing transcriptions of the papers and the discussions. An effort has been made to maintain the spontaneity of a spoken presentation and to avoid the formality of a dissertation. The papers, as presented in this book, follow the order of their presentation in the lecture series. With one exception there are two contributions from each therapist. In general the first deals with theory or some specific problem in therapy and the second involves a case discussion or a research study.

Our lecturers' orientations and the recency of some of their innovations reflect the diversity among psychotherapists as well as the fact that the field is continually growing through a process of re-evaluating existing ideas and techniques and introducing new ones. It is in the hope of facilitating this process that these lectures have been assembled in this book.

Several persons played important roles in organizing the lecture series and in reviewing portions of this manuscript. For this, I would like to express my appreciation to Drs. Howard F. Hunt, William Offenkrantz, Joseph M. Wepman, John M. Shlien, William E. Henry, C. Knight Aldrich and Miss Shirley J. Heinze. In addition I would like to express my gratitude to Russell Smith and Garland Guice for recording the lectures and to Linnea Brandewein and Paulette Lawitz for transcribing them. To June Rosenberg, Mary Insinna, Eleanor Cunningham, and Agnes Niyekawa I am indebted for help in preparing the manuscript.

M. I. S.

New York, 1960

Contents

CONTEMPORARY

PSYCHOTHERAPIES

Introduction

by Morris I. Stein, Ph.D.

THE GOAL of psychotherapy is to help the maladjusted or mentally ill person achieve a state in which he is able "to work well, to feel well, and to expect well" (Whitehorn, 1959). As one reviews the history of therapists' attempts to achieve this goal, one is impressed by the recurrence of certain themes, issues and problems. From these, I have selected the following five areas for further comment: (1) The sources of psychotherapeutic concepts; (2) the growth of schools of psychotherapy; (3) the role of the therapist; (4) the relationship between diagnosis and treatment and (5) the relationship between research and psychotherapy. I hope that a discussion of these five areas will not only provide perspective for contemporary developments that are described in the papers that follow, but that at the same time it will help raise questions of importance for the future.

Sources of Psychotherapeutic Concepts

The development of psychotherapeutic concepts and techniques may be traced to three major sources—the philosophical and religious conceptions of the nature of man, the conceptual models of the biological and physical sciences, and the discoveries made in the use of psychotherapy as a tool of investigation. I shall limit myself to the first two sources since the developments that stem from the third are quite adequately represented in many of the papers that follow.

3

Primitive man with his animistic conception of the world regarded the mentally ill as possessed by evil spirits; the Greeks, believing in the power of the supernatural, had similar beliefs. They, too, regarded the mentally ill as possessed and thought of them as having offended some supernatural power. During the Middle Ages when the world was seen as a battleground between God and the devil, the mentally ill were regarded as allied with the devil. In each of these periods, therapeutic techniques were consistent with the prevailing *zeitgeist*. Primitive man concerned himself with getting the evil spirit to leave the sick person by the use of rituals, the Greeks built their Aesculapian temples in which the mentally ill could sleep, dream of and be exposed to the curative powers of the god of healing. And, during the Middle Ages various techniques were used to make the body an uncomfortable place for the devil to live.

With the growing insistence on the integrity and dignity of man and with the birth of scientific inquiry in the 16th and 17th centuries, psychology was separated from metaphysics and two major parallel trends were begun which are still evident. One sought more humanitarian ways of dealing with the mentally ill and it was later reinforced by the equalitarian ideas of the French Revolution. It led to the major break-through achieved by Pinel in removing the chains from the mentally ill at Bicêtre and Salpêtrière. The trend toward scientific inquiry led to the search for the physical and organic bases of mental illness.

In this sketchy historical survey we can next skip to Freud in whose work we find a continuation of humanistic and scientific traditions, but with this major change. Unlike some of his scientific contemporaries who investigated somatogenic hypotheses, Freud utilized the theories of the physical and biological sciences as models for his own investigations of psychological phenomena. At Brücke's Institute Freud was exposed to Helmholtz's scientific philosophy with its emphasis on forces of attraction and repulsion, the principle of conservation of energy, etc. This influence is reflected in Freud's attempts to elucidate the dynamics of mental phenomena. Darwin similarly had his influence on Freud and the effects of evolutionary theory are manifest not only in Freud's early neuro-anatomical researches, but also in his later theory of psychosexual development.

Contemporary developments in psychotherapy are also influenced by the scientific achievements and philosophical orientations of our time. No longer, however, does the therapist in his theoretical orientation limit himself to the conceptual models of the physical and biological sciences but he has broadened his scope to incorporate the orientations, data and findings of the social sciences. This is evident in the presentations that follow, where we find that Grinker speaks of the importance of differentiating between overt and implicit roles and manifests the influence of the sociologists, especially Parsons. Rogers cites the research on learning theory and the scale he is in the process of developing for measuring progress in therapy can be shown to have antecedents in the work of Goldstein, Piaget and those working in the area of perception. The influence of George Herbert Mead via Sullivan on psychotherapy is manifest in Otto Will's approach. The most significant philosophical influence at the present time is that of Existentialism as seen in the papers by Rollo May, Carl Rogers, and Otto Will to some extent. And the transactional theory of Dewey and Bentley is at the roots of Grinker's thinking.

To point out the influence of other scientific or philosophical developments or of the effects of the *zeitgeist* on a man's thinking contributes to an understanding of new developments and innovations. It in no way diminishes from the significance or value of his contribution. Many creative achievements can be traced to individuals who had several orientations and who did not limit themselves to just one frame of reference. One purpose of this brief survey was to indicate the importance of a broad background of knowledge for developing new approaches to psychotherapy.

There was another purpose in this survey. The theoreticians among the psychotherapists are at times inclined to speak of universals about the "nature of man" as they have come to know them in the course of the therapeutic process. But a look at the therapist's frame of reference, or the physical or biological models that underlie his thinking, may reveal the need for safeguards to prevent the development of too many seductive hypotheses. As the various developments in psychotherapy are studied, one needs to be alert to the question of whether that which is suggested is more consistent with the model than with the data. And as one compares different approaches to psychotherapy, one needs to be alert to the different conceptual models from which they stem.

Growth of Schools of Psychotherapy

The prolific growth of schools of psychotherapy, especially since Freud, is one of the striking characteristics of this field. Each of these schools introduced its own innovation in theory and technique. In general, each of them was founded by a charismatic leader who attracted loyal disciples. They, with their students, worked in partisan-like fashion to demonstrate the value and validity of their orientation.

Many creative developments begin in just this fashion. Highly involved and enthusiastic workers find it necessary to develop their own frames of reference by themselves, in isolation from criticism and censure. At times, they may even find it valuable to set up straw men in the opposition toward which they can rally their forces. But at some point, their findings or orientations, if they are valid, are incorporated in the main stream of thinking and the general body of knowledge is increased so that the whole field prospers from the added growth.

This last stage has not yet occurred in the field of psychotherapy. There is no single body of psychotherapeutic knowledge but several different orientations, approaches and techniques. We speak of Freudians, Jungians, Adlerians, Sullivanians, Rogerians, etc., and each group has little, if any, communication with the others. At times, one gets the impression that there is much duplication of effort and wasted energy in these groups as they go about rediscovering each other's principles and as they go about coining new terms for theories and techniques that are practically synonymous with or special cases of already existing ones. Each group has had its geniuses and keen observers who were especially sensitive to certain phenomena and especially adept at developing valuable and significant techniques. But these tend to remain within the confines of the group and have relatively little influence on others.

No doubt there are many reasons for the state of affairs just described, not the least of which are the therapists' ego-involvement in their ideas and the problem of setting up objective criteria for testing the value of innovations and new theories. Since there is likely much to be gained from integrating the "best" of the different schools of psychotherapy, I should like to call attention to one source of difference that I feel has been a stumbling block in this area and then turn to a brief statement of what appear to be similarities between schools of psychotherapy.

One source of difference between schools of psychotherapy that is often overlooked and which needs to be made explicit is the difference in types of patients on which the founders of the different schools based their initial observations. Maskin (1960) summarizes this point rather well when he says, "Freud used hysteria as the model for his therapeutic method, depression as the basis for his later theoretical conjectures. Adler's clinical demonstrations are rivalrous, immature character types. Jung's examples were constructed to a weary, worldly, successful, middle-aged group. Rank focussed upon the conflicted, frustrated, rebellious artist aspirant. Fromm's model is the man in a white collar searching for his individuality. And Sullivan's example of choice is the young catatonic schizophrenic." To this, one might add that Rogers' original formulations were based on college students.

With these differences in basic data, and sources of observation, it is not surprising that each school should develop its own special theory and technique. One school might well have a good deal more to say than another about one specific type of patient than another. One school might have more to say about one technique than another; and some methods need to be found to assess this information, so that that which is valid can be added to a growing body of knowledge that can be shared by all. It is when schools of psychotherapy overlook the differences in their sources of data and extrapolate from their basic information to other areas which they have not investigated, that conflict develops and hampers integrated development.

There are differences in schools of psychotherapy other than the one I have mentioned. But rather than discuss these, I should like to suggest a tentative formulation of a general statement of psychotherapy which may cover the assumptions and orientations of most, if not all, schools of psychotherapy.

Psychotherapy is a process in which changes in an individual's behavior are achieved as a result of experiences in a relationship with a person trained in understanding behavior. The patient comes to therapy because of a variety of life experiences that have made him uncomfortable, unhappy, or have placed him under stress. His desires to be without psychological pain and to achieve a state of greater psychological well-being motivate him to seek help and serve as significant forces in effecting changes throughout the therapeutic process. The patient has sufficient capacity, latent or manifest, to effect changes in himself if he is provided with a non-evaluative atmosphere in which he can experience his thoughts, feelings, and attitudes in relation to and/or with another person without realistic fear of censure. The patient's experience in the therapeutic relationship is assumed to be a sample in microcosm of the significant factors that brought on or relate to his problems. Observing the patient's behavior (both verbal and non-verbal), and using his empathic understanding of the patient's behavior in relation to himself, the therapist comments on what he observes. The patient, witnessing the same behavior, and viewing it in the light of the therapist's comments as well as in the light of his own reactions is now in a position to re-evaluate his own past behavior and to prepare for or begin to change. While all the factors involved in change are not clear, it is assumed to involve the general principles of learning. No school of psychotherapy guarantees that the patient will be cured or that changes in behavior will occur. Therapists express a willingness to help patients but their efforts are of no avail unless the patient is willing to work in a cooperative relationship. The goal of therapy, as we said at the beginning of this Introduction is "to work well, to feel well, and to expect well" (Whitehorn, 1959).

These are some of the similarities between schools of psychotherapy and no doubt there are others. With this as a base, one cannot help but think that there would be much to be gained if all groups of therapists could control their partisan attitudes long enough to meet and evaluate each other's contributions with an eye to developing an integrated picture of psychotherapy. Continuing with this fantasy, such a meeting might arrive at a more complete general statement of a theory of psychotherapy and from this statement, each existing school might well represent a special case with specific significance for certain types of patients.

Such a group might also develop plans for studying the relative effectiveness of different types of therapy with different types of patients. For example, studies might be developed in which psychoanalysis, transactional therapy, non-directive therapy and reparative adaptational therapy, interpersonal therapy, etc. would all be tried on "equated" groups of hysterics, obsessives, schizophrenics, etc. In this fashion, psychotherapy might become a problem-oriented field rather than a technique- or theory-oriented field with partisan points of view represented by diverse and separated schools of thought.

Role of the Therapist

There are several problems in the therapist-patient relationship to which our contributors address themselves. I should like to elaborate on one of these problems—conflict between the patient's quest for, and ascription of, omnipotence to the therapist and the therapist's perception of himself as a "helper" in a therapeutic relationship.

Several of our contributors point out that one of the major problems in therapy is the patient's expectation that the therapist will be omnipotent. Patients expect therapists to solve their problems, to provide them with solutions to their difficulties and to provide them with new patterns of behavior that will always result in happiness and psychological health.

Two major factors are involved in this orientation. One is psychological, the other, sociological. The contributors who addressed themselves to this problem considered psychological factors primarily—the patient's wish that the therapist would use some (magical) process, method, or technique which would rapidly and painlessly insure his happiness. This problem, when it occurs in therapy and when it impedes progress, is dealt with by some therapists by concentrating on the effects of childhood wishes and fantasies while others concentrate on the explicit or implicit perceptions of the therapist. The psychological aspect of the omnipotence problem is obviously quite critical. But, it should not result in overlooking other factors that contribute to it. Frank, in his paper on influence, discusses some of these factors and they merit further elaboration here.

Sociologically considered, the therapist is a professional who, like any other professional, earns his livelihood by giving what Hughes has called "esoteric service" to a client "who is not in a position to judge for himself the quality of the service he receives. He comes to the professional because he has met a problem which he cannot himself handle. . . . He has some idea of the result he wants; little of the means or even of the possibility of attaining it" (Hughes, 1952). Thus, one might say that by definition, the professional is in a role that is colored by an omnipotent cast.

Other factors also contribute to the perception of omnipotence. Therapists are almost always called "Doctor." Medical doctors do give treatments and medicines that cure without requiring the patient's active participation. Patients generalize the same orientation to psychotherapists. Historical factors are also significant. The precursors of the contemporary psychotherapist are the shaman and priest. They were regarded as possessing either specific powers, or knowledge, to cure the mentally ill. Furthermore, historically, therapists, and not patients, created the field of psychotherapy. "The patient suffering from appendicitis created the abdominal surgeon, the feverish and delirious man who had a sharp pain in his chest created the specialist in pneumonias, but it was the doctor who created the speciality of psychiatry. He did it uninvited and against terrible odds, against the will of the public, against the will of established legal authority, and against the will of established religious faiths" (Zilboorg, 1941). Since therapists took such an active role in establishing the field of psychotherapy and continue to support it, oft-times in the face of the same opposition that their predecessors met, is it not to be expected that patients would perceive them as omnipotent or at least as taking responsibility for what they had to offer.

Finally, patients are attracted to psychotherapists by virtue of their training and successful experiences in dealing with other patients. On such occasion, the patients often concentrate on the therapeutic product (their friends' recovery or happiness) and not on the process through which he achieved his goals.

Therapists themselves do at times also contribute to the omnipotence problem. They regard themselves as being of value to their patients—leaving the term "of value" open to whatever distortion the patient wishes to impose upon it. By assuming advisory functions in various social agencies where they are quite direct in their advice, they indirectly fan the patient's hopes that they will behave similarly in the consulting room. Still other therapists in their talks before lay groups indicate that they are specialists in human relations problems and imply that they have the answers to these problems. The picture they give to the public is reinforced by publications in the lay literature of successful cases and this encourages the patient to expect a similar experience. All of these factors as well as others are important in the therapist's "attraction value" and such factors not only help bring the patient to therapy, but they are sometimes used in certain types of therapy where it is necessary to induce regression as an important part of the therapeutic technique, if only for a limited period.

When the course of therapy is begun, and when it is in process, the therapist is not omnipotent. He knows that he cannot solve the patient's problems and that the patient has to do it for himself. He also knows that he has had his successes as well as his failures. He can only offer a "helping relationship"—a relationship that implies more mutuality and cooperation than one involved in a relationship of omnipotence-submission. The therapist believes that the patient can reasonably expect help to achieve a state of psychological health, but he cannot reasonably expect cure. He expects the patient to participate in the therapeutic process and not to wait passively for things to happen to him.

Some therapists are beginning to question aspects of their own behavior within the therapeutic process which may have contributed to the omnipotence problem and which may have interfered with the development of a more human-helping relationship. Thus, among the psychoanalysts questions are raised about the "blank screen" conception of the therapist's role. Originally utilized to encourage objectivity on the part of the therapist and the development of transference relationships, psychoanalysts are now becoming increasingly interested in how to deal with countertransference problems and increasingly aware of the effects of the therapist's own personality on the course of the psychoanalytic process (Alexander, 1960). Thus, the artificiality of the blank screen conception is undergoing modification. Other therapists deal with the omnipotence problem, in part, by their willingness to discuss their own feelings and attitudes toward the patient when they feel the occasion demands it. Such behavior no doubt contributes to the patient's perception of the therapist as a human being with whom he can only reasonably expect a human-helping relationship and not an omnipotent one.

I should like to reiterate at this point that I am not concerning myself here with the psychological problems involved in the quest for an omnipotent relationship and the avoidance of a human relationship as they come up in the course of the therapeutic process, but rather with non-psychological issues. I have focussed on the patient's expectations prior to therapy and his perception in the early phases of therapy which may result in early unsuccessful termination. The early terminators and the individuals who need help and who do not seek it after an interview where their expectations have not been met may be prone to unreasonable expectations that for many of them have their source in what may be described as reasonable ignorance of a therapeutic relationship. Indeed there are persons whose psychological makeup is such that they may utilize the factors I have discussed as rationalizations for not dealing with their own problems, but we are not concerned with them here.

Assuming the analysis of the non-psychological factors is correct, there is one suggestion that might be of value. Would it not be helpful to those patients who are prone to the difficulties described above if they could be better "prepared" for therapy before it has begun? This is not the place to discuss the characteristics of such preparation at length, but I do wish to indicate that it might involve discussing with the patient the meaning of a helping relationship and some of his feelings about such a relationship. The attrition rate of patients in therapy might thus be diminished. Therapists might be better able to utilize their time and talents in helping those patients who need their help and who are indeed prepared to receive it.

Diagnosis and Therapy

Let us now turn to another area—the relationship between diagnosis and treatment. Here I should like to summarize our contributors' approach and then discuss diagnostic techniques as aides to the therapeutic process.

Our contributors do not make a sharp differentiation between diagnosis and treatment. For them, diagnosis in the sense of understanding the patient's dynamics is a continuing process that is open to change and clarification as new data are brought to light during the unfolding of the therapeutic process. The therapist's diagnostic function is so intimately intertwined with the treatment that it is often impossible to disentangle the two. For heuristic purposes, we might differentiate between diagnosis and treatment as follows: The therapist performs a diagnostic function in selecting from what the patient has said that which he regards as most significant and critical at the time. He also behaves diagnostically in selecting from what might be said that which he does say, and when he decides to say it. What the therapist says when he says it, and the manner in which he says it may be regarded as designed to achieve therapeutic effects, but they also carry with them certain implications concerning conclusions the therapist has drawn about the patient and his problems.

Since diagnosis is a critical aspect of therapy, I would like to discuss the ways in which psychological techniques may be used as diagnostic aids. These techniques have been questioned. It is feared that testing involves an evaluative attitude; it is believed that psychological reports, especially when they are concluded with some nosological classifications, "disindividualize" the patient and make him into nothing but a statistic, and, it is feared that bringing the psychologist into the picture may complicate the therapist-patient relationship on the assumption that the patient may feel that there is now a third person who presumably has gleaned all the answers to the patient's problems from the psychological tests. The significance of these criticisms is open to discussion, but that would take us far afield. Suffice it to say for the moment, the validity and reliability of the diagnostic techniques can well be improved in future research. "Diagnosis by technique" need be no more evaluative than "diagnosis by person" as it occurs in therapy. Psychological reports need not conclude with nosological classifications; and when they "disindividualize" the patient, they are simply bad reports. Finally, the problem of the psychologist as a third person with a great deal of knowledge can be dealt with in the same fashion that the omnipotence problem, discussed in the previous section, is dealt with, or in the same manner that any outside person is dealt with. These issues can be solved if there is a desire and need for the diagnostic information and if the therapist and psychologist, as diagnostician, can work effectively together in a cooperative relationship.

Diagnostic techniques have to perform a significant function for the therapist. In what areas can this function be fulfilled best? For our present purposes, I should like to discuss three: screening, training, and as an aid to the therapist's own diagnostic function. I will omit from the discussion their value in research and as aids in studying the outcome of therapy.

Diagnostic techniques as screening aids: Therapists are confronted with the problem of selecting patients whom they can help most. To do so, they use a variety of criteria including estimates of the severity of the patient's problem, his capacity, latent and manifest, to deal with his problems and to engage in a therapeutic helping, and not omnipotent, relationship as we discussed it above. Oft-times the therapist does not spell out these criteria and there is little attention paid to whether the psychologist is focussing on the same criteria. Even if the diagnostician uses the same terms as does the therapist (e.g. "ego-strength") there is some question whether he is using them in the same way and if the diagnostic technique that is used can get at the precise meaning that the therapist desires. For maximal usefulness as a screening function, it is therefore apparent that thorough communication between therapist and diagnostician is not only desirable, but absolutely necessary. By the same token, the diagnostician, by keeping pace with research studies of the relationship between diagnostic techniques and patient attrition and continuation and outcome of therapy can call the attention of the therapist to some critical variables that he may have overlooked in the patients he has selected. Whether the criteria are developed by the therapist or whether they are contributed by the diagnostician, there is obviously no need that the diagnosis be limited to the objective and projective techniques which are presently available. New techniques which focus specifically on the screening criteria may need to be developed.

Diagnostic techniques as aids in training therapists: It has been suggested that some therapists are more effective with certain types of patients than others. For example, Alexander (1960) says, "There are sufficient indications, mostly derived from supervisory work with candidates, that the individuality of a therapist may be therapeutically more favorable with one type of a patient than with another." If this is so, then diagnostic techniques oriented to matching therapists and patients may be of significant value in the early training of the therapist while he is developing his own criteria for selecting the patients with whom he can work best. The second type of diagnostic aid that may be of value in training therapists is one which may be applied to therapeutic process and which may serve as what might be described as a pacer technique. An example of the technique I have in mind is the one discussed by Rogers in this book (pp. 113-127). This method, based on the interaction between therapist and patient, may well alert the therapist in training to the extent to which he is pacing his patient and the relationship between his own activity and the patient's progress, or lack of it.

Diagnostic techniques as aids to the therapist's own diagnostic function: Diagnostic reports as they are generally written at the present time concentrate on the patient's personality structure or specific content data that are troublesome to the patient. Both of these are designed essentially to alert the therapist to areas that may be of concern to him and his patient. This is an additional area where diagnostic tests may be valuable to the therapist.

Therapists are almost all in agreement that the therapeutic process is one in which the patient learns how previous learning experiences have affected his capacity to deal with present problems. Knowledge of the patient's learning processes and his problem-solving methods, especially as he has evolved them to deal with emotional problems, would seem to be a valuable auxiliary aid to the therapist. Such process data are not always available with current diagnostic procedures and new methods would no doubt have to be developed.

The development and use of diagnostic techniques as I have discussed them above is dependent on the cooperation between therapist and diagnostician. The diagnostic function in therapy is an important one. Efforts designed to facilitate progress in this area can be most valuable but they may come to naught if existing skeptical and negative attitudes based on previous experiences are permitted to impede new developments.

Research and Psychotherapy

Traditionally, the case study has been the therapist's choice as a research tool. Using this approach, therapists described new discoveries and relationships, or they discussed the manner in which their observations corroborated or validated previously held views. The case study approach is still the choice of many therapists since they, with some significant exceptions, are untrained in research methodology. However, since about the end of World War II, with the entrance of psychologists into this area and largely due to the pioneering efforts of Carl Rogers, research in psychotherapy began to move from a predominantly case study approach to systematic investigations using sizable groups of patients, established research designs and appropriate statistical procedures. Audio and visual recordings of therapy sessions are increasing in number so that now investigators have available basic data for continuous use.

Researchers have concentrated their efforts in three major areas. One focusses on the patient and studies changes in him before, during and after therapy, concerning the relationship between his psychological characteristics and his success and failure in therapy. The second major area focusses on the therapist, and here researchers have concentrated on the effects of his frame of reference, attitudes and values on the patient, or on the course of the therapeutic process. The third major area of research is the therapeutic process itself which has involved analyses of the recordings of therapy sessions as well as the investigation of hypotheses under controlled laboratory conditions.

Among the issues in the research area which still require attention and resolution are how to coordinate the functions of therapist and researcher. Should the therapist also be researcher and test his hypotheses with his own patients? If he does, then he might feel most comfortable in the thought that he has subjected his thinking to the best possible test. Other therapists might not be as sensitive as he in making the necessary observations. However, if he becomes too involved in the testing of his own hypotheses, he may either overlook the patient's needs or he may, because of the impossibility of developing built-in controls, effect the course of the therapeutic process so as to validate his own hypotheses. If research and therapy functions are separated, there are other types of problems. Many researchers trained in both experimental technique and statistics are not trained in therapy, and some of them who are interested in learning about therapy find it difficult to obtain the necessary training. Furthermore, researchers untrained in therapy have difficulty in communicating with therapists. They find the latter's hypotheses too general and ill-defined. Therapists, on the other hand, complain that researchers do not understand the basic and significant issues but do research on problems to which answers are either unnecessary or already known by experienced therapists. As in all novel situations, so here, problems are bound to arise but it is no doubt likely that as both therapists and researchers gain more experience in working together, some of these problems will be resolved.

Another set of issues in research on psychotherapy includes the determination of appropriate sets of variables for studying the transactions between therapist and patient and the problem of finding a systematic set of variables including overt and covert factors for studying the patient's personality, especially if research is to be focussed on changes in the individual. These problems are not relevant solely to research in therapy, but are critical issues in social psychology and personality theory as well. As advances are made in these other two areas, research in psychotherapy will no doubt benefit.

A third set of unresolved problems on the effectiveness of therapy includes such questions as: what criteria should be used to differentiate successful from unsuccessful cases? What effects can be attributed to therapy and what effects can be attributed to environmental factors or result from spontaneous remission? How permanent are the changes that occur in therapy? To solve these problems requires the definition of mental health criteria, the development of techniques to investigate these criteria, the matching of cases in therapy and those who recover by spontaneous remission in terms of significant psychological variables rather than such factors as social class and nosological classification, and a study of the congruence between problems dealt with in therapy and those encountered in other life situations.

These then are some of the problems that confront both therapist and researcher as they embark on research in this area. Hopefully, the future will bring us closer to resolving some of them.

In reviewing the five major areas covered in this discussion, it is apparent that the field of psychotherapy is an open system which, like any living system, changes and grows over time. The papers that follow present significant aspects of its status at the present time. They are presented in the hope that they will facilitate the work of therapists in their efforts to help their patients and that they will stimulate both therapists and researchers to new advances.

The Role of Influence
in Psychotherapy*

by Jerome D. Frank, M.D., Ph.D.

IN THIS PAPER, I shall not offer a comprehensive theory of psychotherapy or attempt to discuss all aspects of psychotherapy. I wish to concentrate on one aspect of psychotherapy, which we all know about, but which is often neglected—perhaps regularly neglected—for reasons which will become apparent, and that is the role of the influence of the therapist on the patient. This subject is more fully developed in my book, *Persuasion and Healing* (Frank, 1961).

All forms of psychotherapy attempt to promote beneficial changes in a patient's attitudes and symptoms through the influence of the therapist with whom he has a close relationship. In general terms, all psychotherapies are concerned with using this influence to help patients to unlearn old, maladaptive response patterns, and learn better ones. But they differ considerably in their specific goals and methods. Examples of goals are: helping the patient to recover early memories, to develop insight, to work through transference relationships, to release spontaneity, or to modify his self-concept. Methods include, for example, free association, client-centered interviews, and progressive relaxation.

These differences in therapeutic approach are reflected in differ-

*We wish to express our appreciation to the journal *Psychiatry* for allowing us to republish portions of this paper which appeared previously in *Psychiatry*, 1959, 22, 17-39.

ences in the patient's behavior and in the kinds of change resulting from treatment. In addition to these different effects of the psychotherapist's influence, which depend on his particular orientation and method, all forms of psychotherapy seem to produce certain similar effects based on the common quality of the relationship they offer. This common feature is the patient's reliance on the therapist to relieve his distress. This reliance, which may be forced or voluntary, arises from the interplay of environmental pressures and the patient's subjective state—the relative contribution of each differing from case to case. An example of forced reliance, produced primarily by environmental pressure, would be the situation of a paranoid patient, placed in a hospital against his will, believing his incarceration to be unjust but forced to depend on the staff to gain his release. An example of forced reliance arising from subjective pressure would be the patient in a panic who flees to the psychiatrist for protection.

More commonly, especially in office practice, the patient's dependence on the psychiatrist is voluntary and arises from the interplay of more subtle environmental and subjective factors. These lead the patient to expect relief from the psychiatrist, an expectancy which sometimes may be strong enough to justify the term, faith.

The purpose of this paper is to review data from various sources bearing on the determination and effects of the patient's emotional dependency on his psychotherapist for relief, regardless of the particular type of therapy. These effects may include modifications of the patient's productions in the interviews, the duration of treatment itself, and changes in the patient's attitudes and bodily states. Certain mechanisms which may transmit the therapist's expectancies to the patient will be considered. Some implications of these data for research and practice will be reviewed.

The major sources of the material about to be reviewed are reports on brain-washing, so-called miracle cures, experimental studies of the psychotherapeutic interview, and the placebo effect. I will try to pull all these various topics into one coherent whole as we go along. Before getting into them, however, let me start with a consideration of the patient's reliance on his psychotherapist. This may be discussed under four headings: the culture, the treatment situation, the therapist, and the patient himself.

With respect to the culture, the beliefs of what constitutes illness and its treatment are formed and supported by generally held cultural attitudes. A member of a particular society can regard himself as having an emotional illness, for which the proper treatment is psychotherapy, only if his society recognizes the existence of such illnesses and sanctions psychotherapy as the appropriate treatment for them.

The same symptoms, which, in the Middle Ages, were viewed as signs of demoniacal possession to be treated by exorcism, are now regarded as manifestations of mental illness to be treated by a psychiatrist.

In World War II, Russian soldiers did not have psychoneuroses, which can only mean that the Russian army did not recognize the existence of this condition. Presumably soldiers with functional complaints were regarded either as malingerers, subject to disciplinary action, or medically ill, and, therefore, to be treated by regular physicians. In the American army, by contrast, many commonplace reactions to the stresses of military life were initially regarded as signs of psychoneuroses. Soldiers with these complaints, therefore, often received psychotherapy, not infrequently culminating in their discharge from the service. Today, many of these same soldiers would be promptly returned to active duty.

In mid-century America, mental illness has not fully shaken off its demonological heritage, as evidenced by the stigma still attached to it. Both psychotics and neurotics, however, are seen as suffering from *bona fide* illnesses, and the dominant treatment for most of the conditions subsumed under mental emotional illness is psychotherapy. Moreover, the psychiatrist is generally regarded as the best qualified dispenser of this treatment, although other professional groups are challenging his right to pre-eminence. Therefore, an American today, once he has accepted the label of being mentally or emotionally ill, is culturally predisposed to expect relief from psychotherapy and to look to a psychiatrist for this relief.

Now turning to the therapeutic situation itself, certain situations in which psychotherapy is practiced, notably mental hospitals, force the patient, to a varying degree, to become dependent upon the treatment staff. Even when there is no external compulsion, however, many aspects of the psychotherapeutic situation, in both hospital and office, supply cues which tend to impress the patient with the importance of the procedure and also tend to identify psychotherapy with other healing methods. In both ways, they strengthen the patient's expectations of relief and, thus, his dependency upon the therapist.

These cues start to operate even before the therapist and the patient meet. Most patients reach the presence of the psychotherapist only after some preliminaries. If the patient is hospitalized, the commitment procedure heightens his sense of dependence upon the hospital staff for release. Voluntary admission procedures usually require the patient to sign a witnessed request for admission which contains a three day notice clause. This impresses him with the importance of the step he is taking and underlines the staff's control over him while he is in the hospital.

✔ If properly conducted, the admission procedure can heighten the patient's hope of benefit from his stay and his trust in the treatment staff. Psychiatrists working with out-patients are rightly concerned that the referral heighten the patient's expectations rather than, as frequently occurs, making him feel that he is being brushed off. One of the purposes of the intake procedure of psychiatric out-patients' clinics is to predispose the patient favorably to psychotherapy. At the Phipp's Clinic, for example, each new patient is first briefly interviewed by a trained nurse rather than a secretary as a deliberate reminder that he is under medical auspices. More commonly, patients who come to a psychiatric clinic first have one or more intake interviews with a social worker. Ginsberg and Arrington (1948) found that early contact with a social worker made more difference than anything else with respect to whether the patient stayed in treatment.

The avowed purpose of these interviews with the social worker is to determine the patient's suitability for psychotherapy and to prepare him for it. Implicitly, however, the patient may perceive the intake process as a probationary period to determine his worthiness to receive the psychiatrist's ministrations. By thus impressing him with the importance of psychotherapy, it heightens his susceptibility to the psychiatrist's influence. In this sense, the intake procedure is analogous to the preparatory rites undergone by suppliants at faith healing shrines, with the social worker in the role of acolyte, and the psychiatrist as high priest.

Once in the presence of his therapist, the patient's favorable expectancies are reinforced by the setting. Psychotherapy has developed its own trappings which symbolize healing almost as much as the physician's prominently placed diplomas and license, his stethoscope, opthalmoscope, and reflex hammer. Psychotherapists also display diplomas prominently, but they must rely on other symbols of their healing art, such as heavily laden bookcases, a couch, the easy chair, and usually a large photograph of the leader of the cult who looks benignly down on the proceedings.

Psychiatrists who practice in medical institutions don't need these props. Their effects are achieved simply by being in the medical institution, which carries the implication of healing. I'm sure all of us who work in institutions have had patients who say, "You know, I just walked by the clinic, and I feel better." Simply the knowledge that that place is there and that the clinic workers know about them and are interested in them is enough to make them feel better (Reider, 1953).

The therapist's activities in the initial interview may also have the function in part of heightening the patient's favorable expectan-

cies. Psychiatrists usually take a history loosely following the model
of a medical history, thereby reinforcing their identification with the
medical profession in the patient's mind. Psychologists frequently
begin by giving the patient a battery of psychological tests, their
badge of special competence. Both are apt to conclude the interview
by offering the patient some sort of formulation which impresses him
with their ability to understand and help him. As treatment progresses,
the therapist instructs the patient in certain activities which are based
on a particular theory. Whatever their specific nature, all implicitly
convey that the therapist knows what is wrong with the patient and
that the special procedure is the treatment for it. In addition, the
underlying theory supplies a frame of reference which helps the
patient to make sense of behavior and feelings which have been mysterious, and to learn that they are not unique but represent important
and widely shared experiences.

Thus, from the moment the prospective patient approaches psychotherapy until his treatment contact terminates, he is confronted with
cues and procedures which tend to impress him with both the importance of the procedure and its promise of relief.

Turning to the personal qualities of the therapist, in addition to as
yet ill-defined personal characteristics, two attitudes of the therapist
foster the patient's confidence in him. One is his faith in the patient's
capacity to benefit from treatment, which is implied in the mere act
of accepting him as a patient. This may be influenced by his own
feelings. In his first, and what to me is still his best, publication on
psychotherapy, the one in Breuer's and Freud's *Studies in Hysteria*
(1936), Freud wrote, "The process ... presupposes (in the physician)
a personal sympathy for the patient. I could not imagine myself entering deeply into the psychic mechanism of an hysteria in a person who
would impress me as common and disagreeable, and who would not,
on closer acquaintanceship, be able to awaken in me human sympathy; ...." Similar considerations make some psychotherapists unwilling to accept alcoholics, or patients with anti-social character disorders,
for treatment, and accord with the findings of Schaffer and Myers
(1954) that middle-class patients more often than lower-class ones are
assigned to senior staff members, who presumably have first choice.
They relate this to the fact that middle-class patients appear to offer
better prospects of therapy because their values are closer to those of
the psychiatrist. The therapist's faith in the capacities of his patient is
a strong incentive to maintain that attitude of "active personal participation," which helps the patient to develop confidence in him (Whitehorn and Betz, 1954).

The other therapeutically potent attitude of the therapist is his confidence in his theory and method of treatment. How these enhance the therapeutic meaning of the treatment situation in the patient's eyes has been touched on above. Adherence to a definite therapeutic procedure and theory also helps to maintain the therapist's self-confidence. The clearest example of this I remember is a young doctor in analytical training with a classical analyst, who remarked quite seriously, "The good thing about this training is, even if the patient doesn't get better, you know you are doing the right thing." In fields where there is a common body of validated knowledge and the effectiveness of treatment has been demonstrated—for example, abdominal surgery or the treatment of infectious disease—the physician's confidence rests on his mastery of the pertinent knowledge and diagnostic and therapeutic techniques. In psychotherapy, which lacks such a body of information, therapists tend to rely for their emotional security on allegiance to a group which represents a particular view.

Allegiance is fostered by a long period of indoctrination, as many writers have pointed out. The effectiveness of indoctrination in psychotherapy is suggested by replies of a group of psychotherapists, mainly Freudian, Adlerian, or Jungian in orientation, to the questionnaire distributed by Werner Wolff (1954). Seventy per cent stated they believe their particular form of psychotherapy to be the best, a high figure considering the absence of any objective data that one form of therapy is superior to another. Only twenty-five per cent professed themselves satisfied with their theoretical orientation. It is interesting that these consisted mostly of disciples of Adler and Jung. Wolff comments, "The degree of the identification of every member with the leader of the group is greater in minority groups, which defend their new system against the system of the majority group."

What is even more interesting is that seventy per cent believe their treatment to be the best, yet only twenty-five per cent were fully satisfied with their theory. This means, if you subtract these figures, that forty-five per cent, about half of those who responded, believed their therapy to be best, not only in the absence of objective evidence but also without being sure of the soundness of the theory on which it is based. This is striking testimonial to the faith of these therapists in their procedures.

It seems safe to conclude that training in psychotherapy tends to develop a strong allegiance in the young therapist to his therapeutic school. This contributes to his confidence in his brand of treatment, which in turn helps him to inspire confidence in his patients.

Now, finally, we turn to the patient as the fourth variable involved. The extent to which the patient accepts the cues offered by the culture, the treatment situation, and his therapist, as representing potential relief, depends, of course, also on his own attitudes. Many complex and as yet poorly understood factors influence the patient's ability to develop trust in his therapist. In a recent study of patients in a psychiatric clinic, which we did, more of those who remained in individual treatment at least six months than of those who dropped out in the first month were suggestible, as measured by a sway test. That is, suggestibilty seems to be positively related to staying in treatment.

This study also confirmed the results of Schaffer and Myers (1954) with respect to social and educational status and remaining in treatment. Patients whose values were such that the goals and methods of psychotherapy made sense to them, that is, the middle class, better educated ones, were more apt to stay in treatment.

Perhaps the major personal determinant of the patient's faith in treatment is the degree of his distress. The literature is consistent in the finding that with neurotics the degree of reported distress is positively related to remaining in treatment. There are at least two possible and compatible explanations of this. One, which is consistent with the little that is known about miracle cures, is that presumably the more wretched a person is, the greater is his hunger for relief and his predisposition to put faith in what is offered. The other possibility is that the patient's revelation of distress is in itself a sign that he is favorably disposed to trust the therapist and therapy. It indicates a willingness to emphasize aspects of himself which show his vulnerability or weakness and, therefore, is a sign that he wants this kind of treatment and is prepared to trust it.

Up to this point, I've tried to review the major factors which predispose a psychiatric patient to rely on his psychotherapist for help, thereby enhancing the latter's influence on him. These factors include the cultural definition of mental and emotional disturbances as illnesses, for which psychotherapy is viewed as the treatment of choice, cues offered to the patients en route to the treatment situation and in the treatment itself, which enhance its meaning as a potential source of help, the therapist's faith in his procedures and in the patient's ability to benefit from them, and certain socially and personally determined attributes of the patient himself.

I would now like to turn from determinants of the influence of the therapist to some ways in which this influence is transmitted to the patient. That the psychotherapist influences his patient is generally accepted. Early psychotherapeutic techniques such as mesmerism, direct suggestion under hypnosis, and the moral persuasion of DuBois deliberately exploited the therapist's power. More direct forms of psychotherapy still dominate the treatment scene in their modern forms of hypnotherapy, progressive relaxation, directive counseling, and simple advice-giving. Of Wolff's respondents, many of whom, you remember, were trained in the broad psychoanalytic tradition, only twenty-seven per cent said they used a strictly non-directive approach. Nevertheless, beginning with Freud's substitution of so-called free association for hypnosis, the dominant trend in writings on psycho-therapy has emphasized the desirability of the therapist using more indirect methods of influence. The goals of treatment are expressed in more ambitious terms than the relief of the patient's distress and improvement of his functioning. He must be helped toward greater self-actualization, spontaneity, maturity, creativity, and the like. The therapist facilitates the patient's movement by empathizing with him, accepting him, collaborating with him, respecting him, and being permissive. The patient's natural tendency to become dependent upon the therapist is to be combatted. The therapist is not to persuade or advise, since such activities impede the patient's growth towards emotional maturity.

The trend toward minimization of the therapist's direct influence may spring in part from our democratic values, which place a higher worth on apparently self-directed spontaneous behavior than on that obviously caused by outside influence. The swing from directive techniques also derives in part from the experience that many cures achieved through these means prove to be transitory, though whether a larger percentage of enduring results is achieved by more permissive techniques is still unknown.

I should like now to present data form two sources which indicate some of the ways in which a therapist may transmit his expectancies to the patient, and so influence the latter's production in treatment, sometimes without the awareness of either. One source is a report on Chinese thought reform, or "brain washing," the other is content analyses of patients' and therapists' verbalizations in treatment.

At first glance, nothing could seem more remote from psycho-therapy than methods used by Chinese Communists to obtain con-fessions from their prisoners. The objects of psychotherapy are patients; those of thought reform, prisoners. Patients and therapists operate within the same broad cultural framework; the cultural values of interrogators and prisoners clash. The goals of psychotherapist and patient are roughly similar; those of interrogator and prisoner are diametrically opposed. In psychotherapy the welfare of the patient is uppermost; in thought reform that of the prisoner is of no account. Thought reform relies on the application of extreme force; psycho-therapy typically eschews overt pressure on the patient.

Though the differences between psychotherapy and thought reform far overshadow their similarities, several psychiatrists have been impressed by certain parallels between them. These spring from the fact that in both thought reform and psychotherapy someone in distress must rely on someone else for relief, and that the patient or prisoner is required to review and to reinterpret his past life in detail.

Studies of pathological processes increase understanding of normal ones by throwing certain of their characteristics into relief. In the same way, a study of thought reform, which may be regarded as a pathological form of psychotherapy, highlights some aspects of the latter which have received inadequate attention.

There have recently appeared two articles in which startling parallels appear, which I recommend to any of you who are interested in this. They are in the report, put out by the Macy Foundation, of the Third Conference on Group Processes (1957). One, by Robert Lifton, is on Chinese thought reform; the other, by Erving Goffman, is on the social structure of the mental hospital.

The influence of thought reform is exerted through various group and individual pressures, but I shall concentrate only on the interrogation. The prisoner spends many hours with the interrogator, whose task it is to obtain the prisoner's full confession of his "crimes." Certain features of the interrogation situation are relevant to this discussion. It is characterized by rigidity in some respects, ambiguity in others, and insistence on participation and repetition.

The rigidity, first of all, lies in the interrogator's attitude of infallibility. His position is that the Communist viewpoint on every issue is the only correct one. The prisoner's guilt is axiomatic, and all of his productions are judged in the light of this assumption. The interrogator indicates that he knows what the crimes are, but that the prisoner must make his own confession. He is encouraged to talk or write freely about himself and about his alleged crime, but he is not told what to write. He may be punished severely, however, if his production does not accord with the desires of his interrogator. It's a kind of permissiveness with a threat always in the background: "I'm not going to tell you what to do, but if you do the wrong thing, look out." Those statements which do meet the interrogator's wishes gain approval which reinforces them the more effectively because of the prisoner's previous apprehensiveness. No matter what he confesses, it is never enough, but the hope continues to be held out to him that once he makes a proper and complete confession, he will be released. The prisoner is, thus, placed in perceptually ambiguous situations which compel him to scrutinize the interrogator for clues as to what is really wanted, while at the same time offering to him no target against which to focus his resistance.

The participation of the prisoner in bringing about his change of attitude is implicit in this procedure. By putting the responsibility for writing an adequate confession on him, his captors force him to commit himself to this process. Schein describes the same procedure in Korean prison camps. "It was never enough for the prisoner to listen and absorb. Some kind of verbal or written response was always demanded. The Chinese apparently believe that if they could once get a man to participate, eventually he would accept the attitudes which that participation expressed" (Schein, 1956).

Finally, repetition is an important component of thought reform. One of the chief characteristics of the Chinese, and I quote Schein (1956) again, "was their immense patience in whatever they were doing. They were always willing to make their demand or assertion over and over again. Many men pointed out that most of the techniques gained their effectiveness by being used in the repetitive way, until the prisoner could no longer sustain his resistance."

Under these pressures, the prisoner's self-searchings produce material increasingly in line with the interrogator's desires, and eventually the victim may be unable to tell fact from fantasy. In extreme cases, he accepts his fabricated confession as true. Lifton tells of a man who confessed with conviction and in detail that he had tried to attract the attention of an official representative of his country who had passed by the door of his cell, only to discover later that this episode could not possibly have occurred.

The world of the victim of thought reform seems a far cry from that of the mental patient, yet the analogies are sometimes startling. Some patients are in the same state of terror and bewilderment that the Communists tried to produce in their prisoners. This is most true of patients in mental hospitals, which I'm not going to try to discuss now. Here I should like to consider only the faint but discernible parallels between thought reform and out-patient psychiatry, whether in clinic or in private practice. The psychiatrist's potential influence on the out-patient depends in part on the latter's expectancy of help. A few office patients turn to the psychiatrist as a last resort, after having vainly tried other possible sources of help. Their favorable expectancy, like that of the victims of thought reform, is based on desperation. A larger group are not sure why they have come to the psychiatrist or how the latter can help them. The psychiatrist then has the task of mobilizing their favorable expectancies by convincing them that they are ill and that the illness is best treated by psychotherapy. This is usually expressed as arousing the patient's consciousness of illness. For example, Kubie (1936) writes, "Without a full-hearted acknowledgment of the sense of illness, a patient can go through only

the motions of treatment. . . . It is often necessary during analysis to
lead a patient through a sustained period of relative isolation from his
usual activities and human associations." It may not be entirely far-
fetched to read into such a statement a recognition that a patient, like
a prisoner, can more easily be brought to change his ideology if he is
removed from the groups which reinforce his present one.

Viewing psychotherapy in the light of thought reform calls attention to another feature which tends to enhance the therapist's influence.
This is the interpretation of all the patient's thoughts, feelings, and
acts in terms of a consistent and unshakable theoretical framework.
The psychotherapist doesn't assert his infallibility directly, but, I
think, he does it by indirect means. In accordance with his theory,
the therapist assumes that the patient's distress is related to repressed
infantile memories, parataxic distortions, or an unrealistic self-image,
to take three examples. Therapy continues until the patient acknowl-
edges these phenomena in himself, and deals with them to the therapist's, and his own, satisfaction. The possibility that he has not experienced the phenomena in question, or that they may be irrelevant to his
illness, is not entertained.

Freud's (1935) handling of his discovery that an individual may
confabulate an infantile memory may serve as a prototype of this way
of thinking. As he was quick to see, "This discovery . . . serves either
to discredit the analysis, which has led to such a result (the invention
of an infantile memory) or to discredit the patient, upon whose
testimony the analysis, as well as the whole understanding of the
neurosis is built up." Well, that is quite a spot to be in, but Freud got
out of it in less than a page and a half, being a very brilliant man.
The way he did it was this. He points out that "these fantasies possess
psychological reality, in contrast to *physical reality*, and *in the realm
of neurosis, the psychological reality is the determining factor*"
(Freud, 1935). Therefore, the fact that these infantile experiences
were fantasies rather than actualities, far from refuting his theories,
confirms them. I don't mean to imply that this explains away the
Freudian theory of neurosis, which rests on a great deal of evidence
besides infantile fantasies. I offer it as an illustration of the type of
thinking which is characteristic of some psychotherapists and which
contributes to their influence on patients.

The therapist may protect the infallibility of his theoretical orientation in several ways. For example, behavior of patients which does
not conform to his position is apt to be characterized as resistance, or
manipulation, words which have a derogatory implication. Patients'
criticisms can always be dismissed as based on transference, implying
that they are entirely the result of the patients' distorted perceptions.

Faced with such behavior, the therapist is admonished not to become defensive, that is, not to admit even by implication that his viewpoint requires defending.

The therapist also has ways of maintaining his faith in his theory and procedures in the face of the patient's failure to respond favorably. He may take refuge in the position that the patient broke off treatment too soon. Or he may conclude that the patient was insufficiently motivated or otherwise not suitable for treatment. Occasionally, he may entertain the possibility that he applied his technique incorrectly, but failures rarely lead him to question the technique itself, or the premises underlying it. In short, the vicissitudes of treatment are not permitted to shake the therapist's basic ideology.

In calling attention to the means by which psychotherapists maintain their conviction of the correctness of their theories and procedures, no derogation is implied. On the contrary, this conviction probably is partly responsible for the success of all forms of psychotherapy, as already discussed. It is stressed here as one of the ingredients which heighten the therapist's influence on the patient.

The methods of psychotherapy, finally, are slightly analogous to those of thought reform with respect to repetition, participation, and ambiguity. In long term psychotherapy the patient repeatedly reviews material connected with certain issues toward which the therapist maintains a consistent attitude. That this may tend to influence the patient in accordance with the therapist's viewpoint is consistent with what is known concerning the role of repetition in all learning.

The desirability of the patient's being an active participant or collaborator in the treatment process is universally recognized. One of the many reasons for encouraging such an attitude is that it forestalls or combats the patient's tendency to become dependent upon the therapist, or so it is claimed. The perspective of thought reform suggests that, though securing the patient's participation may combat dependence, it may also heighten the therapist's influence in at least two ways. The more the patient's participation can be obtained, the more he commits himself to the change which the therapist is trying to educe. Moreover, the patient has greater difficulty mobilizing his resistance against a collaborator than against a directive therapist.

It is in the ambiguity of the therapy situation, however, that its greatest potentiality for influence probably lies. Like the interrogators in thought reform, some psychotherapists convey to the patient that they know what is wrong with him, but he must find it out for himself in order to be helped. This is one means of enlisting his participation, but it also gives the patient an ambiguous task. This ambiguity is heightened by the fact that the end point of this process, whether it is unearthing his infantile memories, making his unconscious conscious, correcting his idealized image, or what not, is indeterminate, like that of the confession. The patient is to keep on trying until he is cured, but the criteria that demonstate cure has been achieved are not clearly specified.

In the meanwhile, the therapist by his attitude of interest, or disinterest, and his interpretations, reinforces those behaviors of the patient which he approves and inhibits others.

Psychotherapists have always been alert to the possibility of directly imposing their own ideas in the long term repetitive relationship of psychotherapy, and have advocated certain attitudes to diminish this possibility. One is "permissiveness," i.e., the therapist leaves the patient free to use the therapeutic situation as he wishes. The perspective of thought reform suggests that, given a patient who expects the therapist to relieve his distress, the latter's permissiveness—by creating an ambiguous situation—may enhance rather than diminish the power to indoctrinate the patient. Again it is permissiveness with an implied threat, though the threat is very subtle in this case. It is the threat that the patient won't get better, or that the therapist will lose interest in him if he fails to do the right thing, but the therapist won't tell him what the right thing is.

An ambiguous situation tends to create or increase the patient's confusion which, as Cantril (1941) suggests, tends to heighten suggestibility. It also makes him more anxious, therefore, presumably heightening his motivation to seek relief from the therapist. By failing to take a definite position, the therapist deprives the patient of a target against which to focus his opposition. By avoiding clear communication of his wishes, he intensifies the patient's search for subtle hints as to how well he is doing. Even when the therapist is out of the patient's sight, as in psychoanalysis, the patient is acutely aware of changes in his respiration when he lights his pipe, shifts his chair, and so on, as any analysand will testify.

In summary, this review of thought reform and its parallels with psychotherapy suggests that a patient's susceptibility to influence may be heightened by placing him under severe emotional stress, for relief of which he must depend upon the person trying to influence him, by attacking his sense of personal identity (which hasn't been stressed in this presentation), and by transferring him from groups representing his usual values to one which confronts him with a self-consistent and unyielding alternative value system. Under these circumstances, the influencing agent can intensify his power by leaving ambiguities in the task which the victim must complete in order to gain release, by demanding his active participation, and by repeatedly going over the same ground. Similar factors, in greatly attenuated form, may be ascertained in psychotherapy and may in part determine the strength of the psychotherapist's influence.

V Now, I should like to turn to quite a different mode of influence which has been called to our attention by studies of so-called operant conditioning. Operant conditioning, which is a term devised by B. F. Skinner (1953), consists in reinforcing spontaneous activities of an animal. Ordinary conditioning involves eliciting a response with a stimulus, and then linking that stimulus to another stimulus, and thereby getting the response to the new stimulus. In operant conditioning, the experimenter waits for the animal to do something spontaneously, and then rewards it. For example, a pigeon is placed in a certain kind of cage, and starts to peck. If he pecks a certain spot, a grain of corn falls down. This kind of conditioning proceeds very rapidly and, strikingly enough, the learning that occurs as a function of the nature of the reinforcement is the same throughout the animal kingdom. It has been said that this is the only method which fails to reveal differences between pigeons and men.

It has occurred to some people that in psychotherapy the same process may be operating, in which the patient's spontaneous behavior is his speech, and the rewards are certain changes of expression or remarks of the therapist. The first experimental support of this notion was obtained by Greenspoon (1955), who simply had graduate students in his department repeat words at random, and he would grunt "um hum" whenever the subject said a plural word. Even when the subject didn't know that he was being given signals at all, the amount of plural words he gave increased.

This led therapists to see if any of the same kind of forces were operating in patients. I won't try to review the growing literature on this, but will mention two examples, which seem to me quite startling. One is the work of Salzinger and Pisoni (1958) at the New York State Psychiatric Institute, in which they took a group of schizophrenic patients coming into the Institute and subjected each patient to an interview with each of two interviewers, on different days. These interviews were structured. For the first ten minutes, the interviewer just got information. He tried not to reward anything. For the next ten minutes, he deliberately rewarded affect statements, that is, statements which involved an expression of feeling, and these were carefully defined so that the interviewer knew exactly what kind of statement he should reward. He did this by simple grunts, looks of interest, "go on" —this kind of thing. For the last ten minutes he again offered no reinforcements.

Salzinger and Pisoni discovered that in both interviews with both interviewers, even a ten minute period of reinforcement significantly increased the frequency of affect statements; that is, the middle band of these interviews had more affect statements than did either of the control periods.

The other study I wish to cite is that of Murray (1956), who did a content analysis of two protocols, one of his own, and one of the case of Herbert Bryan, which is published in Carl Rogers' *Counseling in Psychotherapy* (1942). The defensive statements of Murray's patients, as defined by him and of which he disapproved in theory, fell from 140 to nine per interview, over seventeen sessions. Expressions of hostility, which he permitted and perhaps subtly reinforced, rose from practically none to nearly eighty by the fourth interview.

Murray then took the case of Herbert Bryan, which is especially interesting because it is offered as an example of non-directive therapy. He found that two raters could very easily rate the therapist's comments as approving or disapproving with a high degree of agreement. That is, although the therapist thought he was non-directive, his comments could easily be classified as having a rewarding or punishing effect. Then he studied the content of the patient's remarks in relation to these approving or disapproving statements of the therapist. He found that statements in categories disapproved by the therapist fell from forty-five per cent of the total number of statements, in the second hour, to five per cent in the eighth. Statements in approved categories rose from one per cent in the second hour to forty-five per cent, almost half, in the seventh.

This offers a mechanism for explaining the repeated observation, and one to which I have already referred, that patients tend to express their problems and attitudes in the therapist's language. Stekel (Wolff, 1954) said long ago, "Dreams are made to order, are produced in the form that will best please the therapist." Patients treated by Carl Rogers and his group (1951) show a shift of perceived self toward their ideal self. Those treated by Murray, who operates in a framework of learning theory, showed a decrease in defensive verbalizations and an increase in direct expression of feeling. Patients in psychoanalysis express increased amounts of hitherto unconscious materials as treatments progressed. And, Ralph Heine (1953) found that veterans who had undergone psychotherapy expressed the reasons for their improvement in terms of the theoretical system of their therapist. Rosenthal (1955) found, in a small study, that improved patients showed a shift in their value systems toward those held by the therapist.

So it seems to me that we can conclude that the elimination of suggestion in the crude sense of directly implanting ideas in the patient does not exclude reinforcement which may influence his production in the direction expected or desired by the therapist. It would be a mistake, however, and I want to emphasize this, to generalize too hastily from these very scanty findings. They apply only to what the patient says, and not to how he actually feels, and from one study we have evidence that what he says may not go along with what he feels. This study found that the patient talked less and less about the topic of mother, which the therapist did not like, but, when he was questioned, the relative importance of mother in the patient's own feelings remained just as high (Parloff, Goldstein and Iflund, 1960). So we have to be cautious about generalizing from these results.

However, there is a real possibility that if you keep saying the same thing long enough, you begin to believe it, and therefore, that if you verbalize, in certain ways over and over again, in time it may actually change your attitude.

Now finally, I'd like to turn to some of the direct effects of this influence on patients. The evidence I shall present suggests that the amount of treatment to the point of significant improvement is affected by the patient's expectancies, presumably transmitted to him by the therapist; and that faith alone, the state of mind of faith or hope, can produce profound and lasting changes in attitudes and bodily states.

Let me give you some examples of the possibility that length of treatment may reflect in part the therapist's and the patient's expectancies. The first example consists of two studies of group therapy of patients with peptic ulcer that were done on different populations, and which therefore cannot strictly be compared. In both these studies, the peptic ulcer was definitely diagnosed by X-ray, or by blood in the stools, or some other clear clinical sign. Fortin and Abse (1956) treated ten college students with an analytic type of group therapy, and the patients also received medical treatment at the same time for the relief of their discomfort. In this group, discussion of ulcer symptomatology was ignored, and attention became focussed on basic personality problems. Most of the patients had a flare-up of symptoms during the first month. Three required bed-rest in the infirmary. However, during the latter part of group therapy, presumably after several months, in addition to favorable personality changes, the ulcer symptoms lessened in intensity and frequency. They state that at the end of the year, "Among the four members who were diagnosed initially, prior to group therapy, no recurrence was reported. Among the remaining six members with chronic peptic ulcers, where the expected rate of recurrence is over seventy-five per cent, for a period of three years observation, only one student reported a hemorrhage." They got good results after several months of treatment, although the patient got worse first. This is in accord with the expectancies implied by analytic approach.

Twenty-two years ago there appeared a study which has been resolutely ignored, by Chappell, Stefano, Rogerson, and Pike (1936). They took thirty-two patients with demonstrated peptic ulcer, which had been refractory to medical treatment, and gave them a six week course of daily didactic group therapy, which is absolutely different in its intent from analytic therapy. Therapy lasted for six weeks only, and attention was focussed on how to live with an ulcer. In the group they stressed ways of promoting what they call visceral rest. They compared these thirty-two patients with a group of twenty matched controls. All fifty-two patients got the best medical treatment that was available at the same time, so that was constant. They found what might be expected, that in both groups the patients rapidly became symptom free. It is interesting that in the experimental group, all but one, who had a disastrous home situation which could not be influenced by the treatment, became symptom free within three weeks. This is the period in which Fortin's (1956) patients were getting worse. The difference in the two sets of patients showed up in the follow-up. At the end of three months, all but two of the thirty-two group patients were symptom free (one could not be located), whereas eighteen of the control group of twenty, after an initial good response to the medical regimen, had full recurrences of symptoms in this period.

At the end of three years, twenty-eight of the original group therapy patients were re-examined. Twenty-four "considered themselves to be healthy." Of these, fifteen had remained completely or nearly symptom free. Only two were as sick as at the start. Chappell's (1936) patients began to get better while Fortin's were getting sicker, and the end results seem equally good, or at least equally durable. It appears as if patients reflected differences in the therapist's expectancies, by the speed with which they improved.

Shlien (1956) at the University of Chicago Counseling Center, in a preliminary study compared the improvement of a group of clients on certain measures, who were told at the start that they would receive twenty therapeutic sessions over a ten week period, with another group of twenty-nine clients, who were continued in treatment until they terminated voluntarily. Both groups received client-centered therapy and the same improvement measures were used for both. The groups were closely matched at the start of the therapy by the criteria used. The group receiving time-limited therapy reached the same average level of improvement at twenty interviews as the others did in an average of fifty-five interviews. Moreover, at the end of fifty-five interviews, when they did a follow-up, although the group receiving time-limited therapy had been out of treatment several months, their improvement on these measures was still maintained.

Now, I would like to switch to the other, and perhaps most controversial aspect of the effect of faith or hope, and that is its direct effects on the patient. It is generally agreed that a patient's hope for a successful outcome of the treatment can make him feel better, but it is usually assumed that improvement based solely on this is transient and superficial. An example of this type of response is afforded by an obsessional patient who tried several forms of psychotherapy, each lasting many months. He stated that as long as he hoped the treatment would help him, his symptoms greatly improved. When his hope eventually waned, his symptoms recurred and he sought another therapist.

Changes following brief therapeutic contact, however, in which little seems to have occurred beyond the arousal of the patient's faith in the therapist, are sometimes deep-seated and persistent. The most plausible explanation for the permanence of these so-called transference cures, is that the relief the patient experiences from this relationship frees him to function more effectively. He becomes better able to utilize his latent assets, and finds the courage to re-examine himself, and perhaps to modify his habitual maladaptive way of responding, leading to genuine personality growth.

There is a good possibility, however, that the emotional state of trust or faith in itself can sometimes produce far-reaching and permanent changes in attitude or bodily states, though the occurrence of this phenomenon cannot be predicted or controlled. The major evidence lies in the realm of religious conversions and miracle cures.

It is common knowledge that faith in its religious form can have profound and lasting effects on an individual's personality, attitudes, and values. After a conversion experience the convert may have changed so much as to be scarcely recognizable as the person he was before this experience. This is seen not only in persons like St. Augustine and St. Francis, but even in an occasional denizen of skid row who becomes "saved" by the Salvation Army meeting. Most such conversions are transient, of course, and backsliding is the rule. In this, they resemble the transference cures that I have already mentioned. As with such cures, perhaps the conversion sticks when it leads to new forms of behavior which yield more rewards than the old patterns.

For the purposes of this discussion, the only important points are that religious conversions can lead to profound and permanent changes of attitude in persons who have undergone prolonged hardship or

spiritual torment, and that they usually involve intimate and emotionally charged contact with a person or group representing the viewpoint to which the convert becomes converted. Conversions which
occur in isolation are often, perhaps always, preceded by such contact with others. Even when the hermit goes off into the hills, he is
coming out of a group with which he has been closely identified and
which values this kind of change.

According to William James (1936), "General Booth, the founder
of the Salvation Army, considers that the first vital step in saving out-
casts consists in making them feel that some decent human being cares
enough for them to take an interest in the question whether they are
to rise or to sink." The role of divine intervention in producing conversion experiences may be left open. The significant point for this
discussion is that they are usually accompanied or preceded by a certain type of relationship with other human beings which in some ways
resembles the psychotherapeutic one. The psychotherapist, too, cares
deeply whether his patient rises or sinks.

That faith can also produce extensive and enduring organic changes
is amply attested to by so-called miracle cures. There can be little
doubt that these cures can activate reparative forces which in rare
instances are powerful enough to heal grossly damaged tissue. And
anyone who looks into this, I think, will be convinced that the evidence for miracle cures (even of obviously gross pathology, like non-
healing ulcers and non-union of fractures) is just as great as for anything else we accept as true.

The only point I would like to emphasize about them is that it is
the state of faith, and not the object of the faith that seems to release
this healing force. All religions report cures and they are also produced by individuals who, by the accepted standards of society, are
charlatans.

That the healing force appears to reside in the patient's state of
faith or hope and not in its object has been neatly illustrated by an
experiment performed by a German named Rehder (1955) with three
chronically and severely ill, bedridden women patients. One had a
chronic gall-bladder disease, one had failed to recover from an operation for pancreatitis, and one had advanced cancer. Rehder happened
to run into a faith healer who worked by absent treatment, and who
asked to be allowed to work on these three patients. So the faith
healer worked away without the patients knowing it, and nothing
happened. Then Dr. Rehder told these patients and said, in effect,
"there's a faith healer in town, a very good man who has had a lot
of success, and I've asked him to work on you by absent treatment.
He's going to start treatment tomorrow morning at eight o'clock."

Rehder picked a time when he knew the faith healer would not be in operation. At eight o'clock the next morning, all three of these patients dramatically improved. The lady with the pancreatitis, who did not have a disease process which was still active, got out of bed where she had been for eight months, began to put on weight and went home and resumed her normal life. The life of the patient with cancer was not prolonged, but she became symptom-free, and physiologically changed; that is, she lost massive ascites and edema, and her blood count went up to normal, and she went back home, and lived a normal life as a housewife until she died of the cancer. The lady with gall-bladder disease also stayed well for several years before she had a recurrence. All this came out of faith in something that hadn't happened. I think that is the interesting part of the study.

✔ Certain features are common to most miracle cures. The patients are usually chronically ill, debilitated and despondent. Their critical faculty has been weakened, and they are ready to grasp at straws. The journey to the religious shrine is long and arduous, and Janet (1925) points out that miracle cures don't work for people who live in the neighborhood of the shrine. After arrival there are many preliminaries before the patient can enter the shrine, and during the preparatory period the patient hears about other miraculous cures and views the votive offerings of the healed. As Janet says, all these things happen today at Lourdes just as they used to happen of old at the temple of Aesculapius. In his despair, the patient's state of mind is similar to that of the victim of thought reform, and the symbols of cure are present, as in the psychiatrist's office, though of course much more potent in the religious shrine. All three types of experience are similar in that another person or group of persons is involved who represents the promise of relief.

Finally, the emotionally charged atmosphere should be mentioned. People who visit Lourdes say one cannot help but be swept up in it. And faith cures can occur in skeptics as well as believers, but they have to be ardent skeptics. They have to be involved emotionally. Apparently the emotional excitation has something to do with the change that occurs.

In the realm of medicine, evidence abounds that faith can facilitate bodily healing. In these cases, the patient's faith is activated by the doctor's administration of an inert pharmacological substance, which symbolizes his healing function. Such remedies are called placebos, implying that they are means of placating the patient, and therefore, not genuine treatment. But placebos can have deep and enduring effects. The most commonplace example is the treatment of warts by painting them blue, or muttering incantations, or using other rituals.

This phenomenon has been investigated quite thoroughly by dermatologists with good controls, and those who have done large series of cases claim that the cure of warts by suggestive methods is just as frequent as by any other method and is better than spontaneous remission (Block, 1927). A wart is a virus disease, not a psychogenic phenomenon. Apparently in certain patients, the belief that they are being helped can produce changes in the physiology of the skin which tips the balance so that the wart virus can no longer thrive.

Placebos can also heal serious tissue damage, if it is directly related to the patient's emotional state. I've found one study on this, which I offer with caution because it is reported from abroad with very little data. It was a study in a municipal hospital in Budapest in which two groups of patients with bleeding peptic ulcer were compared. The placebo group received an injection of sterile water from the doctor who told them that it was new medicine which would produce relief. The control group received the same injection from nurses who told them it was an experimental medicine of undetermined effectiveness. The placebo group had remissions which were "excellent in seventy per cent of the cases lasting over a period of one year" (Volgyesi, 1954). The control group showed only a twenty-five per cent remission rate.

The cure of warts and peptic ulcers by suggestion is not as spectacular as religious miracle cures, but qualitatively the processes involved seem very similar. The example of miracle cures and placebo responses suggest the probability that a patient's expectancy of benefit from treatment in itself may have enduring and profound effects on his physical and mental state. It seems plausible, furthermore, that the successful effects of all forms of psychotherapy depend in part on their ability to foster such attitudes in the patient. Since it is the patient's state which counts rather than what he believes in, it is not surprising that all types of therapy attain roughly equal improvement rates. This finding also suggests that the generic type of relationship offered by the therapist plays a larger part in his success than the specific technique he uses.

The aspects of the therapist's personality that affect his healing power have not yet been adequately defined, but it seems reasonable to assume that they lie in the realm of his ability to inspire confidence in his patients.

Lest this talk leave the impression that I attribute all the positive effects of psychotherapy to the patient's expectancy of help, let me cite an experimental study of psychotherapy with psychiatric outpatients, the results of which strongly suggest that certain kinds of improvement can be explained on this basis, but others probably cannot.

In this study, adult psychiatric out-patients were assigned at random to individual psychotherapy, group therapy, and minimal psychotherapy, with three different psychiatric residents. Each resident conducted all three types of treatment. The resident's obligation extended only to six months of treatment, at which time he was free to drop the patient. The patients were told that at the end of six months the decision as to further treatment would be made by the patient and the therapist. Two scales were used to measure the patient's progress. One was a symptom checklist, a measure of distress, filled out by the patient. The other was a social ineffectiveness scale, a measure of the adequacy of his functioning, filled out by interviewers on the basis of interviews with the patient and an informant.

It is the similarities and differences between these two measures that I want to describe. The treated patients as a group showed a marked improvement at six months in both social ineffectiveness and discomfort scores. But the scales behaved differently in an important respect. With respect to social ineffectiveness, the amount of treatment made a difference. That is, patients who received group therapy or individual therapy, which involved a good deal of treatment contact, improved more than patients who received minimal therapy, where they were seen about a half hour once every two weeks, and they improved more than patients who dropped out of treatment. Moreover, the improvement in social ineffectiveness gradually increased for the group of treated patients over a two year follow-up period. In contrast, the average decrease in discomfort at six months, showed no relation to anything. It was as great for the people who dropped out of treatment after four sessions as for those who had had individual therapy for six months, and there was no difference between any of the treated groups. We broke down the discomfort scale into symptoms of anxiety and depression and somatic symptoms, and found that the anxiety and depression symptoms started out higher and decreased more than the somatic symptoms. That is, the decrease in discomfort was due mainly to decrease in anxiety and depression. The initial drop in discomfort was maintained over two years on the average although some patients relapsed, and others continued to improve.

The first question we wanted to answer was: Is this an artifact? Was the initial score on discomfort falsely high because the patients were uneasy in the situation and, therefore, reported more discomfort than they felt most of the time? Then, later discomfort scores would be their real level and all we would have measured would be their increasing familiarity with the scale. The other question we wanted to answer was: How fast does this change occur? We measured it first at six months. Maybe it occurred in two weeks, or even in an hour. We tested both these questions by a little experiment. We took twelve of the patients who were coming back for their routine follow-up study after two years and who had had some recurrence of their discomfort, although it was not up to the original level; and we gave them placebos. We had them come back in two weeks, and they showed a drop in discomfort of the same order of magnitude after two weeks that they had shown initially after six months (Gleidman, Nash, Imber, Stone and Frank, 1958). This rules out repetition of the scale as a cause of the drop because they had had the scales several times by then. It also shows that the drop can occur in two weeks. Now we are running an experiment in which we check the patient before and after he receives a placebo, and find that it happens within one hour.

This suggests that there are at least two interrelated factors operating in producing results in psychotherapy: activation of the patient's favorable expectancies, and changes in attitudes and behavior which depend on specific situational influences. These could be summarized as the unlearning of faulty attitudes and the relearning of better ones, though we believe that many processes are involved besides learning in the narrower sense.

The activation of favorable expectancies results chiefly in the relief of the patient's subjective distress, especially that part of it related to anxiety and depression. These may be viewed as manifestations of the patient's apprehensiveness about his condition.

Changes due to exposure to a social learning situation would be expected to appear in the patient's social behavior. Such changes would be expected to differ in at least two respects from those due simply to a patient's belief that he is being helped. They should be more gradual, and the kind of change should be related to the kind of situation to which the patient is exposed. In this study it was found that the change in social ineffectiveness tended to improve throughout the period of observation, and the amount of change at six months seemed related to the amount of therapeutic contact, whereas, change in discomfort, which is based probably just on the expectancy of being helped, was very rapid and quite independent of the kind of treatment.

In this presentation, I have attempted to focus on two interrelated themes. One is that because of certain properties of all therapeutic relationships the therapist inevitably exerts a strong influence on the patient. This influence arises primarily from the patient's hope or faith that treatment will relieve his distress. This favorable expectation is strengthened by cultural factors, aspects of the referral or intake process, cues in the therapy situation which indicate that help will be forthcoming, and the therapist's own confidence in his ability to help, springing from his training and methods. Analogies between psychotherapy and thought reform have been used to clarify some of the sources and modes of operation of the influencing process in psychotherapy. Some examples of the influence of the therapist's expectations on the patient's productions and on the duration of therapy have been given.

The other theme is that the patient's favorable expectation, which is a major determinant of the therapist's influence over him, may have direct therapeutic effects, which are not necessarily transient or superficial. Certain implications of these propositions for practical research may now be very briefly mentioned. Since this review points out areas of relative ignorance which need further exploration, rather than areas of knowledge, its implications for psychotherapeutic practices must be regarded as extremely tentative. It should be noted, first, that the likelihood of a common factor in the effectiveness of all forms of psychotherapy does not imply that all methods or theories are interchangeable for all types of patients. It may well turn out that the specific effects of different approaches differ significantly, and that different types of patients respond differently to different therapeutic techniques. Until these questions are clarified, it is important that every therapist be well versed in his theoretical orientation, and skilled in the methods most congenial to him in order to maintain his self-confidence and, thereby, the patient's faith in him.

Since the leading conceptual systems of psychotherapy are not logically incompatible, but represent primarily differences in emphasis, or alternative formulations of roughly the same ideas, adherents of each school may feel no compunction about their own positions, while tolerant of alternative views, pending the accumulation of facts which may make possible decisions as to the specific merits and drawbacks of different approaches. The psychotherapist should be prepared, however, to modify his approach within the limits possible for him in order to meet the expectancies of different types of patients. Interview types of therapy, for example, tend to fit the expectations of most middle-class patients, but many lower-class patients cannot conceive of a doctor who does not dispense pills and jab them with needles. These patients are very apt to drop out of interview psychotherapy because they cannot perceive it as treatment for their ills. For them, the tactics of therapy may involve accommodating their initial expectations, so that they return for more treatment. The developing therapeutic relationship may then lead to modification of the patient's expectancies in a more psychotherapeutically useful direction. Thus, it may be hoped that adequate diagnosis will eventually include an estimate as to the type of therapeutic approach most likely to activate and potentiate the patient's faith.

This review also suggests the desirability of the psychotherapist being more aware of his influence on patients. The physician cannot avoid influencing his patients. The only question is whether he should use this influence consciously or unconsciously. As Modell (1955) says in his book on treatment, "It would be well to remember that in all therapy, trouble is apt to follow the ignorant application of important forces." And this applies particularly when the important force is the doctor or the therapist himself.

Finally, we must be cautious about attributing improvement to other causes until more is known about the direct effects of the patient's positive expectancy, and the expectancies of the psychotherapist as related to him. Until we know the factors in the patient, therapist, and treatment situation which determine the degree and form of influence exerted by the therapist, and what the effects of his influence are on the patient's behavior, and on the nature and duration of his improvement, we cannot adequately isolate either the factors specific to each form of psychotherapy, or those involved in all forms of psychotherapy. In the meantime, we are in danger of falling into a trap of attributing the patient's improvement to the particular kinds of production he gives in a kind of treatment, overlooking the possibility that both the production and the improvement may be determined, at least in part, by his faith in the therapist.

Therapy in a Group Setting

by Jerome D. Frank, M.D., Ph.D.

THE THEORETICAL FRAMEWORK for my activities in group and individual therapy may be stated as follows: The general idea is that the neuroses are maladaptive responses that result from disturbances in the normal processes of growth and maturation. These disturbances arise from conditions, especially in early life, which do not afford suitable opportunities for growth, or which lead to chronic anxiety-producing situations, with which the inadequately equipped child must deal. As a result of these unfortunate early experiences the patient suffers, when he is grown up, conflicting urges and feelings which he cannot effectively resolve, such as being utterly dependent on a parent whom he at the same time fears.

These conflicts and the individual's futile efforts to deal with them lead to habitually distorted ways of perceiving himself and others, resulting in inappropriate responses to current interpersonal situations. He carries his childhood conflicts over into adult life. The sources of the conflicts, as well as the distortions to which they give rise, are often more or less concealed from the patient for various reasons which we need not go into at this moment. He is aware mainly of being distressed, which he often does not directly relate to his problems.

The major question is why the neurotic gets fixated with these maladaptive responses and is unable to learn from experience. There are several obvious possibilities, which probably all operate. One is that anxiety reduction tends to reinforce the immediately previous learned behavior, and a lot of neurotic behavior brings immediate relief of anxiety at the expense of long term relief. The classic example is the neurotic alcoholic who drinks to relieve feelings of depression, even though he knows that when he sobers up, he is going to feel a whole lot worse. He gets an immediate relief from his drinking and this tends to reinforce it. Another important factor involved in this fixation of maladaptive responses is what Sullivan calls *selective inattention*—the fact that the patient simply avoids perceiving cues that don't fit with his picture of the world. For example, a patient may not see friendly gestures that someone else is offering, or if he does see them, he may misinterpret them as hostile. One step beyond this is the "self-fulfilling prophecy." Since all behavior tends to elicit corresponding behavior from other people, if you expect a certain response from someone else, you may behave in such a way as to elicit this response, which then confirms your expectation. The paranoid patient is a very good example of this. He approaches the stranger "prophesying" that this person will be against him too. No matter how friendly this stranger starts out to be, if the patient continually repulses advances and is surly and suspicious, soon the stranger is going to become hostile toward him, and his prophecy is fulfilled. This reinforces his expectancy that the next person he meets will be against him.

From the standpoint of treatment, perhaps the most important source of this rigidity is that the patient's self-respect is so damaged. After repeated experiences of frustration and failure, he lacks the courage to look at himself afresh or to try something new, which always involves some risk. His neurotic patterns may be painful, but at least he is used to them, at least he knows what to expect, and it is very hard for any of us to change habitual ways of functioning, even when we know they should be changed, unless we can find some courage to run the risk of what might happen if we do change. So I would think that anxiety reduction, selective inattention, the self-fulfilling prophecy, and damaged self-respect are the kinds of things that tend to keep patients in their ruts.

Three important sources of damaged self-respect should be mentioned. One is that patients feel that they are not living up to their capacities, which is a very damaging feeling, although it is a rather subtle one. They feel that they are not able to produce the way they should, or enjoy life the way they should, that they are unduly dependent on other people. A second source of damaged self-respect is that they are aware of lustful or hostile feelings of which they are ashamed. Thirdly, the attitude of society toward these illnesses helps to diminish the self-respect of our patients to a considerable degree. No matter how much we deny it, neurosis is a stigma, and coming to a mental hospital or psychiatric or psychological clinic is still regarded by many patients as stigmatizing.

There is one other point which I think is useful in conducting therapy, one can usually focus on some one issue or theme that seems to summarize a great many of the patient's conflicts. It is very useful to get an interaction with the patient focussed about an issue of this sort, even though many other things may be wrong. A very common theme with a schizophrenic, for example, is his craving for intimacy on the one hand, and his tremendous fear of being dominated and hurt on the other, which can be traced through all kinds of situations.

The goal, then, of any form of psychotherapy is to supply a new interpersonal situation, which can help the patient find more effective and satisfying ways of handling his chronic interpersonal and internal conflicts. As the patient begins to experience some successes in his dealings with others, this reinforces the new ways of behaving, and so, if all goes well, the maladaptive patterns are progressively weakened and the more successful ones strengthened, and his potentialities for further emotional growth are progressively mobilized. An example is a physician who, among his many other problems, was very resentful and envious of his more successful colleagues, and this added to his depression. It was a kind of self-fulfilling prophecy. Apparently, when he was with these colleagues, he would act in such a way that they would be inclined to brag about their successes. There was one man in particular, an ophthalmologist, whom he would visit occasionally. He would come back upset because the man would do nothing but brag about how much money he had and how many cars he had and all that sort of thing. In the course of treatment, something shifted in the patient's value system and he began to be a little less concerned about income. The next time he saw this ophthalmologist, he acted differently, though he couldn't quite say how. He said he thinks what he did was to be able to congratulate the man quite comfortably on his success when he started to brag, whereupon the ophthalmologist did a 180° flip-flop and began to complain about all his troubles. This reinforced the patient's new perception that, after all, money didn't always bring happiness, and a useful process was set in motion.

This is in general the framework in which I operate. Now I shall try to be more specific. I think a therapist tries to do three basic things. He tries to support the patient emotionally, he tries to stir him up, get him activated, stimulated, and he tries to offer a situation in which relearning is easy. Let me elaborate.

I think there are two aspects of support. One I dwelt on at length in my previous paper. The first support you give the patient is to convey to him that you can help him. This is partly implied in his coming in the first place and certainly partly implied in the doctor's or the therapist's manner right along. This usually is a very powerful allayer of anxiety, and puts the patient in a better state for learning. The other kind is support of the patient's self-esteem, which also is conveyed in a primitive way. It comes from the fact that a person in whom he has confidence sits and listens to him with respect and with interest, and tries very hard to understand him. This is tremendously supportive, especially for the kind of patients I work with mainly, lower- and lower-middle class patients. Many of them have never had a chance to talk over their problems with somebody whom they regard as superior, and who listens sympathetically. Usually, if they are exposed to authority figures, it's because they've done something wrong. It's the judge or the teacher or somebody who is after them about something. And here comes someone with prestige who takes them very seriously and listens and says, in effect, "You are a good guy, I think there is a lot to you, I respect you." I don't think any therapy happens, no matter how skillful the rest of the process is, unless support is there first, unless the patient feels that he can be helped and feels his morale boosted by the therapy situation.

Then it is necessary and desirable to maintain an optimal amount of emotional tension. We know that if a person is panicky, he can't learn —and if he is completely blasé and indifferent, he is not going to learn either. There is a zone of optimal activation of the patient or evocation of his feelings, which is necessary for attitudes to change, as if emotions supply the motive power for the change. So we try to damp down emotion when it gets too strong, which may happen in groups, and we try to stir it up if it is too weak. I think the way we do this mainly is by leaving the situation ambiguous, that is, by so-called permissiveness. If the patient doesn't know quite what he is supposed to do, this evokes tension, and commits him to the task. In Dollard and Miller's book (1950), they put it in terms of the fact that a response can't be changed unless it is operating; that is, unless you evoke the pathological response there is not much chance of it changing.

The third basic aspect of all forms of psychotherapy is facilitation of learning which, for want of a better term, I am calling implicit direction. It usually isn't explicit direction. The treatment situation has certain characteristics which help to guide the patient. Feedback is a kind of guidance. The therapist singles out certain things and reflects them back to the patient so that he gets a better picture of what he is doing, and how he actually affects other people. I think of a very simple example of a girl in group therapy who complained that no one ever seemed to like her, nobody would talk to her. Actually the whole group was afraid of her because she was always scowling. The group pointed out to her that with such an expression on her face, everyone was afraid to open his mouth, but she wasn't aware that she was wearing a constant scowl. It is this kind of very simple feedback which I think is important in redefining situations and clarifying perceptions. And then there is the vast area of interpretation. I agree with Dr. Jacob Finesinger that it doesn't really matter whether or not the interpretation is true; it only matters that you and your patient think it is true. This facilitates learning in several ways. It conveys acceptance because it indicates that you have understood the patient. It helps the patient to make sense out of feelings which frighten him. Most of our patients, if you search long enough, will admit that they are afraid of going crazy, because they have feelings and they do things that they can't make sense of. Interpretation makes sense of them, which relieves anxiety to some extent. I think there is a dramatic component of interpretation which is important too, especially if the interpretation is in terms of a theoretical system. If a patient is told he has an Oedipus complex, this by implication links him with a host of other people who had Oedipus complexes. It gets him back in a group somehow. Our patients often feel terribly isolated, and this is one way of breaking this feeling down. I do not put too much stress on the niceties of interpretation because I think it is mainly in these non-specific ways that it is important.

In addition to feedback of the reflective kind—interpretation—there are two other aspects of the therapeutic situation which facilitate learning that we may overlook sometimes. One is that there is a low penalty for failing. The patient is free to experiment; he can always come back. In a group meeting, patients may be badly shaken by a quarrel but they know they can come back again and that communication between them will be maintained in spite of the upset. This, I think, is important in fostering a situation for relearning. And the final aspect is that we act as models for patients, for better or worse. We represent a certain set of values, a certain way of behaving, a certain perception of life, which they can take or leave, but they are very much influenced by it.

These then are to me the common factors in all therapeutic approaches—support, evocation, and implicit direction. Support lies in help-giving and enhancement of self-esteem; evocation I discussed as trying to maintain optimal emotional tension; implicit direction involves feedback and interpretation, and a situation in which the patient does not get punished for failing and in which the therapist acts as a model.

There are several implications of this theoretical framework for the way one conducts therapy. The first is, I have learned to accept the fact that whether I like it or not, I have a powerful influence on my patients, and, the conclusion from this is that I should use this influence directly. Why beat about the bush? First, I quite openly explain the rules of the game to the patient, and try to reinforce behavior which seems to fit in with the therapy. I seldom openly disapprove, but rather ignore behavior which doesn't fit in with therapy. That is, I am quite conscious about trying to inculcate the therapeutic code into the patient, by direct words as well as by example. And second, I state my reactions and insights rather bluntly and directly to the patient. Sometimes too much so, because it sets him back and he gets defensive, but more often than not, I think, helpfully. That is, I don't use a non-directive technique in the sense of just following the patient's lead. I interact quite directively with him.

Then, as I mentioned previously, I try to keep listening for some major issue. I keep coming back to it and try to relate different things the patient tells me to it. I feel the patient is more likely to feel that he is being helped if we both agree that here is a sore spot and these are things related to it, than if I remain noncommittal about everything that is happening.

And then, as a final step, and this usually has to come a good deal later, because it is threatening, I try to get across to the patient what he is contributing to the situation that prolongs the difficulty—to get him to see his responsibility for the mess he is in. If you do this too early, it is an attack on the patient. You have to wait until you feel that he really feels comfortable with you and trusts you and will realize it is not an attack, that you still respect him afterwards. I think when this works the patient says to himself, in effect, "By gosh, I'm doing something to keep this trouble going." This is probably the most powerful support for him to have, because it lets him feel that things are under his control after all. He really has some say about what goes on, and he is not just the helpless victim of great forces.

Now, let me apply this thinking very briefly to group therapy even though I'm focussing on individual aspects of it.

The point that strikes me most about group therapy, as compared to individual, is its tremendous evocative power. There are many ways that a group evokes patients' feelings and pathological attitudes and also their constructive qualities. A group in which there is a good deal of free discussion, forces the patients to interact with each other, to define themselves to the other people, and so on. They are strangers and they've got to get themselves identified, and this is apt to evoke a great many neurotic and healthy patterns.

Our groups have the standard that you express your feelings honestly and freely, but not wildly. There is no credit given for just blowing up. The code is that you say honestly what you are feeling without reservation, but you are also responsible for it. That is, you must examine what it is in you that produces this feeling. Let me add, parenthetically, the fact that everybody knows that he can be the victim as well as the aggressor, tends to keep everything under adequate control, so unless the group contains a really deviant person, it doesn't generate too much hostility. The problem that a patient states need not necessarily be worked out between patient and therapist; it can be worked out between the patients in the group. For example, in one group, two Jewish men, who happened to have known each other years before, outwardly represented opposite attitudes toward being Jewish. One man was militantly Jewish, and the other concealed it—tried to pass, you might say. They got more and more angry with each other over this for a period of weeks, and then finally each one began to see that he was fighting in the other person what he was fighting in himself. That is, the man who was fighting his Jewishness began to realize he had some secret pride in the fact that he was Jewish, and the man who was militant about it had to admit there was some disability that he was trying to conceal from himself. So each had worked himself through to a more livable position through his interaction. The group provided a situation where they could keep communicating in spite of their anger. This, I think, is one of the great values of group therapy. In individual therapy, the protagonists are so hopelessly unequal, they cannot really quarrel. The therapist has got to be a genius to fight with a patient and still hold him. But in group therapy all kinds of conflicts can go on between equals, while the therapist is a neutral umpire. He can, if necessary, come to the defense of one side or the other, or dampen things down, or encourage them to go on, so that the evocative and working-through aspect of conflict is facilitated. These conflicts, of course, are often based on transference reactions and mirror reactions like the one I just mentioned, where each person sees in the other person what he denies in himself. They also are often based on real life differences in values. A worker and a small business man in a group won't change their values as a result of the conflict, but they will become a little more secure, having tested out what they believe in the fire of conflict. Thus, the evocative power is very important in a group.

Ⅴ A puzzling feature of group therapy is why it is as supportive as it is. Neurotics traditionally have contempt for themselves, and, therefore, for each other, and they feel stigmatized at coming to a clinic, yet soon the group becomes supportive for them. It enhances their self-respect. There seem to be several reasons for this. The one that everyone points to is that it breaks down the feeling of isolation that our patients have. The one common denominator of people who feel that group experience has been successful, whether they are captains of industry, teachers, social workers, or patients, is the discovery that difficulties which they thought were unique to themselves are shared by other people. Apparently each of us is taken in by the other's mask, you might say. We know what our problems are, but we're fooled by the other person's front. In a group the masks go down and we find we are all in the same boat after all. This is immensely reassuring.

And, then, group therapy affords an opportunity which does not exist in individual therapy for patients to be helpful to each other. In individual therapy, all the help flows from the therapist to the patient. In group therapy, Patient X can say something that is very helpful to Patient Y. The discovery of Patient X that he can actually be of use to someone else raises his self-respect. Furthermore, any group which meets for a while develops a kind of cohesiveness. The members get a feeling of group belongingness which is supportive for them. I suppose that it goes back to combatting the feeling of isolation. This is often expressed in this way: "We've got more sense than our friends who have the same kind of troubles we have, but they don't have sense enough to come to the group." Thus, even though the patients first meet on the basis of defects, in the end the group becomes supportive. Dreikurs (1951) has stressed this very well in a brilliant little paper in which he points out that therapy groups are the only groups in our society in which the ticket for admission is a weakness rather than a strength.

In composing our groups we do not try to mix the grossly different diagnostic categories—hospitalized psychotics and neurotics and so-called psychopathic personalities. Also, we try to avoid having nothing but very passive, silent people, or nothing but over-aggressive people. We try to get some kind of balance. I haven't found that the clinical diagnostic categories are much help in this respect. A group can have everything in it from a mild character disorder to an ambulatory schizophrenic and function well. There are some limits to class differences, or educational differences, but they are usually wider than one thinks. One of the patients in my current group is a very rough kind of fellow, speaks bluntly and says "deez" and "doze" and so forth, but he happens to be quite intelligent and he gets along with a couple of perfect ladies in the group, who are very middle-class housewives.

I've covered briefly the evocative power of the group, and mentioned some aspects of support. Finally, there is the matter of implicit direction. There are multiple sources of this instead of just one. Feedback comes from several people in the group, and the group affords multiple models, so the patient has a wider choice of behaviors to identify with or reject. And as in individual therapy, the situation is such that the penalty for failure is greatly attenuated. If a member makes a boner or does something bad, he is easily forgiven. For one thing, the members are strangers to each other, and they know that any ill feelings that are generated in the group will go on ice until next week. Also, the ground rule that one is supposed to express one's feelings honestly and freely, tends to imply there is no penalty for this, or no prolonged penalty. There may be rough going for a while, but we have found that patients learn that if they stay with it, they feel better in the end.

There is one particular aspect of the group as a learning situation which I should like to mention, and that is its real-life quality. The therapy situation with just one person is perceived as artificial by many patients. The therapist's reaction is not a gauge of how other people will react, but group members tend to accept each other's reactions as valid. Members can readily carry group experiences over into their daily lives. Let me give one example of this. Often with a patient in both individual and group therapy, the same material will come up in the group as came up in individual treatment with entirely different repercussions. The example is a rather unusual one, I suppose, and that is why it sticks in my mind. It involves a man also still in individual treatment, a man who has a hard enough problem in all conscience. His eyesight is failing because of a degenerative eye disease. It is just a matter of time before he loses his vision, but this is not what gives him a neurotic problem. Several other members of his family are afflicted with the same condition, and to a greater degree than he is. They are all desperately shamed by this and try to hide it. They get into a perfect self-fulfilling prophecy situation. They feel that if people knew about "our affliction, they would scorn us, they would laugh at us, so we won't tell them." So what happens? At a party someone passes a plate full of canapes, and the patient's brother (who can barely see) drops it on the floor, and everyone laughs, and that just proves that everybody would laugh if they knew what was wrong with their eyes. This patient is night-blind, he stumbles at night. People with him think he is drunk, and he feels humiliated. This had been gone over repeatedly in individual interviews and nothing had happened at all, and it took him six months in the group before he could even mention that there was anything wrong with his eyes. When he finally mentioned it, he burst into tears, and of course, nobody scorned him and nobody laughed and everybody was helpful and sympathetic. From this point on, the whole problem began to ease up for him. After it came up in the group and he could see for himself how other people reacted to knowledge of his disability, he became able to tell acquaintances he could not see at night and could ask to hold their arm, for example, which he couldn't do before. Concomitantly his chronic depression lifted in spite of the progressive failure of his vision.

With this framework in mind let me present and discuss one group session at which there were four patients, although we shall concern ourselves with only three. One, Mrs. B, is a 33-year-old housewife who has a tremendous real-life problem. This was only her fourth meeting. Two years ago, her husband had an operation for a malignant tumor, and they told her that he would be dead in six months. He is still alive and there have been no recurrences, but the sword of Damocles has hung over her head all this time. She reacts to this mainly by the pathological symptom of intense depersonalization feelings. All of a sudden, she doesn't know who she is and her body seems changed. She had a post-partum depression three years earlier. In the background there is an enormous amount of anxiety and guilt over her mother and her brother, two years older, whom the mother favored, almost psychotically. She worshipped the ground he walked on. The patient was an ugly duckling. To compound the matter, this brother made sexual advances to her all during her adolescence. She denied any actual intercourse, but this whole situation is fraught with most unpleasant feelings to her. Like a schizophrenic, she has almost too much insight. She talks about how she transfers the feelings from her brother to her husband, all this kind of thing. She brings this up quite often in the group.

In the group, she was a well-groomed, self-assured, suburban housewife, who dominated her first meeting by acting like a therapist; she questioned another patient a lot, then told too much about herself. She talked about her husband's cancer and about the incest with her brother almost immediately, before there was any chance for group support to develop. Near the end, Mr. K, whom I shall describe presently, said that he was getting very angry at her, and that she talked too much. She broke down and cried. She was very shaken all the rest of the week, so she said, and somehow this intensified her transference feelings. She identified her older son and her husband with her brother, and hated them. This brought up the issue we have been focussing on. She wants desperately to be liked, to be close to people, and yet her manner drives them away, because she is so dominating. This is one of those conflicts one can see operating in the group, and she started it off again in the meeting I shall describe.

Another member of the group is Mr. C, a 48-year-old barber who for ten years had had many bodily symptoms of emotional tension such as compulsive sighing and much overt anxiety. For one period in his life, he was an alcoholic, but he stopped eight years ago, with the help of Alcoholics Anonymous. This was his twenty-third meeting. His history was not very revealing except that his barbershop was in a neighborhood that was changing from white to colored. He had had to move his home recently, and he realized that sooner or later he would have to move his barbershop. And I seized on this—mistakenly, in the sense that we made no progress on this issue. In the group, his behavior was quite interesting. At first, he was blandly humorous on the few occasions that he spoke. He never revealed anything personal but talked only about his complaints. One day when another therapist led the group, after about fifteen meetings, he compared notes with another patient about the poor treatment doctors had given them both, and then told about being an alcoholic. A few meetings later, again in my absence, he finally brought up a theme that seemed useful. He revealed that he constantly feels that everybody is taking advantage of him. He documented this to a paranoid degree. He told how years ago he had gone with a girl who eventually married somebody else, and then the girl pursued him with hostile intent and he was afraid she was going to poison him. He then revealed that he distrusted everyone. When I came back to the group at the next meeting he was able to say that he distrusted me, because I had focussed on the neighborhood changing color and this had nothing to do with his symptoms. His tremendous distrust became the issue we emphasized. First we accumulated examples and then in the meeting I shall describe raised the question of what he does to keep his distrust alive by behaving in such a way that the other person gets his signals mixed, and so tends to act in such a way as to fan his suspicion.

With respect to this patient's distrust, he brought up an early memory in a group meeting, and, of course, early memories often tell a lot about a person's present attitudes. He is an only child, and he described how when he would come home late, either his father or mother would dress up as a ghost and stand in the alley and he would be scared to death and run off. Other children would tell him the ghost was one of his parents, since sometimes it was a short ghost and sometimes a tall ghost, but he would never believe it. While telling this, he stressed how much he loved his parents and how wonderful they had been to him. One can surmise the source of his generalized distrust.

One more man must be kept in mind, a patient who teaches me humility because I didn't think the group or I could treat him at all, Mr. K. This was his twenty-fifth meeting. He is a 33-year-old single man who initially had been seen three years before, because he was in the hospital for evaluation of a congenital heart disease, which he has, but he also has a whole superstructure of neurotic symptoms. At that time, he stayed in psychiatric treatment for about two years, stopped for a while, came back to individual treatment and this time gravitated toward the group. His complaints were nightmares, and a fear that people might hurt him, or that he might hurt them. He was afraid of the dark and of being out alone. He had a pattern of pseudo-masculinity. He was a tough guy, wore worker's clothes and spoke in a gruff manner, drank too much at times, and ran around with women. I felt that this wasn't the kind of fellow I could work with; our values seemed to be utterly different, and yet, he turned out to be the best patient in the group and has improved. This came out of his discovery in the group of his fear and hate of women, to the point that when he began to argue with one of the women he panicked and dashed out of the room. From that point on, we began to focus on this problem with him—fear of women and fear of his own lack of masculinity, which turned out to be almost psychotic. He really thought his female cousin was going to put poison in his food. I can see now, in thinking about this man, that I didn't appreciate that he was favorably disposed towards psychotherapy and had come back voluntarily for another course because the first one had helped him. One might say that he had accepted the value system of psychotherapy!

The account which follows is of the group's twenty-fifth meeting. It begins with Mrs. B, who is talking about people accusing her of being dominating and overbearing; and she accused me of using the latter word.

Mrs. B—I liked him the first time I saw him [Mr. K]. And I can't—if I could put my finger on it and say: "Well, I don't like this about him or I don't like that." I guess that it's that I don't like to be criticized, probably.
Dr. F—When one's feelings are hurt, one strikes out.

[This was a kind of reflective attempt at reassuring her. She had been talking about disliking people and her fear of being criticized.]

Mrs. B—All I did. . . . Well, tears came to my eyes, and I said something. . . . They searched around for a word that described the way I was talking, and we settled on "overbearing." And, I know, when you said that—I mean when he said it and she said it and then when you said "overbearing"—I don't know, it was the same almost identical situation that I grew up with. My mother has used the word "overbearing" I don't know how often. And I had to agree with them because I realize it's overbearing. And yet, I guess it's the only way I ever had of making my point.
Mr. C—Just what do you mean by that? "Overbearing"—just how would you mean that?
Mrs. B—Well, I'm gonna [laughs]—I'm gonna make my point. I mean, my mother would say I'd give her the last word on my stomach to show her that I meant. . . . You know, if I'd be arguing with her, she'd never be able to get the last word. She'd say I always did, that I just keep driving at it all the time.

Mr. K—You have a demand, is that what it. . . .

Mrs. B—It was almost a need to make myself heard, I think. I don't know. I have no other way to do it. I couldn't reach her or my brother in any other way except through my mouth, I think.

Mr. C—I don't see where you're that way. That's why I don't get it—just exactly what you mean.

Mrs. B—Oh, I know I am!

Mr. K—You know what? That you're overbearing?

Mrs. B—With some people I am.

Mr. K—Well, I might have the wrong definition—you don't sound overbearing to me.

Mrs. B—I have very strong. . . .

Mrs. J—[To Dr. F] What would you mean by "overbearing"?

Dr. F—I'm trying to think whether I used the word first or whether Mrs. B used it first about herself.

[I don't know which of us was distorting, but I think it was the patient in this situation, because I usually am apt to reflect rather than start with a word like that. If it is true that it is the patient who is distorting, the purpose of this was to try to clear up this distortion.]

Mr. K—I don't—I never heard him say anything.

Mr. C—[To Mrs. B] I think you said it.

[This is interesting too. The group comes to my defense right away. One of the fears therapists have about group therapy is that the group will gang up on them. It is true that the patients can often express their feelings much more easily in a group than in individual therapy, and they do express their anger with the therapist more openly. But it is my experience that they never will gang up on him for long because they can't destroy their source of help. After all, they're depending on the therapist to help them, and sooner or later, the group swings around.]

Mrs. B—I thought you said it.

Dr. F—It doesn't matter at this point.

Mrs. B—No. [With embarrassed laugh] I got mad at you. I did. I'll be honest about it.

Dr. F—Getting mad at the doctor is one of the things to talk about. That's one of the most important things to talk about.

[That was an effort to set standards. She was getting apologetic about being mad at me, and I was rewarding her being able to say she was mad at me, to encourage her to talk about feelings toward the doctor.]

Mrs. J—Well, what do you mean by being overbearing? Do you say that, in other words, you'll press your point?

Mrs. B—Uh huh.

Mrs. J—And you think you do that here when you have something to say?

Mrs. B—Well, I–I, uh, think sometimes I talk out of nervousness, just to get it out of my system. And I think I felt these people were [laughs] helping themselves, and I almost felt obligated. . . .

Mrs. J—To help them?

Mrs. B—To help them.

Mr. C—In other words, you think you talk too much. Is that what you mean? I still don't get what you mean.

Mrs. B—Well, I might be offensive when I do it. . . . I don't know. As I say, I feel very strongly what I think. I mean, I have things set up just the way they're gonna be, and [laughs] nobody's gonna change me—on some things. I mean, I'm willing to listen to reason on some things, but there're some. . . . And I don't see why I'm not allowed to have those [laughs] thoughts or ideas, and when I do have them and I express them strongly, then I'm considered overbearing.

Dr. F—Have you ever thought how fortunate your husband and children are that you are a strong person?

[Here I tried to point out that this aspect of her personality wasn't entirely a liability, but also was an asset. To what extent it helped, I don't know.]

Mrs. B—I'm very grateful. But then I got to thinking—I thought, well, Tom reacted to me that way and Robert reacted to me that way, how about my children? Are they going to react the same way to me as Tom and Robert? And it kind of worried me.

[This was the thing, really. She is grateful that she is strong, but if the group reacts this way, do her children react in the same way? This is what she really was concerned about and which I missed, perhaps, in rushing in to reassure a little too early.]

Mr. K—You know, I just got that headache back, right now.

[Now Mr. K is about to enter the discussion in his characteristic indirect way. He is very aware of his body and when it kicks up, he announces he is under strain. This is the man who is terribly sensitive to overbearing women. It was he who started this subject by accusing Mrs. B of talking too much, then panicked over it, and now is able to talk about it. As a result of this one issue being discussed, this man is facing up to his dreadful fear of women, testing it, and finding he can stand it in the group.]

Mr. K—On the subject of overbearing, well, a woman has a right to be overbearing if she wants.

Mrs. B—Well, with my own children—

Mr. K—That's what hit me Saturday with my cousin. I kept her husband out; he was supposed to come home to go to the store [laughs]. I was the one!

Dr. F—She gave you the devil?

Mr. K—No, but I could see she wanted to jump on me, see? And, boy, that headache really got terrific.

Dr. F—And, here it is again.

Mr. K—Right here again.

Dr. F—Was it the word rather than what she was saying or the way she was saying it?

Mr. K—Just maybe the word, or what she was saying—I don't believe I could accept that, that a woman could be aggressive.

Dr. F—Without being dangerous?

Mr. K—Being dangerous, passive—They have a right to be—I mean, they're human. [Laughter] I don't know, maybe that—that struck me funny there in a way—just the way she was talking and the word "overbearing."

Mrs. B—About what I said about my own children, I didn't actually realize. . . .

Dr. F—I think the problem, Mrs. B, as I see it now, is that you feel you've got to be liked all the time. At the same time, you're a strong person.

Mrs. B—Yes, and it's a conflict.

Dr. F—Well, maybe it's a soluble one. Maybe you're not using your strength in the right way in trying to be liked.

[That was an attempt to formulate the issue for Mrs. B. You've got to be liked all the time, and at the same time, you are a strong person. I put it in a non-threatening way to the patient.]

Mrs. B—And I couldn't be mad at Robert [Mr. K].

Mr. K—Why?

Mrs. B—Well, I—I don't know, but I just couldn't.

Mr. K—Women—they couldn't be mad at me—not me [sarcastically].

Dr. F—They can't be mad at you?

Mr. K—Naw, they can't be mad at me. Not me. [Laughs] I don't know why.

Dr. F—It's sort of humiliating, I suppose, to feel that people can't be mad at you—makes you feel like a little boy, something like that.

[This is the only example here of reflective technique. I tried to reflect the feeling that he was being a little boy, so insignificant no woman could really be mad at him.]

In the next section, I tried to develop the theme of suspicion with Mr. C, which, incidentally, has relieved him—although I am unsure of this patient because he has gotten relief before, temporarily. His symptoms tend to shift. He no longer has the symptom he came in with, but he now reports others. He also does indicate considerable relief in many situations since he got on the topic of suspiciousness. Here he describes his experience with a dentist, who said what a nice patient he was, and thereby immediately aroused all his suspicions.

Dr. F—[To Mr. C] If you could have told me the minute you distrusted me that you distrusted me, it would have died down again, probably, because you talked about it. If you let it wait, it goes on piling up steam.

Mr. C—Well, that's—like I told you, last Monday I went to the dentist. He took me at 7:30. Anyway, I got in the chair and he got to going. And he started saying, "Well, you're a right nice patient," and I thought to myself, "Now, ain't he trying to build up a lot of stuff inside me." We've known each other for a while, you know, and he said, "You're a right nice fellow." I thought to myself: "How about this stuff?" Now I have to go back again, and he's gonna find more work there where he's gonna get more money—the teeth, he's gonna give me treatment on my gums, and here's one tooth he filled twice. And I laughed to myself coming down. I thought to myself, now, look at that stuff he was giving me. What I figured—of course, he does seem a right nice sort of a man—but, you know, I thought, well, he's just doing that now just to dog me for maybe fifteen, twenty dollars—

Mr. K—Suppose I told you you're a pretty good guy—what could I want offa you?

Mr. C—Well, that's something different.

Mr. K—Why?

Mr. C—Because you're not in a position to—

Mrs. J—You, in other words, don't trust doctors.

Mr. C—No. And a lot of people, too, as far as that goes.

Mrs. B—This seems to be tied up an awful lot with money.

Mr. C—Yeah, it does that too. I've noticed that, too, just here lately since you mentioned that. That's on my mind an awful lot.

Mrs. B—Like my mother, all her troubles stem right around money, money, money.

Mr. K—Like some time ago, he made a statement to me down in the room when he was paying the bill about somebody only paying $2.00.

Mr. C—Yeah, I noticed some was only paying $2.50 and some was paying $5.00. Well, I began to wonder: "Now, what is this?"

Mrs. B—According to what you can afford to pay—

Mr. K—[Laughing] Special privilege.

Mrs. B—Some people can't pay much and some can't pay anything.

Mr. C—I thought it was all one price—the way it is in everything. Lot of times, I'd get in there right close so I could see—I hate to ask anybody. [Laughter and everybody talking at once.]

Mr. C—If some was paying $2.50, I felt a little hurt. Why should I—

Mr. K—If it makes you feel any better—

[Laughter and talk.]

Mr. C—Huh?

Mr. K—I said, I'll let you know right now if it'll make you feel any better.

Mr. C—What?

Mr. K—How much I pay.

Mr. C—Oh, you're paying $5.00.

[Laughter and talk.]

Mrs. B—He's already checked that.

[Everybody laughing and talking.]

Mr. C—You're paying $5.00. You pay $5.00, too. Mrs. R was—

Dr. F—Is it your feeling that we're favoring Mrs. R or that we're gypping you? Or both?

Mr. C—Both.

Dr. F—And why are we doing it?

Mr. C—Why should I pay $5.00? I mean, I can figure I can't afford it anymore than anybody else. Many bills as I've got. That's the way I look at it.

[Everyone starts talking.]

Dr. F—If it's a hardship and you don't have the money, I'll refer you to the admitting officer who'll be glad to review the situation.

Mr. C—Here's the way I look at it. If I thought it would do any good, I'd go out and give them a thousand dollars tomorrow—if I could borrow the money.

Dr. F—It isn't a matter of the money here that's the point. You get the same service for zero, $2.50, or $5.00. Money doesn't make the difference. The money is determined by whether you can pay or not without hardship. If it's a hardship, then by all means go back and talk to the admitting officer again. . . . But that is not your problem. Your problem is your reaction to this, these feelings of favoritism, or of your being taken advantage of.

Mr. C—In other words, I'm being soaked.

After he first revealed his suspiciousness a few weeks ago, this man was able to tell with a great deal of shame that he had spied on every member of the group to find out how much each was paying in the out-patient department. This was a great step, to open up and talk about it, and although it caused a good deal of laughter and tension, at least it was out in the open. He feels that we are gypping him, that he has to pay more than some of the other people, which is the point I emphasized. What I did was to attempt to clarify the situation. I told him that if it was a real hardship, there was a way of getting his bill adjusted. I tackled the reality aspects of it. And then he went back to the feelings involved.

It seems to me that when an obvious distortion of a situation comes up, it can be corrected simply by referring to the facts rather than just reflecting feelings immediately. It is sometimes better to clarify the distortion and then say, "But this is the way you feel about it," as a useful teaching experience.

Returning to the group, let me summarize its progress. Mr. C gave more examples of episodes in which he felt gypped, until he came to one in which he had taken his iron to be repaired and the shopkeeper had told him "this iron can't be repaired, you need a new one." So what did he do? He bought the new iron, thinking all the time he had been gypped. He took the old iron home and still has it, thinking, "I'll take this to another repairman, and if he tells me it could have been fixed, I'll know I've been gypped." We were then able to bring up his way of prolonging these situations of feeling suspicious. He could have resolved this suspicion by taking the iron to somebody else, but he would rather leave it hanging. And then—I don't know if it was in this meeting or another one—he gave another example in which he ordered a Bromo Seltzer in a drug store, and he thought the girl said fifty cents, when he knew perfectly well that it cost ten cents. He held out fifty cents and the girl hesitated whether or not to take it, and then said ten cents. This confirmed for him that she was just ready to cheat him by taking the fifty cents. Here was an even clearer example of his contributing to the situation. Clarifying his role in keeping his suspiciousness alive was the most important single thing that happened in this meeting.

Implicit in this example is that I focus a great deal on the present. I discouraged Mrs. B over and over again from dwelling on her feelings toward her mother and her brother, and tried to keep her in the here and now—for example, her feelings that her children think she dominates them, and how she can behave differently in the group so that she will still be a strong person, but won't antagonize everybody. When pathogenic behavior appears in the group and everybody can see what is happening and feel it at the moment, it affords the major opportunity for therapy.

In summary, I am constantly seeking to support the patients, to evoke feelings in them, and to increase their learning potentialities in the situation rather directly, by clarifying distortions; and I also am frank about the fact that I am influencing the patients. I accept this about myself and, therefore, am quite open about it. These are the main points I have tried to present, and which the examples were intended to demonstrate.

The Adlerian Approach
to Psychodynamics

by Rudolf Dreikurs, M.D.

I SHALL PRESENT the position of Adlerian psychology only in regard to: personality development, psychopathology, and therapy, without comparing its position to other systems and approaches. Its similarity and difference to the approach of the neo-Freudians, Carl Rogers, George Kelly, and others, who are all moving more or less in the same direction, will be apparent.

First, let us discuss some of the fundamental tenets in regard to personality development and personality structure. It is strange that it has become necessary to re-emphasize again the social nature of man, to counteract the influence of other theories of personality development. Adler was one of those who proposed that man is thoroughly a social being, and all his problems are social problems. Whatever we call "human" is an expression of a social interaction, of social intercourse. For this reason, we can presume one basic desire in all human beings: the desire to belong, which Adler called "social interest." Whatever anyone does, he is trying to integrate himself into society, to participate in his social group. This may sound strange when we realize all the asocial and antisocial trends in human beings and the relative inability of man to function adequately socially. Adler maintained that every human being tries to participate in his own way in society; he is primarily concerned with finding his place in the group. It is only mistaken ways which some individuals seek, mistaken ideas,

60

mistaken approaches about finding the way, which lead them astray and create social tensions and pressures. But even these detours and miscalculations have to be understood on the strength of the underlying conviction that one has to have a place in the group, because only within the group can one function. Outside the group one is nothing.

Perhaps one of the most convincing examples of the social significance of anti- or asocial attitudes are the hermits, those who withdraw from society and openly display their disdain for people. They move away from the group. But, it is a fair guess that no hermit who lives a safe distance from a town would stay there if the town burned down and the people moved away. He has to emphasize his distance from people, and its recognition by them, in order to be a hermit. In other words, even in isolation, even in going away from people, the concern is *with* people, with society; the group is, for man, the natural element in which he has to move.

The term "group" is not restricted to any group but includes every group in which one finds oneself or with which one identifies. In the final analysis it is society and all mankind. Our movements within the group depend on our concept of social order and social life, and these concepts can be traced to the experiences and their interpretations which we have had with our family, our friends and our community. We all have some correct and incorrect, positive and negative notions about mankind. We all move in accordance with our ideas. Whenever we are within a group, we try to establish a place for ourselves. For instance, we have a group right here in this room, regardless how loosely we may belong. However, whatever anyone of us is doing here depends on our concept of the possibilities we have to integrate ourselves. Some, for instance, may want to show that they are superior intellectually to others, or even to the speaker; others may want to impress their sub-group by showing either interest or the lack of it. Still others may consider the needs of the situation and act accordingly. Each one's behavior will depend on his concept of how he can find his place in this given group. The same holds true for any other group where one may participate, temporarily or permanently. This holds equally true for membership in anti-social groups. They will attract those who find their goals in line with those of the group. A child who rebels against adult society will tend toward other such children with whom he forms the group. Together they express individually and collectively their anti-social feelings and rebellion.

We are often asked how Adler could attribute all psychopathological reactions and behavior deviations to inferiority feelings. The answer is this. As long as one feels equal to the situation and adequate to the task at hand, one is willing and able to participate in a constructive and useful way. Adler calls the motivation toward participation "social interest," and he considers the desire to belong the basic human motivation toward belonging. Only if one considers oneself as less than others, as inferior to them, then one moves, instead of toward others, toward self-elevation. Self-worth and self-esteem is a prerequisite for inner security because only then can one be sure of one's place in the group. In contrast, the feeling of inadequacy and of deficiency motivates movement not toward others, but away, either through useful compensations toward personal glory, or, if the feeling of failure is too pronounced, to the useless side. In either case, it results in mistaken approaches.

The individual's goals always manifest, often in a peculiar, even in a perverted way, his direction toward integration in the group. The child who demands attention does so not for the sake of attention; for him it means having a place, not gratification of any desire. The child who has power as his goal and tries to defeat the adults does so not in order to get into a fight for fighting's sake, or because of any inner drive or aggression; for him, defeating others means being somebody. Giving in means that he has no place, no value, that he is a nobody. The child who tries to get even considers hurting others as his only way to prove that he is somebody. It is a very perverted form of integration, but these are the only forms for certain children to find significance in the group. Of course, goals may be long range toward some fictitious idea of security in life, and then they may not be clearly connected with immediate goals. The latter, in turn, are tied in with the overall movement of the person toward what he thinks should be his place in life.

With regard to the social nature of man, Adler's psychology finds itself today more easily accepted and comprehended. But there are other fundamental concepts in Adlerian psychology which are probably responsible for the fact that it has found little acceptance until recently. As we consider the various fundamental tenets of Adlerian psychology, it will be seen that Adler was fifty years ahead of his time. Some of his basic concepts contradicted contemporary scientific assumptions. Today, his concepts are increasingly supported by scientific developments in other fields. There is first the *holistic* concept of Adlerian psychology. The term *Individual Psychology* (Adler, 1932) is very often misunderstood, as if it were in contrast to "social" and "mass" psychology. What is meant by the term *Individual Psychology* is that the individual is indivisible. He has to be seen as a whole. It is the emphasis on this *Ganzheit*, and it is this *holistic* approach to each individual, who has to be seen as a whole, which characterizes Adlerian psychology.

✓ Now, this holistic concept was utterly unperceivable at the time of Adler. It has only become acceptable since Smuts (1926) developed his theory of *Holism* and gave it a more fundamental basis. Since then it has become fashionable for everybody to speak about *Ganzheit* and *Holism,* particularly in psychology. The peculiar fact is that most people who use the term *Holism* are not quite clear as to what it means, and usually use it incorrectly. Particularly in psychoanalytic literature there is a great deal of emphasis on holistic perception, which implies that if one takes into consideration the total picture of an individual, then one has, so to speak, a holistic picture of him. This is contrary to what is meant by the term *Holism. Holism,* a concept which Gestalt psychologists were the first to develop in psychology, maintains that the whole is *more* than the sum total of its parts. This concept is often overlooked by people who assume that they use the holistic approach. A great deal of time and effort in the field of psychology is actually devoted to an unholistic effort—namely, to explain the whole from an examination of parts, and of partial mechanisms. Take the theory of psychosexual development to explain behavior, or the behavioristic approaches as they appear in various forms, assuming that behavior is based on stimulus-response reflexes. All these efforts indicate an intent to understand the whole through an understanding of partial phenomena, which is just the opposite of the holistic concept. The holistic approach assumes that you can understand the whole only as a whole in which the individual parts have their place, their function; but the whole is *not* explainable through the knowledge of any part—or all parts.

Now, are there any practical consequences of such theoretical assumptions? Do we have any access to an understanding of the whole without looking at its parts? Here is where Adler, for perhaps the first time, combined the holistic concept with another concept which initially was completely rejected and unacceptable: the *teleological* approach. Teleological means "goal directed," from *teleos,* an end, the goal; it is finalistic. This teleological approach was not new in his time; Bergson and others mentioned it. The neo-Vitalists in medicine emphasized the purposive nature of pathology in serving a curative purpose. For instance, fever became recognized as not just an expression of pathological processes, but a means to stimulate healing forces by combatting invasion of germs or other toxic substances. Adler, recognizing that the whole individual cannot be understood by parts, cannot be understood by any individual characteristic or partial phenomenon, found that the individual *can* be understood by the goals which he sets for himself, and towards which he moves. In the movement of the whole toward a goal, the whole of an individual is expressed. His whole past, which may have conditioned him to this choice, his present attitude, which activates this movement, and his future ideals which direct him—the whole of the individual is involved, his body, his mind, all his functions—in the one movement toward a goal. And without the realization of goal-directed behavior, one cannot perceive, one cannot see, the individual as a whole.

This teleological consideration is so fundamental in Adlerian psychology that Neufeld (1954) has correctly called our form of therapy a "teleo-analytic" approach. It will be seen in a discussion of therapy later on that the understanding of goals and helping individuals to change their goals are prime objectives of Adlerian psychotherapy.

These teleological mechanisms were contrary to scientific premises because teleology in the past has been linked to theology, which assumed that each individual serves goals set for him by God, by destiny. Therefore, due to its historical meaning, the term has been unacceptable to scientists. We find such objections far fewer in this country than in Europe.

There is another objection which many have to teleological considerations. It presupposes creativity which does not fit into our scientific orientation. Goal seeking remains a meaningless notion unless one is ready to assume that the individual is free to choose his own goals. Therefore, he is to a certain extent free from strictly deterministic, causalistic influences. It is this implication of teleology, and it is this teleological aspect of *Holism*, which makes holistic concepts so difficult to comprehend for our generation of scientists. They are steeped in the traditional mechanistic, causalistic principle which stimulated the tremendous scientific progress of the last centuries.

Interestingly enough, were it not for recent development in physics, and in the natural sciences, Adlerian psychology would be passé by now. It is the support from new scientific trends which is responsible for Adler attaining today his place in the field of psychology. An interesting incident may perhaps demonstrate this. Last year, during a summer course at the University of Oregon, I gave an advanced seminar for psychologists. It was difficult for many students to understand what I had to say. They rejected the assumption that there could be anything except causal relationships; that anything like free will, like self-determination, is possible. However, there was one student who defended my position, and tried to help me to explain these concepts to others. I asked him whether he had studied Adlerian psychology before. He said, "No, but I first studied physics before I switched to psychology." And that was the reason why he understood what I was saying.

If you wish to acquaint yourself with these new forms of thinking, you have to step out of the field of psychology and look into the field of physics and natural science. May I recommend an excellent little pamphlet, *Teleological Mechanisms*, which was published by the New York Academy of Science in 1948. It contains a paper by Lawrence Frank (1948), which, I think, is one of the best papers on teleological mechanisms.

Causality is only an aspect of statistical probability. Only because of the great number of cases in which the same cause seems to have the same influence, does it *look* as if there were a causal relationship. But this does not hold true for the individual organism, which is not determined by statistics. Frank (1948) points out that the causal principle is a linear relationship: one cause—one effect. This is no longer true in our scientific perspectives. The assumption of a completely passive object is incorrect. There is always an interaction between an object and the force to which it is exposed; this interaction may be very minimal in the physical bodies, but it is very pronounced in biological and even more in social processes. Furthermore, the causal principle assumes, in this linear approach, that one force affects a body, while we know today that the whole field in which the force operates is often more important than the force itself. It requires some fundamental reorientation to understand the newest developments in science in general, and in psychology in particular. It is this resurgence of non-mechanistic thinking, of non-Aristotelian and non-Euclidian principles, which makes the position of Adlerian psychology more acceptable today.

To clarify what is meant by linear relationships, let us say that here is an object; here is a force. This is the traditional form of interaction. If there are multiple forces, all that is necessary is the addition of more lines.

Even though more forces are added, it is still a simple relationship. Forces are affecting an object. When two other factors are taken into consideration, the field and the interaction of the object itself, then you see a completely different picture. Here is an example about fields. In the traditional study of physics, we learned that the electrical current which is used in various electrical appliances travels in the wire, from the positive to the negative pole. The electrical energy for a clock on the wall, a microphone, or a lamp, was assumed to be in the wire which connects the appliance with the socket. Now the concept of electricity is quite different. We know today that the electrical energy which is responsible for lighting the lamp travels outside the wire. It is affected by the magnetic field around the wire. By changing the magnetic field around the wire, the current can even be reversed. This is not a case of multiple causation, but a different perception.

ᐯ Let us take for another example, one which Adler used when he first discovered and developed his own orientation. We all assume that the individual is influenced by a variety of factors in multiple causation. Two of the most important sets of factors are supposed to come from heredity and environment. The emphasis may switch at times from one to the other. We have evidence that in an autocratic society, man is supposed to be primarily determined by his heredity; while in a democratic setting, man is considered to be more influenced by environmental forces. In general, most people regard heredity and environment as crucial factors in determining the development of each individual. Adler for the first time proved that all these considerations are fallacious; they are inadequate. One little detail was forgotten— namely, the child himself. Adler pointed out in his early study of organ inferiorities that what a person is born with is less important than what he does with it afterwards. His study of hereditary deficiencies showed that one child will take his deficiency for granted, without any effort of compensation, and will develop a lasting deficiency where he originally was only confronted with a difficulty in function. Another child may encounter the same deficiency and decide to make up for it, and in his compensatory efforts, he usually tends to overcompensate. As a result, he will end with a special accomplishment in the very area where he had originally been deficient. Now, all those who are mechanistically and causally oriented will seek to discover what makes one child give up and the other compensate; they may look for all kinds of factors in the environment to find the cause of the child's choice. But both children may have a very similar situation. Two children may be treated in the same way and one be discouraged and the other one will try harder. We cannot explain the child's behavior merely by all the causal factors to which he is exposed, but by his own interpretation of what he encounters, within himself or around him, by his conclusions, which is a creative act. This interaction cannot be explained by any multi-factor consideration; there is a new element, and this is the act of choosing, what Lawrence Frank (1948) calls the "response" of the object. This kind of interaction exists in nature and is most pronounced in the most complex organism, in man with his mental and psychic faculties.

In our work, we actually do not speak of forces. We speak about the movement of the whole being. The individual may set his goals in a conflict of preferences, and ambivalence serves as a good point for illustration. Ambivalence is always self-deception. A person is not driven in two directions. He may pretend to be for specific purposes, either to shed his responsibility, or in order not to move at all. I will give you an example which Kuenkel (1928) presented, which shows you the role of ambivalence in holistic perception. A man at a swimming pool tries to jump off a diving board. He runs, and suddenly he is afraid and stops. He goes back, angry at himself, and tries again. Again he stops in the last moment. The third time, he runs and jumps in. This is a very good example for so-called ambivalence. On one side, he wanted to jump in; on the other, he was afraid—of either the water or the fall, or whatever it may be—so he seemed to be torn between two motivations. From a holistic point of view, it doesn't look like that at all. What did this man really want to do? If he wanted to jump, why did he first hesitate? If he didn't want to jump, why did he finally jump? We are so trained to look at one isolated fact of "I want; I don't want," that we don't see the whole movement. From an holistic point of view, that is purposive behavior. This man is one of those who try to conquer themselves, who try to show their will power. "I will prove that I can do it." Now, if he had merely run and jumped, he couldn't have proved anything. He had first to build up his fear of the water, which he then afterwards overcame to prove his strength to himself. Of course, such a man does this not only in the swimming pool, but in life generally. It is a very important procedure, because after he has conquered himself so many times and demonstrated his will power, then when he wants to do something he shouldn't do, he simply fails to conquer himself; and he has a wonderful excuse, because this time his will power wasn't strong enough. Furthermore, it gives him an opportunity to look down on all the people who do not have the will power to control themselves. We have to see this behavior as part of the movement in life. It is one movement; ambivalence is a part of it. That is how we approach the problem. Whatever one is doing, it is one approach. Ambivalence is *one* approach, being torn apart is *one*, indecisiveness is *one*. Indecisiveness is not "caused" by opposing interests or desires. A person may not want to take a step, he does not want to make a decision, or he wants somebody else to make a decision for him. Perhaps he wants to be free of obligations afterwards, because he really did not want to do it. So everything he is doing is one movement and has one purpose. There is never a possibility of a divided movement, because he can only move in one direction, and that is the only direction that counts.

In line with these basic concepts, we try to understand the individual in his two aspects: in his goals, which express his *total personality;* and in his *field of action,* since only within a particular field does any behavior have a specific goal. If the individual were driven by unconscious forces, by desires, drives, and so on, then he could fulfill his drives, his desires, independent of the situation in which he finds himself. If, on the other hand, we want to understand the goal of behavior, then we have to see the area in which it takes place. The same behavior in a different situation may express a completely different goal, always in a social sense, since human problems are primarily òf a social nature. We have to understand the social movement, the social significance of what we call behavior. In our frame of reference, character and personality traits indicate movement. Every action of the individual has to be understood within the field in which it takes place, and within the framework of the total personality.

Goals can be divided into long range or immediate goals. Long range goals have to be understood by another aspect of Adlerian psychology, i.e., the assumption of the *constancy of personality*. We remain fundamentally the same person after our personality has been well established in early childhood. That is perhaps one of the most outstanding contributions of Adler (1929), the concept of the *life style*, which characterizes each individual.

The child is born into a world of which he knows nothing. Social life is so complex that one cannot rely on a few instincts as do many animals, who at birth have almost all the knowledge they need for survival. They know the food which is suited for them, and which is dangerous; they know where to go, how to move, what to do. In contrast, social life is extremely complex, and the infant is one of the most helpless creatures. Everything which we need in order to live has to be learned and trained. The child devotes his first few years to learning. He learns by trial and error and then draws his conclusions. Whatever he considers as helpful in his attempt to find his place is maintained. In this way, the child develops some basic concepts as guides for life. He develops his ideas about what he can do and what he can't. Unfortunately, children are excellent observers, but bad interpreters. They observe keenly what goes on, but do not always draw the correct conclusions. As a consequence of incorrect conclusions, mistaken concepts are formed, mistaken beliefs about oneself, about others, about life. Such mistaken beliefs are the reasons for the child to proceed—in his desire to find a place for himself—in ways which are disturbing and destructive for himself and others. The child experiments with an almost unlimited number of schemes and approaches and draws definite conclusions of which he is not aware. He observes himself in comparison with parents, brothers and sisters, and tries to establish himself in his interaction with them. From a mechanistic point of view, one is inclined to believe that the child is driven on the one hand by his hereditary endowment, and on the other, is compelled by the social forces around him. But this is not true. The process of interaction which takes place between all members of the family is much more complex. We have evidence that children often influence their parents much more than the parents influence them. Mother and father and siblings may follow more the conviction of one child, wrong as it may be, thereby fortifying convictions rather than causing them.

To use a frequent example, we know that most young children are convinced that by themselves they are nothing—only through others can they have a place. We call them dependent, speak of dependency needs, and consider it quite normal for children to feel and act in this way. Many theories are developed to justify the existence of the dependency needs of young children. But what actually takes place is quite different from what most workers in the field assume. The child is not dependent because he is weak and small, but he uses a real or assumed weakness, which is mostly exaggerated, to put his parents in his service. He plays weak, he plays dependent. A mother who is told to give him more security so that he eventually may become independent is thereby induced to intensify the child's feeling of weakness because he finds it most effective in order to get service and attention. On the other hand, if the mother is advised to stop serving the child, he very often—almost in one leap—jumps out of his condition of dependency and may become independent overnight. His dependency has lost its value for him, and, therefore, he discontinues it.

Another example: we witness today a considerable amount of genuine interest in children. Most parents are devoted to their children; they do everything for them. At the same time, there are more and more children who feel rejected and are convinced that nobody cares for them. Since it has been the practice in child psychiatry and child guidance that the workers in these fields see only the children and listen only to what they have to say, they come understandably to the conclusion that the children are rejected. But we know today that this is not true, in most cases. Most children who feel rejected are not rejected, but assume they are because their impressions and interpretations of what they experience are faulty. For instance, a child may assume that mother does not love him if she is not constantly busy with him or does not always do what he wants. Getting constant attention or having his own way are his premises for feeling accepted and having a place and being loved. Or a child who has had the mother all for himself and suddenly has to share her with a little brother or sister may come to the conclusion that mother, who now spends so much time with the baby, does not love him any more. And now a sad sequence of events takes place. As soon as the child gets the notion that he is no longer loved, regardless of how incorrect this notion may be, he behaves in such a way that it is difficult for mother to show him how much she loves him. He becomes provocative, tries to prove that his opinion is correct. He behaves according to what he expects, namely to be treated in an unfriendly way, and he succeeds in collecting the proof. Particularly provocative are the children who believe that only power over others and defeat of authorities can give them status and a place. In trying to prove their significance they provoke anger, fights, and criticism, which adds to the validity of the assumption that they are not loved. Actually, they are mistaken. They are loved and would be treated differently if they did not operate under faulty premises. Now we can see why so many child psychologists who work only with children and not also with their parents come to the mistaken conclusion that these poor children really *are* rejected. We can also understand, although we have to deplore the fact, why they tell the mothers to be more permissive, to show more love, while actually what the mothers need to be told is not to give in so much, not to yield to the children's undue demand for attention and power, so that the children can find out that they are loved, and don't need all the attention and all the fuss and all the power which they succeed in arrogating for themselves. In our child guidance work, we do exactly that. We help the parents to extricate themselves from the domination of their children, to which they are usually exposed in our time. The success of children in tyrannizing the parents does not give them the feeling of being loved, it only makes them more determined to have their own way, which is their mistaken idea of finding their place. A child who thinks that he is important only as long as he can do what he wants may very well succeed in doing what he wants, at least most of the time, but he will never feel sure of his place following this approach. There are other ways in which parents can convey their respect and love than by giving in to their children or making slaves out of themselves for the assumed welfare of their children.

Since many people may feel that parent-child relationships are more important than sibling-sibling relationships, let me digress for a moment to discuss this. Let us imagine, for example, two boys, one of whom is preferred by mother; he looks like her father, or her brother, and she adores him. The other seems to follow her husband's family, he looks and acts like him, and she dislikes him. She does everything for her favorite, and lets the other one shift for himself, or even pushes him down. How will the first one develop? This depends to a larger extent on his relationship to his brother and his accomplishments than on what the mother does. If the neglected or rejected child really becomes discouraged and consequently fails, academically or socially, then the first will have a chance to be a good boy and a good student. But, if in the interaction between the two, the other considers the first as mamma's boy and is determined to show him that he is a real man, that he can study and be independent, then he may win out, if the first one lets him. All of his mother's love will not save the favored child and will not prevent him from becoming deficient unless he succeeds in asserting himself against the challenge of his brother. Whether he becomes a failure or not, he still can maintain his mother's love; however, her behavior to him will be greatly influenced by what he decides to do with himself.

During the early formative years, each individual grows up in a particular setting of the family, which we call his "family constellation." In the interaction with other members of the family, he develops his own notion about how to integrate himself into the family group. Affected by the competitive spirit of our time, he tries to stay ahead of his main competitors, which are usually in the next older or younger siblings. The first and second child are almost always in strong competition. Where one fails, the other moves in; where one succeeds, the other gives up. As a consequence, each becomes different in temperament, character, interests, and personality. Actually, the interaction between the children influences the personality development of each much more than do the parents. The parents are generally helpless bystanders who don't know what to do. Since they do not know how to reconcile the conflicts of the children and how to mitigate the competitive strife between them, their corrective efforts, misguided as they are, usually tend to increase the conflicts and the competition.

We all develop a very concrete notion about what we are, what we can do, how we can succeed and under which circumstances we feel we belong and have a place. Throughout our lives we operate on these basic assumptions of which we are unaware. This does not mean that the ensuing constancy of personality does not permit a wide range of overt behavior patterns. Let us assume, for instance, a person who has to be the first; he has been the first born and tried all during his life to remain on top. He succeeded in keeping his other siblings down. He was the best student, best behaved, most considerate, always right. He had to be the first, otherwise he would have been nothing at all. As long as he can be first in a positive way, he will do what is good and right; but if he encounters a life situation where he can't be better than all the others, he may give up, either turn into a new direction of activities, or switch—as we say—from the useful to the useless side. If he can't be the best, he may want to become the worst.

Here is an example for this rather frequent dynamic pattern. A young girl grew up in a small western town as the youngest of three siblings. Her two older brothers, like everybody else, paid considerable attention to her and made a great fuss over her. She was just a "darling"; nothing ever happened to this family that was as beautiful and precious as this little girl. She grew up with the conviction that she was something special. But soon she was not satisfied with being just a little girl. She wanted to be as good as any boy. So, she became the leader of a gang of boys. It was not a gang in an antisocial sense; rather they did all kinds of adventurous things, climbing trees and mountains, playing wild games, etc. She was their undisputed leader. It was her way of showing that even though a girl, she could be as good as any boy, or even better. At the age of nine or ten, it became obvious that it was not quite the thing for a girl to behave like that; it detracted somewhat from her glory. Almost over-night, she decided to give up the role of a boy; she now tried to prove that she could also be better than any girl. She began to study, turned into a bookworm, a very sophisticated young lady who managed to have a whole coterie of boys courting her. Naturally, for her, this was the only possible way—she graduated as valedictorian, as the outstanding girl of the community. At the outstanding university to which she was sent, she found that despite all her excellent training, she was unable to be the best student in her courses, although she was pretty good, and had good grades. Neither was she the outstanding girl; other girls were more sophisticated, were better dressed, and consequently were more popular with boys. For her that meant that she was nothing, a nonentity. Since she was not the first in anything, she had no place at all—until she hit on a new approach. In one of the classes the instructor spoke about epilepsy. That was her cue. She visualized herself lying in the street in convulsions with foam at her mouth. That's what she was, an epileptic. In her understandable distress, she sought psychiatric help. Naturally, she wanted to be well again, because she suffered. But at the same time, she tried to impress me that she was the worst patient I ever had seen. What could be worse than lying in the street in convulsions with foam at the mouth? This was the epitome of sickness, of failure. She was completely devoted to this idea, could not think of anything else. Classes, grades, popularity, and boys became meaningless. She made a complete switch from the useful to the useless side, creating a side show, so to say, where she again could maintain her assumption of being something special. She never actually fainted or had an attack; but that was not necessary since she visualized it vividly. It was her third pattern of being outstanding, first as a gang leader of boys, the adventurous devil, then as a sophisticated young lady with highest popularity and academic rating, and now the worst epileptic case one could imagine. Even visualizing herself lying helpless on the street was a triumph, although a perverted one. Her basic concept that she had to be the first led to a great variety of movements, all understood by the constant factor in her life. "Only being the first one and having everybody noticing me, only then do I have a place in life."

In psychotherapy, the life style of each patient has to be clearly determined. We have developed a technique which enables us to do so within one or two interviews. There are two areas for investigation of the life style. First, we determine the family constellation, the interaction between all the members of the family, and thereby perceive the movement of the patient in contrast to the movement of his parents, siblings, and others in the family group. The second most important single technique is one of the most significant contributions of Alfred Adler (1929), which has been almost entirely overlooked for the last forty years and is now slowly being rediscovered. It pertains to the significance of *early recollections*. They permit a rather clear and reliable perception of the person's outlook on life, because he remembers, of the millions of early childhood experiences, only those which fit into it. Knowing what a person remembers from his early childhood in terms of concrete incidents as they occurred gives a picture of what life is like for him. On the strength of the exploration of the family constellation and of the early recollections, we are in a position to determine with considerable certainty the concept of the patient, his mode of moving, and what we call his "basic mistakes," which need correction if we want to help him. This is a relatively simple technique which nevertheless requires skill and training to be used adequately. It permits insight into the personality structure of the patient. His life style* could not be recognized without such an approach.

I would now like to discuss briefly some psychological dynamics which we see differently than others. One is the problem of unconscious processes which dominate, to a large extent, contemporary considerations about psychodynamics.

Consciousness and unconsciousness are qualities which may characterize certain psychological processes. In other words, what we think, feel, or intend may be conscious or not. But we find no evidence that there is an "Unconscious." There is no particular part of our psychological structure devoted to unconsciousness as the construct of an Unconscious may indicate. In contrast, it seems that there is a continuum in degree of awareness of what goes on in us. As Adler said, there is nothing of which we know nothing, and nothing which we know perfectly clearly. The unawareness and the short moment of full conscious perception may hide the incompleteness of it. I have

---

*For additional information on determining a patient's life style, the reader is referred to: Adler (1938), Ansbacher and Ansbacher (1956), Dreikurs (1950, 1954) and Way (1950).

found the function of the eye as a good example to demonstrate the various degrees of awareness. We perceive visual pictures with the retina. The retina is a highly organized layer with light cells of different functions. Those on the periphery provide merely a dim view of the surroundings; those closer to the middle permit increasing perception of color, form, and shape. However, only a small central group, the *fovea centralis*, enables us to perceive the objects clearly in shape and color. If you hold your finger at the side of your head you don't see it, but if you move it you can perceive that something is moving. We perceive motion before we perceive form. As you move your finger forward, you see now that there is something, but you can't see what it is until you bring it clear in front. It is obvious for what purpose the eye is organized in such a way. If we had no *fovea centralis*, we would see everything that goes on, but not clearly; and if we had nothing but the *fovea centralis*, the rest of the field would be cut out, as in tunnel vision. You could see very clearly what is in front of you, but you would not know what is going on around you. You need this wide field of perception, but it does not have to be clear at the periphery. If you need a clear perception, you can turn your head so that you can focus on what you want to see. What is true for vision is true for life in general. In order to orient ourselves, we need a dim vision of everything, and a clear vision of just what is important at the moment. Consciousness and unconsciousness means little or greater awareness, and is similar to clear or dim perception of vision.

There is much that we sense without being fully aware of it. We become fully aware and conscious only of that on which we focus our full attention. The vast majority of the biological, physiological, and psychological processes which take place in our body and in our mind do not reach the conscious level, and remain, therefore, in a state of various degrees of unawareness. Consciousness, full awareness, then, is an exception and is extremely limited. We are not aware of what we are doing most of the time, even when we think we are. When you ask a child why he did something wrong he actually does not know. If he says so, he is usually right, although it infuriates parents and teachers. And when he gives you a reason, it is usually a rationalization or excuse, either deceiving himself or others. The trained psychologist can explain to a child the reasons for his transgressions. Not knowing them is the rule; knowing, the rare exception. We are trained to assume that awareness is an important factor in motivation, that it makes much difference whether our behavior has conscious or unconscious reasons. Consequently, if we realize that we are not aware of our motivation, we use this unawareness as a kind of excuse as if our bad behavior would be more excusable if we don't know its reason than if we do. The motivation for bad behavior is equally wrong regardless of whether we are aware of it or not.

In general, awareness of motivation is very rare. Most of the time we either do not pay attention to our real motivation or we delude ourselves about it. We see fully only what we need to know and what we want to know. In most instances, our actions are so well trained that they do not demand our full attention, and therefore our consciousness. In other instances if we knew completely what we wanted to do, our consciences would not permit us to do it. Conscious motivation and action in the light of full awareness is a rare exception and occurs only in a minute part of all our actions and activities.

It is a great mistake to assume that the unconscious is to blame for most detrimental and antisocial actions. As was said, unconscious processes characterize a wide range of our activities; and from them come some of our best motivations, the highest aspirations, the best accomplishments. If we could compare the percentage of detrimental actions which result from conscious or from unconscious thought processes, we would find the conscious processes as more often damaging. They, and not hidden thoughts, interfere often with our functions, hinder more than help, and stifle our potentialities. They, rather than unconscious thoughts, are the seat and cause of disturbances.

This brings us to another mistaken assumption, namely that objectivity is advisable and subjectivity deplorable. It is high time that we correct our value system with regard to motivation and behavior. Presently, consciousness is regarded as good and unconsciousness as bad, objective as good and subjective as bad, rational as good and emotional as bad. This value system seems unjustifiable. Let us first take subjectivity. It is not only not detrimental but highly desirable. We need to be subjective in order to live socially. A completely objective person cannot inject himself in the give and take of life. He has to choose, to take sides, to prefer, to reject, to stand up for his interests and his viewpoint. Subjectivity is not only unavoidable, but a prerequisite for social participation. Adler recognized this fact when he described "biased apperception" as an integral part of the normal personality. It permits us to perceive things only as we want to see them. If we were to see them differently, our schemes and movements would be stifled, so that we could not move any more. Anyone who tries always to be correct and right before he moves finds himself usually unable to move very much, because he cannot ever be quite sure. Therefore, biased apperception is a prerequisite and subjectivity a means for social movement. It may often be necessary to see the other side; but if one always sees the other side, how can one oppose anyone, since he undoubtedly has some good reasons for what he does? We have to take chances, to choose in accordance with our inclination to prefer what we like and to decide what we want. And we cannot have any bias if we become aware of it. For this reason, I assume a psychological uncertainty principle which will prevent us from ever seeing ourselves with complete knowledge and clarity. Oppenheimer pointed out that we either function as actors or as observers. Introspection intereferes with doing, objectivity with forceful action. Therefore, analysis of our actions and conscious understanding of our motives is only necessary when our actions become disturbing and detrimental to us. Only then can introspection and analysis in a therapeutic setting bring certain psychological dynamics to our consciousness, so that we may reconsider our premises. Afterwards, new and improved concepts, the result of our corrective efforts, become again inaccessible to our conscious attention and we again are unaware of our motivations which now may be more adequate. At any rate, we have to learn to trust our subjectivity, our unconscious processes, because they are us and not merely part of us. Certainly they are not a part from which we can dissociate ourselves as if we were not responsible for them.

This brings us to the problem of emotions. Emotions are in disrepute today, and it seems that somebody should come to their rescue. Contrary to accepted conventions, emotions are never the cause of disturbances. People are not emotionally disturbed; they are deficient in their social movement, in their goals, in their form of social integration, because they have wrong concepts about themselves. Anyone moving toward an anti-social goal will naturally need emotions to stimulate him in this endeavor, and his emotions will be as anti-social as his actions. But this is not the fault of emotions. They are not our masters, they are our tools. Our goals are not determined by our emotions, but our emotions suit our goals which we set ourselves in line with cognitive processes of which we are not aware. Adler spoke about "private logic" as the basis for whatever we do. We only do what we intend to do for reasons which are always logical, although not necessarily conscious or objective. Our actions become understandable only when we know their underlying logic. Emotions, therefore, are not responsible for wrongdoings, they are not compelling us, they are not opposed to reason. Rather reason and emotions have a continuum similar to consciousness and unconsciousness. Their coordination is similar to the use of both hands which seem to oppose each other, but which naturally are coordinated and work together. We use them as we see fit.

If someone unacquainted with human anatomy and physiology were to see a man using his hands in his effort to take a glass of water, he might well describe an apparent antagonism between the right and left hand. They might seem to oppose each other and cause the water to spill. Actually, the left hand never works against the right hand, they never really "oppose" each other. Both hands do only what the person makes them do, and this may include spilling the water. Similar to the function of the right and left hand is the relationship between the reason and the emotions, the conscious and the unconscious, the possibilities of being objective and subjective. In each case, one of the pair opposes the other, but only for our own benefit, as most muscles are operating as antagonistic forces, abductor and adductor, opposing each other in order to obtain a stable motion. Their opposition is a functional necessity.

For me, emotions are means, expressions of thoughts. For others, they come from some depths of personality, from the instincts or any other source over which the individual has no control. As we see it, emotions are necessary to take a forceful stand. You have to love or hate, to want or dislike, in order to move forcefully. You have to generate those emotions which permit and support what you intend to do. Outwardly, emotions may appear as a cause for forceful action, particularly when the action is antisocial, undesirable. One may be inclined to say that emotions sway us. Actually, people don't know that emotions don't sway anyone if he does not want to be swayed, so that he can do what he knows he shouldn't. We are conditioned to blame our emotions, particularly when we have intentions which we do not want to admit to ourselves. We pretend to be good, and therefore cannot admit intentions which are not so good, but we are perfectly willing to blame our emotions for having made us do what we really do not want or mean to do.

Guilt feelings have a particular significance for such self-defenses. As I see it, guilt feelings are the demonstration of good intentions which we do not have. They occur only when we want to dissociate ourselves from what we are doing, blaming past transgressions for our inability—or better, unwillingness—to behave properly now. We feel guilty only when we are up to some mischief. Anyone who intends to do the right thing and is confident that he can do it cannot afford the luxury of, nor does he need, any guilt feelings. Guilt feelings have a purpose, and the purpose is never a good one. While we demonstrate forcefully our goodness by feeling guilty, we deceive ourselves and others about our real intentions.

Let us take another example. A generally accepted modern concept is that of psychosomatic medicine. It assumes a dualism of psyche and soma which actually do not exist as entities. There is no psyche without a body, and a body without a psyche would cease existing. Von

Bergmann, like many others, suggests that they are only adjectives but not entities. We can speak about psychological factors in somatic processes which undoubtedly exist, but only in the same way as we can distinguish the movement of the right and of the left hand. It is not the psyche which influences the soma or vice versa; it is the individual who has a soma and a psyche, who can think and feel and act, biologically and socially. All these functions are at the disposal of one individual, as he moves toward his goals. It seems that we are entering a new era in medicine which will not be affected by psycho-somatic considerations and distractions. Instead of studying the effects of emotions on body functions, we will recognize the tremendous power of the individual over all his functions, be they physiological, emotional, rational or unconscious. In general, sociologically as well as scientifically, we are beginning to recognize the tremendous strength of the individual just as we discovered the tremendous power within the atom which heretofore was considered the smallest particle of existence and the symbol of smallness and insignificance. We are becoming aware that pathological processes, not only in the psychic and mental, but also in the somatic field, are subordinated to the individual's movement in life toward specific goals. One group of physicians, the surgeons, have early shown great understanding for and interest in psychodynamics. They know only too well that the will to live or its absence may in many cases determine the outcome of an operation more than their skill. All depends on what the patient wants to do with himself. There is evidence that we can make ourselves sick emotionally, as well as physically, and that people can function and survive beyond any medical expectation. We are beginning to realize the power which each individual has in determining his life and death, and all his actions. In this light, the emphasis on partial phenomena such as emotions, consciousness, psyche and soma, become unwarranted and misleading. Holistic medicine is replacing psychosomatic medicine.

Willpower is a fiction. It doesn't exist, because it could only exist if there were something like lack of willpower with which it could be contrasted. But there is never any lack of willpower, since everybody does only what he intends to do. Willpower is a self-deception used to justify our reluctance to do what we are supposed to do, or an opportunity to look down on those who don't have it. Actually, the so-called "weak" person is much stronger than all the strong people around him. They may try to make him do something, but will never get anywhere, while he makes them do what he wants and take on responsibility for him. There is no such thing as willpower. It is the outgrowth of our ignorance about ourselves and about human nature. We do only what we decide to do; but if we don't want to take the responsibility for it, then we refer to our emotions, to our unconscious or to our lack of willpower.

Before I conclude, I should like to mention some implications of Adlerian psychology for psychotherapy by turning to some fundamental premises in our therapeutic approach. First of all, we have some definite ideas about the kind of relationship which is essential for psychotherapy. The establishment and maintenance of a proper relationship is the first consideration. Then we try to understand the patient, which means we try to analyze his life style, his goals, his motivations within the given field of operation. Then we try to provide him with insight, awareness of goals and intentions. Most people know what they are doing wrong, but not why they act and feel as they do. If they knew, they might be able to change. For this purpose, we try to help them to understand themselves. But insight is not the final step yet. It only paves the way toward a change of the patient's basic mistakes, his fallacious and erroneous premises, the faulty conclusions which he has drawn in his interpretation of himself and life. He needs our help to see what he is doing and to free himself from his false assumptions. In other words, our treatment is not directed toward a change in emotions, but a clarification of cognitive processes, of concepts. We do not attempt primarily to change behavior patterns or remove symptoms. If a patient improves his behavior because he finds it profitable at the time, without changing his basic premises, then we do not consider that as a therapeutic success. We are trying to change goals, concepts, and notions. Only such changes can bring about permanent improvement. If he thinks and perceives himself differently, he automatically behaves differently. Therefore, termination of therapy depends more on the evidence of significant changes and improvements in the self-concept as revealed by changes in early recollections, than on the overt behavior or disappearance of symptoms at the time of termination. It is less important in what condition a person leaves therapy than in what direction he moves after he leaves. If there is a new direction, new goals in life, then the further improvement in his condition and behavior can be anticipated. Psychotherapy is a learning process. We have no guarantee that the patient will learn, but we have to give him an opportunity. Change is within the reach of everybody. He can learn about himself, about life, and can change his convictions and movements. This premise of Adlerian psychology renders it more optimistic than some other forms of psychotherapy.

The Adlerian Approach to Therapy

by Rudolf Dreikurs, M.D.

PSYCHOTHERAPY, regardless of what individual therapists may consider it to be, is always a learning procedure. A learning procedure is more than an emotional experience. Any learning or any experience, if it is strong, like anything else that is strong and impressive, has some emotional impact. As I see it, all learning is a formation—or change—of concepts or beliefs. No learning takes place unless concepts develop or change.

For instance, somebody is taught to play the piano; then one might think that he learns muscle coordination, or movement of hands and fingers, or skills. This is not true. Dr. Leonhard Deutsch (1951), a fellow Adlerian, studied the problem of piano teaching and came to the conclusion that one can learn piano effectively with a minimum of exercise, if one knows *where* to learn it. It is not learned with fingers, but with the brain. Similar procedures take place in all learning situations and in any form of psychotherapy. The technique of piano teaching which Dr. Deutsch developed consists of teaching sight reading with one principal difference from the customary form of piano teaching. The traditional teacher will advise that if a mistake is made, the phrase should be played over and over again to exercise the movement in question, until the fingers gain the proper dexterity and muscular coordination. Dr. Deutsch takes the opposite stand. When a mistake is made one stops and determines the wrong judgment which was responsible for it. If a higher note was touched, then one over-estimated the distance. One does not *repeat* it, but makes a mental note of what happened, learning to translate what one sees in the music into the movement which it requires. Learning to play, then, is unconsciously developing proper judgment. No finger exercises, no scales and the like are needed. The fingers develop their dexterity with the concepts of their necessary movements.

Now the same is true in psychotherapy. Whatever your rationale is for your therapeutic efforts in the process of therapy, the patient changes some concept about himself, and life, and about what he is doing. That is, in my mind, the basis of all psychotherapy, from faith-healing to psychoanalysis. However one achieves results with a patient, some conviction, some concept, some basic assumption of the patient has been altered, some cognitive processes were involved.

To repeat, the patient changes concepts about himself, about his movements, about life. Those are the things which he learns in psychotherapy. We can then assume, I suppose, that in all forms of psychotherapy certain basic processes are alike, regardless of the assumptions, interpretations, or beliefs of the various therapists. There is something similar going on in every process of psychotherapy. I don't go as far as Fiedler (1953) in his belief that the similar interaction of the experienced psychotherapists of various schools precluded fundamental differences, but I think that in all forms of psychotherapy certain basic processes take place, about which I shall elaborate later.

We can distinguish two forms of psychotherapy: interpretive or analytic, and non-interpretive or non-analytic. In the analytic, interpretive form of psychotherapy, I propose the following basic phases, which overlap, but can still be distinguished in their dynamic requirements. First, the establishment and maintenance of the proper relationship. Second, analysis in the wider sense—understanding of the patient, his problems, and personality. Third, providing insight in order that the patient understand himself. Fourth, what I call reorientation—change. In the non-interpretive, non-analytic procedures, (e.g. Moreno's psychodrama, client-centered therapy, hypnosis, supportive therapy, Low's will-training) we can see that, by and large, step one is followed by step four directly. We establish a relationship and move directly toward the reorientation.

The first question to be considered is: What is a therapeutic relationship? Again, we know that any school of psychotherapy which has a definite technique and an underlying theory has its own interpretation of the therapeutic relationship which is catholic. For instance, the psychoanalytically-oriented psychotherapist assumes that anybody, from the faith-healer to the Adlerian, is actually achieving results through transference, and conversely, the Adlerian assumes that all the therapeutic relationships, including the psychoanalytical one, is based on certain specific mechanisms which Adlerians consider important. We all have similar experiences with patients, but from conflicting theoretical positions, we interpret what goes on in different ways. And now, let us discuss what, in my opinion, takes place in any therapeutic relationship.

The first necessity is to establish some kind of contact, some willingness to participate with each other, to cooperate. But, that, of course, is trivial. Everybody knows that one cannot deal with any human being unless a friendly relationship is established. But is there more in the therapeutic relationship than that? The answer is yes—and no. I reject the assumption that anything closely resembling the various theoretical formulations of transference—and we have dozens of such formulations right now—really meets the issue. It is not a question of a peculiar emotional relationship which I consider essential for therapy. I realize that the relationship between patient and therapist has a certain uniqueness; for many it is the first time that they experience an interpersonal relationship in which they don't have to be afraid, in which they feel understood, in which they encounter a certain amount of permissiveness, of acceptance, in which, for the first time in their lives, they can reveal their deficiencies and their sins without losing status and worth, which in itself is a therapeutic factor. One can be oneself and still encounter respect, which is an unheard of experience for most of our contemporaries. So this kind of a human relationship, where one can be oneself, characterizes, among others, the therapeutic relationship. But there is something else in addition to the proper therapeutic relationship, which not only has to be established, but maintained throughout therapy.

As those of you who are acquainted with Adlerian psychology know, our emphasis in understanding people is always in regard to goals. In line with this goal-directed orientation of Adlerian psychology, we find that the crucial factor in the existence or absence of the proper cooperation between doctor and patient is the nature of each other's goals. In other words, therapy will progress when the goals of the patient and the goals of the therapist are in line with each other. Any resistance whatsoever is, in my opinion, due to the fact that the goals of the therapist and the goals of the patient do not coincide. Regardless of how friendly they are with each other, regardless of how much appreciation, how much love and devotion might exist, if the goals of the two do not coincide, no cooperation is possible. In this sense, then, the therapeutic relationship is in no way different from any other relationship which requires close cooperation. Cooperation cannot exist if two people have opposite, or mutually exclusive, or antagonistic goals. Both in evaluating patients and in teaching students and associates, I try to make them aware of this interaction, to make them determine if goals are compatible between therapist and patient.

In which way, then, is the therapeutic relationship endangered through the therapist's inability to perceive an opposing goal of the patient, or to change it? A few of the more frequent pitfalls need to be mentioned. It is obvious that if a patient comes because he is sent by his wife or somebody else, or if he comes because his wife wants a divorce unless he enters therapy, then from the beginning it is clear that he won't get anywhere, because there is no agreement on goals. He is willing to come; it is perfectly all right to make another appointment with him, but he is not interested in psychotherapy. So, whatever one does with him, one wastes time. He doesn't want to be treated, he only wants to come. If he wants to come merely to complain about his wife, and the therapist has other ideas about his needs, then no progress is made. But those are the most obvious pitfalls, and I think anybody who has any training is aware of them. However, more subtle forms of danger wait.

Another example is that of the patient who comes because he wants help. He wants to get well, but he doesn't actually expect that he ever will get well. He comes only because it is the right thing to do and he wants to try everything; but he is pretty much determined to prove to you that he is hopeless. The therapist, naturally, wants to show him that he is *not* hopeless. This is a clash of goals. Or, the patient wants the therapist to do something to make him well. The therapist can't do that; but as long as the patient expects that, and his expectation is not changed, the therapist can't go on because he is working at cross-purposes with the patient. The patient is willing to take part, but he is not willing to change his opinion, his ideas about life, his values. Then there is the more obvious difficulty that the patient doesn't trust the therapist—he doesn't trust anyone. He doesn't expect to be able to understand.

In each of these cases we are dealing with the basic problem of a relationship. Unless it is resolved, we can go no further. Unless a basis for cooperation is established, no cooperation can be expected. To put the blame on the patient, to say he is resistant, that he is bad, or selfish, or autistic, only expresses the physician's inability to know what to do with the patient. This attitude is widespread in our times. If the patient doesn't do what one wants, it is his fault.

Often, the doctor doesn't even make an effort to establish a rudimentary alignment of goals. He blames the patient for not being ready for therapy, instead of realizing that a *basic* cooperation must be established. But all this is clouded by the big words of transference, and guilt feeling, which are used to indicate the difficulty a therapist has winning the confidence and cooperation of the patient.

Establishment of relationship involves an effort to establish common goals, without which, in my mind, no successful therapy can be expected. Now, how do we accomplish this? I shall give you an example of one of the most difficult forms of resistance. Most patients are pessimistic. If they weren't discouraged and rather pessimistic, they wouldn't come to therapy. One of the most frequent underlying mechanisms of resistance in psychotherapy is that the patient doesn't believe he can get well. A neophyte may be inclined to assure the patient that others with similar conditions had been helped, and that there is no reason for his pessimism. But there is no chance to convince the patient at the beginning that he could get well. However, one can offer him an exploration of the reasons of his doubts. He may well accede to that or to an exploration of his personality. But without an open discussion of this predicament, the patient would not give up his reservation, or even sabotage progress. This whole question of whether he will get well or not is completely sidetracked. Now he may be willing to go along on a limited scope of exploration.

In our multiple psychotherapy (a method of two therapists treating one patient) in which we have double interviews, the consultant psychiatrist sees the patient with his therapist every three or four sessions. One of the purposes of the double interviews is always to make sure what our goal is for the next several sessions. The patient knows what we expect from him, and is willing to go along; when the patient doesn't trust me, it would not be very useful to say, "Now, I am a decent guy. You can trust me." That would be futile. On the other hand, if I don't say anything about it, he still wouldn't trust me. I bring it into the open and say, "You seem not to have much confidence in me. Maybe you have had some experience that justifies it. I don't know whether I can gain your confidence but will you give me a chance to see what I have to offer? Maybe you will find out that you can have confidence in me; I don't know." At this moment we have our goals synchronized. It is not a question whether he can trust me now or not, but he is willing to see whether we can work it out together so that he may perhaps be able to trust me. We have at least made some kind of plan for a concerted effort, and that's all that is needed. Now, what if the patient gets angry or becomes unhappy when we don't make progress? Our work is clogged up somehow, but our therapeutic relationship can remain positive, because we always talk about our aims. Of course, we have the added advantage of multiple psychotherapy. When any conflict with a psychotherapist occurs, another one is called in and takes over, so that the patient can always maintain a good relationship. The patients feel free to talk about their difficulty with one or the other therapist. In this sense, then, the basis of the proper therapeutic relationship is nothing but an alignment of goals with which the patient is willing to go along. What *we* do is in line with what *he* is willing to do. It is a rather involved and subtle interaction which requires skill, but which can be learned.

In our relationships, the patient is free to voice his feelings about the therapist, and the therapist to voice his feelings about the patient. But this does not imply the kind of permissiveness which characterizes contemporary psychotherapy. Many therapists let the patients talk about what they want; there is too much concern with the fear of weakening the ego, of suppressing the patient. There is a fear that the patient can't take it, that he isn't ready yet. And the psychiatrist sits in self-glorified superiority determining what the patient can take, which is degrading and shows lack of respect and confidence in the patient as a human being.

Frieda Fromm-Reichmann made an interesting observation shortly before she died. During an informal discussion, she related the following significant incident. One day a young schizophrenic girl annoyed her as she was leaving the office in the evening. Dr. Fromm-Reichmann became quite angry and scolded her. After she came home during the night she felt rather badly. After all, one should not treat a schizophrenic girl in that manner. She is a sick girl and should be treated with more consideration. She was very surprised when she found a letter from this girl the next morning in her mailbox. The girl expressed her deepest gratitude and thanks, "It was the first time in a long time that somebody treated me like a normal human being." We must keep this in mind in dealing with patients. We don't coddle our patients. When they are extremely depressed, when they are in danger of suicide, in extreme anxiety, we are careful, of course. But it is characteristic of our whole approach not to coddle the patient, but to regard him as a human being.

Let me describe a personal experience I had with Alfred Adler, as another example of this relationship. I had a depressed senile patient in a sanitarium near Vienna. At that time, we had no shock treatments and the depressed, melancholic patients remained in their condition. There was nothing one could do for them. I wanted to get a particular man out of the hospital with a person to take care of him, but the family was opposed to it, so I called Adler for consultation. He came, and I remember it very well—the patient was sitting in front of him, and the residents, the psychiatrists, the nurses, in a big circle around him—and Adler began to interview the man, asking his name, and how he felt. The patient in his very slow way began to answer. Adler didn't wait for the answer, but went on to the next question, and the patient again began to answer very slowly. Again, Adler was not long in asking him a third question. I became quite embarrassed. After all, this was my teacher—I was proud of him. I thought, "Doesn't this man know how to conduct a psychiatric interview? How can he have an interview with a depressed, melancholic patient if he doesn't wait to hear what he has to say?" But Adler kept on like that, and you can imagine that nothing came out of the patient because after two or three words, Adler would ask the next question. I couldn't understand what he was doing, when suddenly the patient, who wanted to say something, began to talk fast. Nobody had thought about the possibility that the melancholic patient could talk fast if he really wanted to. But, that was Adler, and that is characteristic of his psychology, the fundamental belief that it is up to the patient to do things; that we treat him like a responsible human being, not in an accusing way, not in a derogatory way, not in a punitive way, but without being willing to play his game with him. Can we express our opinions? *We do!* If I get angry, I get angry and the patient may respond as he feels.

I don't recommend getting angry, but I recommend very much not being afraid of getting angry. I *can* be human. Anything which would detract from the sincerity of a spontaneous reaction would be detrimental. I even prefer to make a mistake rather than to be so cautious that the poor patient shouldn't be abused by me. I do it with children, with adults, with anybody. It creates a much better therapeutic and human relationship. I don't mind the patient criticizing me. I don't mind admitting that I have made a mistake—I very often make mistakes.

Here is another story that illustrates this point. A patient came to me, dragged in by her husband and physician. She had fainting spells, fears of fainting, all kinds of psychosomatic symptoms, but she felt she didn't need a psychiatrist. She didn't want to come; she felt nobody could help her. I had a long talk with her, and tried to reach a common goal. "Would you give me a chance of one more interview? I would like to explain a little bit of what we are doing. Perhaps you would be willing to come just once?" I didn't argue with her whether she needed treatment or not. It would have been completely futile at this point, but I thought maybe I could get her to come once more. And she cooperated. She was from out of town and I forgot to put her name in the appointment book. When she arrived and discovered that I had forgotten to write her name down and another patient was there, I was sure that that was the end of our therapeutic relationship. She would think I didn't even have time for her. I couldn't send her home, so I arranged that the other patient had only a half an hour. She was then willing to continue therapy. About three or four weeks later, the question came up that she seemed more confident in me that something could be done. What made her willing to come for treatment? She said, "Remember the second time I came? Do you know what gave me confidence? You had no time for me because you made a mistake. If a man like you can make a mistake, maybe there is a chance for me."

We should not be afraid of making mistakes. It is more important that we are human. It is unfortunate that one has to emphasize that today, because it is not the customary practice in psychotherapy to be human. Some psychiatrists wouldn't go into the elevator with the last patient of the day for fear of coming too close to him. They have to wait until the patient has gone down. "Don't come too close because that interferes with the therapeutic relationship." This is just the opposite of what I am saying. I want to function and to be recognized as a fellow human being. At least, this is my formulation of good relationships.

The second step of our therapy is analysis. What do we analyze? Not the unconscious. We analyze movements, concepts, be they conscious or unconscious. We first try to understand the present field of action of the patient. In this procedure, we first try to discover his symptomatology, and then we explore his functioning in his three life tasks: his love and marriage, his job, and his human relationships. Next, particularly in neurotic cases, the purpose of the symptoms can immediately be seen by asking the "key question." It consists of "What would you do if you were well? What would be different if you were well?" The answer to this question indicates immediately what his purpose is in being sick and against whom or against what the symptoms are directed. The answers permit us, in most cases accurately, to distinguish psychogenic from organic disorders.

The differential diagnosis between organic and psychosomatic disturbances are usually made on two grounds which are not reliable. First, by default, if there is no organic pathology found for the disturbance. Second, by inference, if the patient shows other signs of tension, emotional distress, anxiety, and so on. Both are unreliable. But in most cases, doctors don't know any other way of making a diagnosis. In my opinion, the only reliable diagnosis of psychosomatic symptoms is to find and determine their *function*. It is not a secondary gain, as Freud assumed, but a primary gain; and if I find a person with a symptom which has no function, then I send him back to the referring physician and insist it must be organic.

A brief case history may illustrate this. A patient came to our clinic very angry. He had had some stomach ailment for a few years, had gone from doctor to doctor, and finally had been sent to a psychiatrist.

But he didn't go to the psychiatrist for a year because he was furious. "Because the doctors don't know what to do with me, they send *me* to a psychiatrist."

It didn't take too long to get him to explore his personality and it turned out he was one of those superior males, ambitious, who wanted to get ahead, who looked down at others, and who tried to elevate himself—and he always succeeded. Then he came to the point where he couldn't get further in life so the crisis situation arose. His demand for growing superiority was stifled, and he collapsed. At this time he had some gastric distress and he never lost it. His willingness to participate was limited and he withdrew from anything which he didn't like. He gave up his concern with getting ahead and just withdrew. When somebody didn't behave as he wanted—his stomach spoke up and he was sick and stayed home.

He was quite intelligent, and it didn't take too long—about two or three months of therapy—before he really changed and became quite human, able to function on his own level, give up his ambitions, and make peace with life. The stomach cleared up. He suggested that the young doctors probably should see how a patient with psychosomatic ailments fights against the assumption of a psychological cause. Would it be all right with me if he would come once a year just for demonstration to the Junior Class? I agreed and once a year we used him as a demonstration.

About four or five years later he came and said, "Doctor, I am sick again—the same pains as before. They are a little bit lower in the stomach, but the same nature of pains." He had already learned a little bit of psychology from his own psychotherapy, and he was sure it was psychogenic, because the pains occurred when he was on the train coming home from a vacation. "Apparently, unconsciously I didn't want to come back. I didn't want to function, so I got sick again." I examined his psychological condition, and found that the pains didn't interfere with anything. He went regularly to work in spite of pains, didn't stay home, didn't stop seeing his friends. He wasn't more irritable with his wife. He functioned completely well. I said, "My dear friend, this time your pains are organic and not psychogenic." "But Doctor," he replied, "they are the same pains. They are the same pains as before and I am sure that I must use it for something." "But I don't know for what you use it. I can't see any use. I had better send you back to diagnostics." I sent him back for a recheck and found considerable opposition. "Oh, we know him. He is neurotic. He came here for years." "I am sorry. You have to examine him because his symptoms are not neurotic this time." "How do you know?" "They have no function." It took me considerable time to have him examined carefully, and they found some little tumors in the testicles, removed them, and he was well.

You have to understand the patient's present functions, what his movements are. This man was physically sick the second time, despite the fact that he couldn't see any difference in his pains. If the pains have a function, they are psychogenic. That doesn't exclude organic pathology. I find patients with organic ailments who use them for neurotic purposes; but if there is no function then it must be organic. The first thing to explore is the present movement of the patient—ask what does he do in life? For what purpose is he doing it?

In exploring the patient's movements, we have to start with his present field of action and then proceed to his general movement through life, to his life style. In this connection I distinguish between counseling and psychotherapy. In counseling we remain on the present level of functioning. In vocational counseling, marital counseling, and child guidance counseling, we can, in many cases help people to overcome their difficulties without going any deeper than the present level of function. One can resolve marital problems by seeing the interaction between the spouses, and one can change it. For example, we don't believe that emotions disturb marriage but erroneous approaches of one partner to the other. It is not because a man hates his wife that he can't get along with her. We don't take the *emotions* as the basis for the disturbance. It is the interaction, and we try to see the logic behind it. Then we change the interaction, and as a consequence the emotions change. He stops hating his wife if he learns what to do with her, how to cope with her, or with their children. Most parents are not emotionally disturbed and *therefore* have conflicts with the children. Most mothers don't know what to do with their children, get defeated by them and then become emotionally disturbed. When they learn to deal with their children effectively the emotional disturbance, in most cases, disappears. In other words, when we try to deal with an immediate situation, with a current problem, then that is counseling. Only people who don't respond to immediate clarification of the situation because of personality deficiencies are then referred to psychotherapy. The object of the therapy is not the immediate situation, but the total personality structure, the life style.

We don't take a mother into psychotherapy, for example, if she merely comes complaining about her husband or about her child. We first go into the situation and try to resolve it. We explore what the patient is doing to her child and help her see it. We try to help her change. If the mother is doing something to the child which is bound to make the child defiant then she has to stop and do something else. We try to use the logic of social living, the logic of cooperation.

Only if we get nowhere because the patient can't respond, do we recommend psychotherapy. Among parents, we find that approximately 20-25% cannot respond sufficiently to counseling and can't resolve their problems with their children. But parents, by and large, respond well when they are shown what they are doing wrong, and told what they can do right.

If, for instance, the father is the disturbing element, then we teach the mother how to deal with the disturbing father. We always work with the whole family. A mother who has a domineering mother of her own and a domineering son, and who is squeezed out between the two, can suddenly get rid of both dominations when she learns how to counteract them. There are many disturbing family influences which lose their disturbing impact if the mother learns how to cope with them. We object to the generally accepted assumption that anybody who is very disturbed needs psychotherapy. It's not true. He may need many other forms of help besides psychotherapy.

If psychotherapy is indicated, we have to examine the patient's personality structure. I think that is one of the greatest contributions which Alfred Adler has made to psychology; I hope before long it will be widely known. It is the technique of determining a patient's life style. It requires first the examination of the formative years of the person in his family constellation. Within the family constellation, within his early childhood group, each of the children develops his personality through interaction with all of the others. We have a method by which we can make a sociogram of early childhood relationships through the personality differences of brothers and sisters. We can distinguish how the first child moved in one direction, the second in another, and the third in a still different direction, how they formed alliances and competitive struggles, and how they formed subgroups. In this way we can see how an individual was exposed to a number of influences and in turn provoked the others to certain behavior. The individual is never the passive recipient of environmental influence, but always an active participant in establishing his relationship with the others. The child influences his parents at least as much as the parents influence the child. As an example, let us look at a summary of a patient's family constellation. She is the fourth of seven children, the middle of the middle group, who pushed all the others down to elevate herself to the status of a princess, equalling the status of the eldest brother, a prince. The two were the only self-assertive children, who wanted and got their own way, patterning themselves after a strong, ambitious, and domineering father. The patient outdid the father and brother by using her femininity for her own ends. The rest of the children were either submissive or openly rebellious. Only the baby in the family had a special position and function. Now, in each case, after we have the family constellation established, we write a summary and then we have the material which we need, how she moves, the field of action in which she developed her personality.

The second thing to do is to collect early recollections. Adler's discovery of the significance of the early memories, was not utilized until recently, because Freud considered them as mere screen memories which cover up the really important childhood incidents which were repressed. Consequently, nobody except the Adlerians concerned themselves with early recollections until recently. In the last few years, however, many research workers and therapists have begun to collect early recollections. We remember from all the millions of experiences from early childhood only those which fit into our concept of life. Whatever we remember from early childhood indicates how we look at life. This is so reliable that when the patient changes his concept of himself and his life, his early recollections change also. New ones come up which he didn't remember, the same incidents which he remembered before are told in a different way, and—most dramatic— the patient denies ever having had some experiences which we have on his record. A patient who had been in treatment only for five months, remembered that he had told us about a certain incident in his childhood, but he could no longer remember the incident itself. He remembered having spoken about it, but the recollection wasn't there. It had been forgotten, because his outlook on life had changed. Thus, when you collect recollections, you can come to definite conclusions. The summary of recollections for the patient mentioned previously reads as follows:

Life is dangerous and unfair. I cannot do anything to avoid it, and I am innocent about what happened to me. I need help and attention from others. I can only have a place and be happy if others make it possible for me, and do something pleasant for me. Life depends entirely on what others do for me, be it pleasant, or unpleasant.

One of the things for which recollections are analyzed is what I call "Basic Mistakes" because these are mistakes which we have to correct when we want to help the patient. For the material just presented, the basic mistakes were:

1. The patient is not as innocent as she thinks; 2. She tries to blame life and people for her own happiness and unhappiness; 3. If life and people don't do for her what she wants, life is unfair and unbearable; 4. She cannot see how she provokes life or what she can do to improve it; 5. She underestimates her own strength. She feels the victim when she actually is only an indignant princess.

In this phase we explore what makes her tick, both in the present situation and in life itself. In the third phase of therapy we give the patient insight. We don't tell her what to do, or what not to do, but we show her at every turn, what she is doing to life, and on which principles she is operating. We use dreams, because in dreams we portray life as we see it. We try to show the person how he moves, without knowing it, on the basis of his own decisions, concepts, and convictions. In this way, we come finally to the process of reorientation.

I have only a few moments to discuss the dynamics of reorientation. In my mind, in all forms of psychotherapy, from faith-healing to psychoanalysis, from the most primitive to the most sophisticated, there are some identical mechanisms at work in the process of reorientation. Although each school has its own justification, or rationale for a corrective technique, some factors are always present. These factors are so basic that some therapists may even succeed in getting improvement without any understanding or insight in the dynamics of each case. One of the strongest arguments in favor of neglecting insight is that the insight obtained by psychoanalysts and the insight obtained by Adlerian psychologists are so different that each one is almost justified in claiming that the other one has no insight whatsoever to offer. The psychoanalysts will say that any insight which does not consider the unconscious is superficial, and I say that any insight which does not consider the life style is not significant. Psychoanalysts fail to see the life style and we do not concern ourselves with the unconscious. Some therapists don't search for any insight and can go directly to reorientation. According to our experience, insight into one's basic concepts and mistaken assumptions seem very helpful to effect a reorientation and improvement. Of course, I do not agree with this procedure; otherwise we could start redirection without insight, and I don't think it advisable to do so.

What is there in this process of reorientation which is so forceful and effective? In my mind the crucial change in all corrective efforts, be it in education, in counseling, in therapy of any nature, is *encouragement*. It is a very widely used and yet little understood term. In my book *Psychology in the Classroom* (Dreikurs, 1957), I tried to spell it out for teachers, because many teachers don't know how to encourage and need to know. It is a very complex process. Why is it so essential to any therapeutic and corrective action? Because, at the root of all deficiencies lies discouragement. As long as somebody has confidence in himself he will function. Only when he becomes demoralized, discouraged, doubtful of himself, doubting his chances, doubting his place in the group, only then does he switch, as we call it, to the "useless side," becoming deficient and maladjusted and psychopathologic. Therefore, whoever helps a patient to gain faith in his own ability and strength restores his belief in himself, can help him, regardless of the therapeutic method he may use. Whenever the patient believes in himself, he will improve, because functioning presupposes his convictions of his ability.

Thus encouragement is one of the essential factors without which no improvement is possible, but with which improvement is almost automatic. This encouragement can come from a great variety of sources. In our case, it is the realization of the patient's responsibility, which he cannot assume without realizing his own strength. By making him aware of how he makes himself sick, we give him the realization that he can also make himself well. We show him what he is doing. He may not like it because he doesn't want to feel responsible for what he is doing; but he can't escape eventually from finding out that not his emotions, his complexes, his nature, his constitution, nor even his parents are responsible, but he, himself; and only he, not they, can save himself. In my mind, such realization implies becoming a free man. Realizing the tremendous power which we have, we know that we can make ourselves well and sick, that we can play weak when it suits our purposes, and play strong when we prefer to do so. We can create our own fears for whatever advantages may lie in withdrawal, or for putting others in our service; or we can free ourselves of our fears. This kind of reorientation is the effect of all therapeutic efforts. It is a moral rehabilitation, a spiritual one.

Finally, we come to the realization, that in all therapy there is a change in the patient's value system. Until the advent of group psychotherapy, many psychotherapists thought that psychotherapy has nothing to do with values, with morals. We Adlerians always knew it, but we were criticized for being moralistic. We aren't, because we don't sit in judgment.

A new social orientation is implied in all therapy. In faith-healing a person develops faith that Christ will save him; in psychoanalysis he becomes mature, and thereby operates on a higher moral value level, becoming a fellow human being who integrates his own interest with the interests of others. There is always a value and moral problem involved in the cure. The cured patient becomes a better human being. In my mind, that is the goal of psychotherapy. Such a goal is never completely fulfilled. It is less important under what conditions the patient terminates psychotherapy, than in which direction he moves afterward. And there is apparently no correlation. I have seen patients who left prematurely, and with whom I didn't think anything was achieved, who, years after when I met them, were well. On the other hand, if a patient is apparently well, and is still not following a new direction, then we have failed and he will fall back. The direction of movement, the social orientation, the concept of oneself and one's own values, the progress toward cooperation with others—all are responsible for the degree of improvement in psychotherapy.

The Characteristics
of a Helping Relationship*

by Carl R. Rogers, Ph.D.

MY INTEREST in psychotherapy has brought about in me an interest in every kind of helping relationship. By this term I mean a relationship in which at least one of the parties has the intent of promoting the growth, development, maturity, improved functioning, and improved coping with life of the other. The other, in this sense, may be one individual or a group. To put it in another way, a helping relationship might be defined as one in which one of the participants intends that there should come about, in one or both parties, more appreciation of, more expression of, more functional use of the latent inner resources of the individual.

Now it is obvious that such a definition covers a wide range of relationships which usually are intended to facilitate growth. It would certainly include the relationship between mother and child, and father and child. It would include the relationship between the physician and his patient. The relationship between teacher and pupil would often come under this definition, though some teachers would not have the promotion of growth as their intent. It includes almost all counselor-client relationships, whether we are speaking of educational counseling,

---

*This paper was previously delivered at the APGA Convention, St. Louis, Missouri, March 31-April 3, 1958. The next to last section, however, contains elaborations developed at the talk delivered at the University of Chicago.

vocational counseling, or personal counseling. In this last mentioned area it would include the wide range of relationships between the psychotherapist and the hospitalized psychotic, the therapist and the troubled or neurotic individual, and the relationship between the therapist and the increasing number of so-called "normal" individuals who enter therapy to improve their own functioning or accelerate their personal growth.

These are largely one-to-one relationships. But we should also think of the large number of individual-group interactions which are intended as helping relationships. Some administrators intend that their relationship to their staff groups shall be of the sort which promotes growth, though other administrators would not have this purpose. The interaction between the group therapy leader and his group belongs here. So does the relationship of the community consultant to a community group. Increasingly the interaction between the industrial consultant and a management group is intended as a helping relationship. Perhaps this listing will point up the fact that a great many of the relationships in which we and others are involved fall within this category of interactions in which there is the purpose of promoting development and more mature and adequate functioning.

The Question

But what are the characteristics of those relationships which do help, which do facilitate growth? And at the other end of the scale is it possible to discern those characteristics which make a relationship unhelpful, even though it was the sincere intent to promote growth and development? It is to these questions, particularly the first, that I would like to address myself.

The Answers Given by Research

It is natural to ask first of all whether there is any empirical research which would give us an objective answer to these questions. There has not been a large amount of research in this area as yet, but what there is is stimulating and suggestive. I cannot report all of it, but I would like to make a somewhat extensive sampling of the studies which have been done and state very briefly some of the findings. In so doing, over-simplification is necessary, and I am quite aware that I am not doing full justice to the researches I mention, but it may serve to demonstrate that factual advances are being made and pique further curiosity.

Studies of Attitudes

Most of the studies throw light on the attitudes of the helping person which make a relationship growth-promoting or growth-inhibiting. Let us look at some of these.

A careful study of parent-child relationships made some years ago by Baldwin and others (1945) at the Fels Institute contains interesting evidence. Of the various clusters of parental attitudes toward children, the "acceptant-democratic" seemed most growth-facilitating. Children of these parents with their warm and equalitarian attitudes showed an accelerated intellectual development (an increasing IQ), more originality, more emotional security and control, and less excitability than children from other types of homes. Though somewhat slow initially in social development, they were, by the time they reached school age, popular, friendly, non-aggressive leaders.

Where parents' attitudes are classed as "actively rejectant" the children show a slightly decelerated intellectual development, relatively poor use of the abilities they do possess, and some lack of originality. They are emotionally unstable, rebellious, aggressive, and quarrelsome. The children of parents with other attitude syndromes tend in various respects to fall in between these extremes.

I am sure that these findings do not surprise us as related to child development. I would like to suggest that they probably apply to other relationships as well, and that the counselor or physician or administrator who is warmly emotional and expressive, respectful of the individuality of himself and of the other, and who exhibits a non-possessive caring, probably facilitates self-realization much as does a parent with these attitudes.

Let me turn to another careful study in a very different area. Whitehorn and Betz (1954) and Betz and Whitehorn (1956) investigated the degree of success achieved by young resident physicians in working with schizophrenic patients on a psychiatric ward. They chose for special study the seven who had been outstandingly helpful, and seven whose patients had shown the least degree of improvement. Each group had treated about 50 patients. The investigators examined all the available evidence to discover in what ways the A group (the successful group) differed from the B group. Several significant differences were found. The physicians in the A group tended to see the schizophrenic in terms of the personal meaning which various behaviors had to the patient, rather than seeing him as a case history or a descriptive diagnosis. They also tended to work toward goals which were oriented to the personality of the patient, rather than such goals as reducing the symptoms or curing the disease. It was found that the helpful physicians, in their day-by-day interaction, primarily made use of active personal participation—a person-to-person relationship. They made less use of procedures which could be classed as "passive permissive." They were even less likely to use such procedures as interpretation, instruction or advice, or emphasis upon the practical care of the patient. Finally, they were much more likely than the B group to develop a relationship in which the patient felt trust and confidence in the physician.

Although the authors cautiously emphasize that these findings relate only to the treatment of schizophrenics, I am inclined to disagree. I suspect that similar facts would be found in a research study of almost any class of helping relationship.

Another interesting study focuses upon the way in which the person being helped perceives the relationship. Heine (1953) studied individuals who had gone for psychotherapeutic help to psychoanalytic, client-centered, and Adlerian therapists. Regardless of the type of therapy, these clients reported similar changes in themselves. But it is their perception of the relationship which is of particular interest to us here. When asked what accounted for the changes which had occurred, they expressed some differing explanations, depending on the orientation of the therapist. But their agreement on the major elements they had found helpful was even more significant. They indicated that these attitudinal elements in the relationship accounted for the changes which had taken place in themselves: the trust they had felt in the therapist; being understood by the therapist; the feeling of independence they had had in making choices and decisions. The therapists' procedure which they had found most helpful was that of clarifying and openly stating feelings which the client had been approaching hazily and hesitantly.

There was also a high degree of agreement among these clients, regardless of the orientation of their therapists, as to what elements had been unhelpful in the relationship. Such therapist attitudes as lack of interest, remoteness or distance, and an over-degree of sympathy, were perceived as unhelpful. As to procedures, they had found it unhelpful when therapists had given direct specific advice regarding decisions or had emphasized past history rather than present problems. Guiding suggestions mildly given were perceived in an intermediate range—neither clearly helpful nor unhelpful.

Fiedler (1953), in a much quoted study, found that expert therapists of differing orientations formed similar relationships with their clients. Less well known are the elements which characterize these relationships, differentiating them from the relationships formed by less expert therapists. These elements are: an ability to understand the client's meanings and feelings; a sensitivity to the client's attitudes; a warm interest without any emotional over-involvement.

A study by Quinn (1950) throws light on what is involved in understanding the client's meanings and feelings. His study is surprising in that it shows that "understanding" of the client's meanings is essentially an attitude of *desiring* to understand. Quinn presented his judges only with recorded therapist statements taken from interviews. The raters had no knowledge of what the therapist was responding to or how the client reacted to his response. Yet it was found that the degree of understanding could be judged about as well from this material as from listening to the response in context. This seems rather conclusive evidence that it is an attitude of wanting to understand which is communicated.

As to the emotional quality of the relationship, Seeman (1954) found that success in psychotherapy is closely associated with a strong and growing mutual liking and respect between client and therapist.

An interesting study by Dittes (1957) indicates how delicate this relationship is. Using a physiological measure, the psychogalvanic reflex, to measure the anxious or threatened or alerted reactions of the client, Dittes correlated the deviations on this measure with judge's ratings of the degree of warm acceptance and permissiveness on the part of the therapist. It was found that whenever the therapist's attitudes changed even slightly in the direction of a lesser degree of acceptance, the number of abrupt GSR deviations significantly increased. Evidently when the relationship is experienced as less acceptant the organism organizes against threat, even at the physiological level.

Without trying fully to integrate the findings from these various studies, it can at least be noted that a few things stand out. One is the fact that it is the attitudes and feelings of the therapist, rather than his theoretical orientation, which is important. His procedures and techniques are less important than his attitudes. It is also worth noting that it is the way in which his attitudes and procedures are *perceived* which makes a difference to the client, and that it is this perception which is crucial.

"Manufactured" Relationships

Let me turn to research of a very different sort, some of which may seem rather abhorrent, but which nevertheless has a bearing upon the nature of a facilitating relationship. These studies have to do with what we might think of as manufactured relationships.

Verplanck (1955), Greenspoon (1955) and others have shown that operant conditioning of verbal behavior is possible in a relationship. Very briefly, if the experimenter says "Mhm," or "Good," or nods his head after certain types of words or statements, those classes of words tend to increase because of being reinforced. It has been shown that using such procedures one can bring about increases in such diverse verbal categories as plural nouns, hostile words, and statements of opinion. The person is completely unaware that he is being influenced in any way by these reinforcers. The implication is that by such selective reinforcement the other person in the relationship could be brought to use whatever kinds of words and make whatever kinds of statements one had decided to reinforce.

Following still further the principles of operant conditioning as developed by Skinner and his group, Lindsley (1956) has shown that a chronic schizophrenic can be placed in a "helping relationship" with a machine. The machine, somewhat like a vending machine, can be set to reward a variety of types of behaviors. Initially it simply rewards—with candy, a cigarette, or the display of a picture—the lever-pressing behavior of the patient. But it is possible to set it so that many pulls on the lever may supply a hungry kitten—visible in a separate enclosure—with a drop of milk. In this case the satisfaction is an altruistic one. Plans are being developed to reward similar social or altruistic behavior directed toward another patient, placed in the next room. The only limit to the kinds of behavior which might be rewarded lies in the degree of mechanical ingenuity of the experimenter.

Lindsley reports that in some patients there has been marked clinical improvement. Personally, I cannot help but be impressed by the description of one patient who had progressed from a deteriorated chronic state to being given free grounds privileges, this change being quite clearly associated with his interaction with the machine. Then the experimenter decided to study experimental extinction, which, put in more personal terms, means that no matter how many thousands of times the lever was pressed, no reward of any kind was forthcoming. The patient gradually regressed, grew untidy, uncommunicative, and his grounds privilege had to be revoked. This (to me) pathetic incident would seem to indicate that even in a relationship to a machine, trustworthiness is important if the relationship is to be helpful.

Still another interesting study of a manufactured relationship is being carried on by Harlow and his associates (1958), this time with monkeys. Infant monkeys, removed from their mothers almost immediately after birth, are, in one phase of the experiment, presented with two objects. One might be termed the "hard mother," a sloping cylinder of wire netting with a nipple from which the baby may feed. The other is a "soft mother," a similar cylinder made of foam rubber and terry cloth. Even when an infant gets all his food from the "hard mother" he clearly and increasingly prefers the "soft mother." Motion pictures show that he definitely "relates" to this object, playing with it, enjoying it, finding security in clinging to it when strange objects are near, and using that security as a home base for venturing into the frightening world. Of the many interesting and challenging implications of this study, one seems reasonably clear. It is that no amount of direct food reward can take the place of certain perceived qualities which the infant appears to need and desire.

Two Recent Studies

Let me close this wide-ranging—and perhaps perplexing—sampling of research studies with an account of two very recent investigations. The first is an experiment conducted by Ends and Page (1957). Working with hardened chronic hospitalized alcoholics who had been committed to a state hospital for sixty days, they tried three different methods of group psychotherapy. The method which they believed would be most effective was therapy based on a two-factor theory of learning; a client-centered approach was expected to be second; a psychoanalytically oriented approach was expected to be least efficient. Their results showed that the therapy based upon a learning theory approach was not only not helpful, but was somewhat deleterious. The outcomes were worse than those in the control group which had no therapy. The analytically oriented therapy produced some positive gain, and the client-centered group therapy was associated with the greatest amount of positive change. Follow-up data, extending over one and one-half years, confirmed the in-hospital findings, with the lasting improvement being greatest in the client-centered approach, next in the analytic, next in the control group, and least in those handled by a learning theory approach.

As I have puzzled over this study, unusual in that the approach to which the authors were committed proved *least* effective, I find a clue, I believe, in the description of the therapy based on learning theory which the investigators describe in an unpublished manuscript. Essentially it consisted (1) of pointing out and labelling the behaviors which had proved unsatisfactory, (2) of exploring objectively with the client the reasons behind these behaviors, and (3) of establishing through re-education more effective problem-solving habits. But in all of this interaction the aim, as they formulated it, was to be impersonal. The therapist "permits as little of his own personality to intrude as is humanly possible." The "therapist stresses personal anonymity in his activities, i.e., he must studiously avoid impressing the patient with his own (therapist's) individual personality characteristics." To me this seems the most likely clue to the failure of this approach, as I try to interpret the facts in the light of the other research studies. To withhold one's self as a person and to deal with the other person as an object does not have a high probability of being helpful.

The final study I wish to report is one just being completed by Halkides (1958). She started from a theoretical formulation of mine regarding the necessary and sufficient conditions for therapeutic change (Rogers, 1957). She hypothesized that there would be a significant relationship between the extent of constructive personality change in the client and four counselor variables: (1) the degree of empathic understanding of the client manifested by the counselor; (2) the degree of positive affective attitude (unconditional positive regard) manifested by the counselor toward the client; (3) the extent to which the counselor is genuine, his words matching his own internal feeling; and (4) the extent to which the counselor's response matches the client's expression in the intensity of affective expression.

To investigate these hypotheses she first selected, by multiple objective criteria, a group of ten cases which could be classed as "most successful" and a group of ten "least successful" cases. She then took an early and late recorded interview from each of these cases. On a random basis she picked nine client-counselor interaction units—a client statement and a counselor response—from each of these interviews. She thus had nine early interactions and nine late interactions from each case. This gave her several hundred units which were then placed in random order. The units from an early interview of an unsuccessful case might be followed by the units from a late interview of a successful case, etc.

Three judges, who did not know the cases or their degree of success, or the source of any given unit, now listened to this material four different times. They rated each unit on a seven point scale, first as to the degree of empathy, second as to the counselor's positive attitude toward the client, third as to the counselor's congruence or genuineness, and fourth as to the degree to which the counselor's response matched the emotional intensity of the client's expression.

I think all of us who knew of the study regarded it as a very bold venture. Could judges listening to single units of interaction possibly make any reliable rating of such subtle qualities as I have mentioned? And even if suitable reliability could be obtained, could eighteen counselor-client interchanges from each case—a minute sampling of the hundreds or thousands of such interchanges which occurred in each case—possibly bear any relationship to the therapeutic outcome? The chance seemed slim.

The findings are surprising. It proved possible to achieve high reliability between the judges, most of the inter-judge correlations being in the .80's or .90's, except on the last variable. It was found that a high degree of empathic understanding was significantly associated, at a .001 level, with the more successful cases. A high degree of unconditional positive regard was likewise associated with the more successful cases, at the .001 level. Even the rating of the counselor's genuineness or congruence—the extent to which his words matched his feelings—was associated with the successful outcome of the case, and again at the .001 level of significance. Only in the investigation of the matching intensity of affective expression were the results equivocal.

It is of interest too that high ratings of these variables were not associated more significantly with units from later interviews than with units from early interviews. This means that the counselor's attitudes were quite constant throughout the interviews. If he was highly empathic, he tended to be so from first to last. If he was lacking in genuineness, this tended to be true of both early and late interviews.

As with any study, this investigation has its limitations. It is concerned with a certain type of helping relationship, psychotherapy. It investigated only four variables thought to be significant. Perhaps there are many others. Nevertheless it represents a significant advance in the study of helping relationships. Let me try to state the findings in the simplest possible fashion. It seems to indicate that the quality of the counselor's interaction with a client can be satisfactorily judged on the basis of a very small sampling of his behavior. It also means that if the counselor is congruent or transparent, so that his words are in line with his feelings rather than the two being discrepant—if the counselor likes the client, unconditionally, and if the counselor understands the essential feelings of the client as they seem to the client—then there is a strong probability that this will be an effective helping relationship.

Some Comments

These then are some of the studies which throw at least a measure of light on the nature of the helping relationship. They have investigated different facets of the problem. They have approached it from very different theoretical contexts. They have used different methods. They are not directly comparable. Yet they seem to me to point to several statements which may be made with some assurance. It seems clear that relationships which are helpful have different characteristics from relationships which are unhelpful. These differential characteristics have to do primarily with the attitudes of the helping person on the one hand and with the perception of the relationship by the "helpee" on the other. It is equally clear that the studies thus far made do not give us any final answers as to what is a helping relationship, nor how it is to be formed.

How Can I Create a Helping Relationship?

I believe each of us working in the field of human relationships has a similar problem in knowing how to use research knowledge. We cannot slavishly follow such findings in a mechanical way or we destroy the personal qualities which these very studies show to be valuable. It seems to me that we have to use these studies, testing them against our own experience and forming new and further personal hypotheses to use and test in our own further personal relationships.

So rather than try to outline how the findings I have presented should be used, I should like to indicate the kind of questions which these studies and my own clinical experience raise for me, and some of the tentative and changing hypotheses which guide my behavior as I enter into what I hope may be helping relationships, whether with students, staff, family, or clients. Let me list a number of these questions and considerations.

1. Can I *be* in some way which will be perceived by the other person as trustworthy, as dependable or consistent in some deep sense? Both research and experience indicate that this is very important, and over the years I have found what I believe are deeper and better ways of answering this question. I used to feel that if I fulfilled all the outer conditions of trustworthiness—keeping appointments, respecting the confidential nature of the interviews, etc.—and if I acted consistently during the interviews, then this condition would be fulfilled. But experience drove home the fact that to act consistently acceptant, for example, if in fact I was feeling annoyed or skeptical or some other non-acceptant feeling, was certain in the long run to be perceived as inconsistent or untrustworthy. I have come to recognize that being trustworthy does not demand that I be rigidly consistent but that I be dependably real. The term congruent is one I have used to describe the way I would like to be. By this I mean that whatever feeling or attitude I am experiencing would be matched by my awareness of that attitude. When this is true, then I am a unified or integrated person in that moment, and hence I can *be* whatever I deeply *am*. This is a reality which I find others experience as dependable.

2. A very closely related question is this: Can I be expressive enough as a person that what I am will be communicated unambigu-

ously? I believe that most of my failures to achieve a helping relationship can be traced to unsatisfactory answers to these two questions. When I am experiencing an attitude of annoyance toward another person but am unaware of it, then my communication contains contradictory messages. My words are giving one message, but I am also in subtle ways communicating the annoyance I feel and this confuses the other person and makes him distrustful, though he too may be unaware of what is causing the difficulty. When, as a parent or a therapist or a teacher or an administrator, I fail to listen to what is going on in me, fail because of my own defensiveness to sense my own feelings, then this kind of failure seems to result. It has been made evident, it seems to me, that the most basic learning for anyone who hopes to establish any kind of helping relationship is that it is safe to be transparently real. If in a given relationship I am reasonably congruent, if no feelings relevant to the relationship are hidden either to me or the other person, then I can be almost sure that the relationship will be a helpful one.

One way of putting this may seem strange, but if I can form a helping relationship to myself—if I can be sensitively aware of and acceptant toward my own feelings—then the likelihood is great that I can form a helping relationship toward another. Now, to accept what I am, in this sense, and to permit this to show through to the other person, is the most difficult task I know and one I never fully achieve. But to realize that this *is* my task has been most rewarding because it has helped me to find what has gone wrong with interpersonal relationships which have become snarled and to put them on a constructive track again. It has meant that if I am to facilitate the personal growth of others in relation to me, then I must grow, and while this is often painful, it is also enriching.

It does reluctantly seem to me that the degree of help one can give is probably a measure of one's own personal growth. I feel reluctant to come to this conclusion because it puts so much on the basis of personal development and, in a sense, takes it out of the realm of professional training. But it does seem that the individual who has profited most from growth-promoting experiences—whether formal therapy, or fortunate life experience, or good relationships with others—is probably most able to offer helping relationships.

3. A third question is: Can I let myself experience positive attitudes toward this other person—attitudes of warmth, caring, liking, interest, respect? It is not easy. I find in myself, and feel that I often see in others, a certain amount of fear of these feelings. We are afraid that if we let ourselves freely experience these positive feelings toward another that we may be trapped by them. They may lead to demands

on us or we may be disappointed in our trust, and these outcomes we fear. As a reaction we tend to build up distance between ourselves and others—aloofness, a "professional" attitude, an impersonal relationship.

I feel quite strongly that one of the important reasons for the professionalization of every field is that it helps to keep this distance. In the clinical areas we develop elaborate diagnostic formulations, seeing the person as an object. In teaching and in administration we develop all kinds of evaluative procedures, so that again the person is perceived as an object. In these ways, I believe, we can keep ourselves from experiencing the caring which would exist if we recognized the relationship as one between two persons. It is a real achievement when we can learn, even in certain relationships or at certain times in those relationships, that it is safe to care, that it is safe to relate to the other as a person for whom we have positive feelings.

4. Another question the importance of which I have learned in my own experience is: Can I be strong enough as a person to be separate from the other? Can I be a sturdy respecter of my own feelings, my own needs, as well as his? Can I own, and if need be, express my own feelings as something belonging to me and separate from his feelings? Am I strong enough in my own separateness that I will not be downcast by his depression, frightened by his fear, nor engulfed by his dependency? Is my inner self hardy enough to realize that I am not destroyed by his anger, taken over by his need for dependence, nor enslaved by his love, but that I exist separate from him with feelings and rights of my own? When I can freely feel this strength of being a separate person, then I find that I can let myself go much more deeply in understanding and accepting him because I am not fearful of losing myself.

5. The next question is closely related. Am I secure enough within myself to permit him his separateness? Can I permit him to be what he is—honest or deceitful, infantile or adult, despairing or over-confident? Can I give him the freedom to be? Or do I feel that he should follow my advice, or remain somewhat dependent on me, or mold himself after me? In this connection, I think of the interesting small study of Farson (1955), which found that the less well adjusted or less competent counselor tends to induce conformity to himself, to have clients who model themselves after him. On the other hand, the better adjusted and more competent counselor can interact with a client through many interviews without interfering with the freedom of the client to develop a personality quite separate from that of his therapist. I should prefer to be in this latter class, whether as parent or supervisor or counselor.

6. Another question I ask myself is: Can I let myself enter fully

into the world of his feelings and personal meaning and see these as he does? Can I step into his private world so completely that I lose all desire to evaluate or judge it? Can I enter it so sensitively that I can move about in it freely, without tramping on meanings which are only implicit, which he sees only dimly or as confusion? Can I extend this understanding without limit? I think of the client who said, "Whenever I find someone who understands a *part* of me at the time, then it never fails that a point is reached where I know they're *not* understanding me again. . . . What I've looked for so hard is for someone to understand."

√   If a therapist really enters fully into his client's frame of reference, then he is not only aware of what the client might say at any particular moment, but he is also aware of the context of feeling in which the statement exists. He doesn't have to stop and think, "Ah, this fear is due to such and such." He senses the feeling empathically (I can't get away from the word) as it exists in context. If he can respond to it in the context it has for the client, he may go beyond what the client has said in words; he may also do a number of things which might seem odd in a recording of the session, so that one would ask, "Where did that therapist's response come from?" But if he is really "in there" as therapists say, then it comes naturally because he does sense the context. I don't believe he has to go through any considerable amount of intellectual manipulation to decide how to respond at more than just the surface level.

A very common reaction among beginning therapists is that they can accept warmth, but sometimes fear that empathy would be dangerous and unhelpful. They think, "Well all right, I can empathize with a lot that this person is saying or expressing, but now he is talking about something too awful to empathize with, or something that it might be really dangerous to go along with, in his feelings. Here he talks about the fact that he feels he is teetering on the edge of a psychotic break. You mean I should really empathize with all that? Might it not be too much for him?"

I think that my own clinical experience and that of a good many others is that it is precisely at that point that the individual feels most deeply alone. To find that one other human being is not afraid of going with him into that very shadowy and fearful and threatening realm is the very thing that preserves his sanity and permits growth. When we think about the ultimates that are always brought into such a discussion—psychotic breaks, suicides, murder and so forth—the experience which can be most helpful in preventing such extremes is for the individual to realize that he is *not* isolated, that he is not completely different. He is not, as he feels at that moment, the only individual who has had such feelings and who is, therefore, completely abnormal and hopeless. If he finds that another human being can relate to him in these very areas which are most terrifying—that enables him to begin to realize that he can be human and still have these feelings. It also helps gradually to place them in perspective so that they are not all-encompassing. Empathy accurately defined as the ability to accompany a person wherever his feelings lead him—no matter how strong, deep, destructive, or abnormal they seem—is, in my estimation, helpful, and not harmful.

For myself, I find it easier to feel this kind of understanding, and to communicate it, to individual clients than to students in a class or staff members in a group in which I am involved. There is a strong temptation to set students "straight," or to point out to a staff member the errors in his thinking. Yet when I can permit myself to understand these situations, it is mutually rewarding. And with clients in therapy, I am often impressed with the fact that even a minimal amount of empathic understanding—a bumbling and faulty attempt to catch the confused complexity of the client's meaning—is helpful, though there is no doubt that it is most helpful when I can see and formulate clearly the meanings in his experiencing which for him have been unclear and tangled.

7. Still another issue is whether I can be acceptant of each facet of a client which he presents to me. Can I receive him as he is? Can I communicate this attitude? Or can I only receive him conditionally, acceptant of some aspects of his feelings and silently or openly disapproving of others? It has been my experience that when my attitude is conditional, then he cannot change or grow in those respects in which I cannot fully receive him. And when—afterwards and sometimes too late—I try to discover why I have been unable to accept him in every respect, I usually discover that it is because I have been frightened or threatened in myself by some aspect of his feelings. If I am to be more helpful, then I must myself grow and accept myself in these respects.

In regard to what I would want to accept in the other person, I think it is more important that I accept the negative and ungrowing and inhibited feelings in him. If anything, that is more important than for me to accept the positive aspects because he is likely to find a number of people in his environment who accept his positive feelings, but it is rather rare that he finds someone who can really accept his negative feelings. Now, if negative feelings are accepted, where does progress come from? My opinion about motivation in such circumstances is that, given an opportunity, the individual inherently, as does every organism that grows, moves toward self-fulfillment and self-actualization. That I feel very deeply.

8. A very practical issue is raised by the question: Can I act with sufficient sensitivity in the relationship that my behavior will not be perceived as a threat? The work we are beginning to do in studying the physiological concomitants of psychotherapy confirms the research by Dittes (1957) in indicating how easily people are threatened at a physiological level. The psychogalvanic reflex—the measure of skin conductance—takes a sharp dip when the therapist responds with some word which is just a little stronger than the client's feelings. And to a phrase such as, "My, you *do* look upset," the needle swings almost off the paper. My desire to avoid even such minor threats is not due to a hypersensitivity about my client. It is simply due to the conviction based on experience that if I can free him as completely as possible from external threat, then he can begin to experience and begin to deal with the internal feelings and conflicts which he finds threatening.

9. A specific aspect of the preceding question, but an important one is: Can I free him from the threat of external evaluation? In almost every phase of our lives—at home, at school, at work—we find ourselves under the rewards and punishments of external judgments. "That's good." "That's naughty." "That's worth an A." "That's a failure." "That's good counseling." "That's poor counseling." Such judgments are a part of our lives from infancy to old age. I believe they have a certain social usefulness to institutions and organizations such as schools and professions. Like everyone else, I find myself all too often making such evaluations. But, in my experience, they do not make for personal growth and hence, I do not believe that they are a part of a helping relationship. Curiously enough, a positive evaluation is as threatening in the long run as a negative one, since to inform someone that he is good implies that one also has the right to tell him he is bad. So I have come to feel that the more I can keep a relationship free of judgment and evaluation, the more this will permit the other person to reach the point where he recognizes that the locus of evaluation, the center of responsibility, lies within himself. The meaning and value of his experience is in the last analysis something which is up to him, and no amount of external judgment can alter this. So I should like to work toward a relationship in which I am not, even in my own feelings, evaluating him. This, I believe, can set him free to be a self-responsible person.

I am not saying that there is to be no evaluation and hence no control. Within the family setting, for example, I think that if instead of rather rigid evaluational control—"that's bad, naughty," etc.—we could substitute much more the interaction of the child's feeling with the parents' feeling, there would be limitations. The sky would not be the limit. There are things that parents don't like and things they do like. There are times when they are tired, too tired to be nice, times when they have had enough, and times when they won't stand it to have something damaged. But if those feelings could be stated as the parents' own feelings, permitting the child to have his feelings in counteraction to those, then it seems to me it would tend to do away with what I regard as the value standards that get introjected into individuals. If we had a situation in which the child's real feeling of "I want to do this," and "I like that," were continually met by the real feelings of the parent, whatever those might be, then I think the child involved would gradually develop real and growing skills in interpersonal relationships. He would not be a little monster but would be *self*-limiting in his behavior, in terms of the reactions he would like to get from others. This would be quite different from the feeling we tend to induce in children that "No matter how it seems to me, it's awful." "No matter what I think about, it's bad."

There would instead be a relationship between real feelings on both sides. I think this is the kind of thing we develop in our best relationships as adults. This is the way we deal with our friends. We want certain things. They want something else. Then, we decide on some mutually reasonable course of action. There do seem to be within the biological organism feedback mechanisms, evaluational systems—whatever one might call them—which enable the organism to discriminate, although not always with immediate accuracy, between experiences which are favorable to its own growth and development and those which are unfavorable. Although such natural tendencies can certainly be deceived and thrown out of kilter by various distorting experiences, nevertheless, the fundamental ability of the organism to distinguish between experiences which favor its own development and those which do not seems to be the capacity on which not only therapy but a great many other processes depend. It crosses my mind that the organism shows much of this kind of ability with regard to physical illness. The feedback mechanisms often keep the organism reacting reasonably adequately in ways that will promote its return to good health.

10. One last question: Can I meet this other individual as a person who is in the process of *becoming,* or will I be bound by his past and by my past? If, in my encounter with him, I deal with him as an immature child, an ignorant student, a neurotic personality, or a psychopath, each of these concepts limits what he can be in the relationship. Martin Buber, the existentialist philosopher of the University of

Jerusalem, has a phrase, "confirming the other," which has had meaning for me. He says, "Confirming means ... accepting the whole potentiality of the other. ... I can recognize in him, know in him, the person he has been ... *created* to become. ... I confirm him in myself, and then in him, in relation to this potentiality that ... can now be developed, can evolve" (Buber and Rogers, 1957). If I accept the other person as something fixed, already diagnosed and classified, already shaped by his past, then I am doing my part to confirm this limited hypothesis. If I accept him as a process of becoming, then I am doing what I can to confirm or make real his potentialities.

It is at this point that I see Verplanck, Lindsley, and Skinner, working in operant conditioning, coming together with Buber, the philosopher or mystic. At least they come together in principle. If I see a relationship as only an opportunity to reinforce certain types of words or opinions in the other, then I tend to confirm him as an object —a basically mechanical, manipulable object. And if I see only this as his potentiality, he tends to act in ways which support this hypothesis. If, on the other hand, I see a relationship as an opportunity to "reinforce" *all* that he is, the person that he is with all his existent potentialities, then he tends to act in ways which support *this* hypothesis. I have then—to use Buber's term—confirmed him as a living person, capable of creative inner development. Personally, I prefer this second type of hypothesis.

Conclusion

Earlier, I reviewed some of the contributions which research is making to our knowledge *about* relationships. Endeavoring to keep that knowledge in mind I then took up the kind of questions which arise from an inner and subjective point of view as I enter, as a person, into relationships. If I could, in myself, answer all the questions I have raised in the affirmative, then I believe that any relationships in which I was involved would be helping relationships, would involve growth. But I cannot give a positive answer to most of these questions. I can only work in the direction of a positive answer.

This has raised in my mind the strong suspicion that the optimal helping relationship is the kind created by a person who is psychologically mature. Or to put it in another way, the degree to which I can create relationships which facilitate the growth of others as separate persons is a measure of the growth I have achieved in myself. In some respects this is a disturbing thought, but it is also a promising or challenging one. It would indicate that if I am interested in creating helping relationships I have a fascinating life-time job ahead of me, stretching and developing my potentialities in the direction of growth.

I am left with the uncomfortable thought that what I have been seeking to express may have little relationship to the interests of others in similar work. If so, I regret it. But I am at least partially comforted by the fact that all of us who are working in the field of human relationships and trying to understand the basic orderliness of that field are engaged in the most crucial enterprise in today's world. If we thoughtfully try to understand our tasks as administrators, teachers, educational counselors, vocational counselors, therapists—then we are working on the problem which will determine the future of this planet. For it is not upon the physical sciences that the future will depend. It is upon us who are trying to understand and deal with the interactions between human beings—who are trying to create helping relationships. So I hope that the questions I ask of myself will be of some use to you in gaining understanding and perspective as you endeavor, in your way, to facilitate growth in your relationships.

I should like to look at this for just a moment in perspective. It was only eighteen years ago that a group of us at Ohio State gloated momentarily over having achieved our first aim—that of having obtained, for research purposes, a sound recording and a written transcription of a complete interview. Our pleasure was very quickly dimmed as we listened to and read the material. It seemed so complex, so formless, so fluid. How could it possibly be the basis of research? Was objectivity possible in this sphere? To me it seems that we have come a long way from that day.

A Tentative Scale for
the Measurement of Process
in Psychotherapy*

by Carl R. Rogers, Ph.D.

FOR THE PAST several years I have been increasingly interested in the problem of finding concepts suitable to contain the phenomena of the *process* of therapy. I believe we have made progress in conceptualizing the outcomes of psychotherapy in ways which are specific, measurable, and rooted in a context of theory. This has led to promising research in outcomes (Rogers and Dymond, 1954); which I am sure will be followed by further and more adequate research. But in regard to the *process* of psychotherapy we have had no satisfactory conceptions or theory. Studies of process have been largely studies of segmented outcomes, and these have not been too helpful in understanding what is going on in the fluid interchange of the interviews.

More than a year ago, I determined to approach this problem of process in a more focussed fashion. After exploring a number of avenues which seemed rather fruitless, I decided simply to become a naturalistic observer. Divesting myself of as many preconceptions as possible, I listened to many recorded therapeutic interviews, trying to listen freshly and naively to what was going on. The complexity was

---

*This paper was previously presented at the APA Conference in Research in Psychotherapy, April 1958. It is presented here with elaborations that developed at the talk delivered at the University of Chicago.

enormous, and at times I despaired of discovering any order in, or making any sense of, the diversity of interaction, the multi-faceted flow of what was obviously a meaningful relationship.

Gradually my observations began to cluster, and I felt I could discern some order dimly glowing through them. I began to see, or to think that I saw, the nature of a rather fundamental continuum involved. Under pressure of time for an address at the American Psychological Association, I pulled together with much hesitancy the observations I had made of this continuum, and presented the result as a very tentative continuous scale for the understanding of the flow of psychotherapy (Rogers, 1958). Since that time, I have been asking myself, does this represent my experience? Does this way of conceptualizing the process have any operational meaning? Do I stand by its rather far-reaching implications? The current paper is an attempt to bring this matter up to date.

The Process Continuum of Personality Change

The concept which impressed itself upon me as I listened and observed was a continuum which seems to apply to the whole spectrum of personality change and development, and not to psychotherapy alone. It is, very briefly, a continuum which extends from a rigidity and fixity of psychological functioning on the one hand, to psychological flow and change on the other. Let me try to clarify this.

At one end of this tentative scale or continuum we find the individual living his life in terms of rigid personal constructs, based upon the ways he has construed experience in the past. He has little or no recognition of the ebb and flow of the feeling life within him, as it exists in the present. He is remote from his own immediate experiencing (an important term which I will discuss more fully). His communication, even in a receptive and acceptant climate, tends to be almost entirely about externals, and almost never about self. The form of communication tends to be: "The situation is. . . ." "They are. . . ." "They say. . . ." If pressed he might say "My characteristics are . . . ," but he would almost never say "I feel. . . ." "I believe. . . ." "I am uncertain about. . . ." He does not recognize himself as having problems. He does not perceive himself as a responsible agent in his world. He exhibits no desire to change, and on the contrary shows many signs of wishing to keep himself and his relationships to others and to his environment as unchanging and stereotyped as possible. He is characterized by stasis and fixity.

At the other extreme of this continuum we find the individual living *in* his feelings, knowingly, and with a basic trust in and acceptance of his feelings as a guide for his living. His experiencing is immediate, rich, and changing. His experiencing is used as a referent to which he can turn again and again for more meaning. The ways in which he construes his experience are continually changing in the light of further experiencing. He communicates himself freely, as a feeling, changing person. He lives responsibly and comfortably in a fluid relationship to others and to his environment. He is aware of himself, but not as an object. Rather, it is a reflexive awareness, a subjective living in himself in motion. He has incorporated into his psychological life the quality of change. He lives fully in himself as an integrated, constantly changing process.

Between these two extremes there lies a continuum which can be differentiated into any number of points. For purposes of illustration I have endeavored to discriminate seven stages which I felt could be distinguished from one another. There is, however, no magic in this number, and one might equally well discriminate three stages, or fifteen, or even fifty if our observations were sufficiently refined.

The Basis of Scaling the Continuum

It is believed that this continuum of the process of personality change and development has a certain general usefulness simply as a concept. If, however, we wish to make of it an empirical scale in order to test various hypotheses in regard to process, then it is important to state the conditions under which behavior samples should be collected for this purpose.

It seems clear that individuals reveal themselves and their characteristics to differing degrees in different situations. It is therefore important that we endeavor to approximate some standard condition under which samplings of expressive behavior might be drawn. It is proposed that the standard psychological climate should be one in which the individual feels himself to be empathically understood, accepted, and received *as he is*. This also happens to be the situation which is hypothesized as facilitating the process in question, but for our present purpose its importance lies only in providing a climate or set of conditions which could be measured and equated for individuals at any stage on the continuum.

It is important to note the negative fact that the scale of which we shall speak does not apply to samples of expressive behavior taken from situations in which the individual feels misunderstood, accepted only conditionally, or not fully received as he is.

The Nature of the Conceptual Model

As I have tried to fit the observed facts to some type of model, I have gradually recognized that they do not correspond well to the usual picture of a simple continuum. The analogy of a yardstick is not adequate. There are a number of separate elements or strands in this process of change which need to be taken into account. But even these are not a series of yardsticks. The facts do not fit well the model of several parallel continua, on which different measurements might be summed or averaged to represent a stage on a more general continuum.

The distinctive point is that at the fixity end of the process, the various strands or elements are quite separable and distinct, and can be separately evaluated or rated. Whether the individual is exhibiting a rigid personal construct, or expressing himself on non-self topics, or describing feelings in a way which shows no direct ownership of them, these are rather clearly distinguishable elements. But in the later stages of the process, the individual may be experiencing feelings with im-mediacy—knowing them and experiencing them being synonymous. These feelings are his expression of himself at that moment. They represent an immediately experienced change in a personal construct. Here all the previously separable strands are fused into one moment, and to separate them is artificial.

It therefore appears that the most adequate diagrammatic model is of converging lines, separable at first, but becoming less and less separately distinguishable.

If I may push somewhat further this model of converging lines, I will use an analogy which in several ways may help to communicate both the quality and the form of the process I seek to describe. We may think of a stream, originating in a number of completely separate sources in the foothills. If we think of these initial rivulets as being completely frozen, then we have the extremes of fixity in the process, the stasis end of the continuum. But if we think of the individual as being warmly received in his frozenness, then several trickles of flow and change begin. These may be frozen or dammed at some further point, but if the psychological climate continues to be favorable then these separable rivulets increasingly flow into one another, becoming, at the optimal point of flow, a unified stream of change in which the contribution of the separate tributaries can no longer be accurately distinguished, although all are present. Such an analogy appears to fit the nature of the process I am attempting to describe.

THE SIGNIFICANT STRANDS OF FLOW

❦ *The Relationship to Feelings and Personal Meanings*

One of the discernible strands in the changing process is the relationship of the individual to the feelings and personal meanings which exist within himself. I have elsewhere defined a feeling as "an emotionally tinged experience with its personal meaning . . . a brief theme of experience, carrying with it the emotional coloring and the perceived meaning to the individual." (Rogers, 1959)

At the rigid end of the process continuum the individual is largely unaware of his feeling life. Even in a receptive climate feelings are not described, and there is no evidence that they are in any way acceptable. Feelings may at times be *exhibited* in ways which seem quite obvious to the observer, but they are unrecognized as such by the individual. (Stage 1)

As we go up the scale we find feelings sometimes described as unowned past objects, external to self. (Stage 2)

Further on the continuum we find much description of feelings and personal meanings not now present. Even in describing these distant feelings, they are not apt to be pictured as acceptable, but tend to be seen as bad, unacceptable, or abnormal. At this stage, when feelings are clearly *exhibited*, the individual may soon afterward recognize these as feelings. (Stage 3)

In the following stage we find feelings and personal meanings described as present objects, owned by the self. There is considerable acceptance of these known, described feelings. Feelings of an intense sort are still described as not now present. Occasionally feelings are *expressed* in the present, but this occurs as though against the client's wishes. There is often a dim recognition that feelings previously denied to awareness may break through and be experienced in the present, but this seems to be a frightening possibility. (Stage 4)

In the next stage we find many feelings freely expressed in the moment of their occurrence and thus experienced in the immediate present. These feelings are owned or accepted. Feelings which have been previously denied now tend to "bubble through" into awareness, though there is fear and distrust of this occurrence. There is a beginning tendency to realize that experiencing a feeling provides a direct referent to which the individual can turn for further meaning. (Stage 5)

The distinguishing mark of the next stage is the extent to which feelings which have previously been denied to awareness ("stuck" in their flow) are now experienced with immediacy and with acceptance. This experiencing is something which *is*, not something to be denied, feared, struggled against. In other respects this stage is similar to the preceding one, in that feelings are experienced and expressed in the immediate moment with even greater freedom and a deeper sense of ownership. (Stage 6)

In the final discernible stage new feelings are experienced with richness and immediacy, and this experiencing is used as a clear and definite referent from which further meanings may be drawn. Feelings are rarely denied to awareness, and then only temporarily. The individual is able both to live in his own feelings and personal meanings and to express them as an owned and accepted aspect of himself. (Stage 7)

Thus in this strand we find feelings and personal meanings at first unrecognized, and unexpressed, though perhaps exhibited. They are next described as remote, unowned, and not present. They are next described as present objects, with some sense of ownership. Next they are expressed as owned feelings, in terms closer to their experiencing. They are then experienced and expressed in the immediate present, with a decreasing fear of this process. At about this point, even those feelings which have been previously denied to awareness bubble through, are experienced, and increasingly owned. Finally, living in the process of experiencing a continually changing flow of feeling becomes characteristic.

Manner of Experiencing

Another strand of the process, closely interwoven both with feelings and personal meanings, and with other strands to be described later, is the individual's manner of experiencing. This is a concept which has been elucidated by Gendlin (1958). He suggests that the term be employed to refer to the directly given felt datum which is implicitly meaningful.* He says, "Some initial sense of what the term 'experiencing' refers to can be communicated by calling it 'subjective experiencing.' It refers to an individual's feeling of *having* experience. It is a continuous stream of feelings with some few explicit contents.

---

*Gendlin's development of this concept of experiencing is one which I believe will bear significant fruit over the next decade or two. Not only is it a helpful concept in itself for purposes such as the present but it represents another step toward what I believe will be the next trend in American psychology—a phenomenological, existential trend. This does not mean that I believe we will desert the logical positivist experimental tradition, nor the psychoanalytic dynamic tradition. It seems likely however that having selected from these streams of thought those elements with the most permanent value, we will use them to move on to

It is something given in the phenomenal field of every person." For example, I can refer directly to the process in me which is involved in having a feeling, thinking a thought, deciding to act, etc. When I ask, "What kind of an experiencing is this?" there is always an implicit answer, even though no explicit answer has as yet been conceptualized. Thus the answer might be "I am experiencing something vague and puzzling which I do not understand," or it might be a much more definite answer. Experiencing implies many possible conceptualizations. No one answer to the above exhausts the possible conceptualizations.

In relation to our present interest in the process of change, we find that there is a great difference in the manner of experiencing at different stages of the process.

At the fixity end of the continuum immediacy of experiencing is completely absent. Conceptualizations as to the meaning of experience are all past formulations. The distance of the individual from his experiencing is very great. (Stage 1)

It is difficult to differentiate sharply the next stage, in which the individual is very remote from his experiencing, and reacts to internal and external situations as though they were past experiences, feeling them, rather than the present experience. Extreme intellectualization is one way of holding one's experiencing at arm's length. (Stage 2)

Perhaps the next development in this strand is that the experiencing of situations is described as in the past. (Stage 3)

In the following stage there is an unwilling, fearful recognition that one is experiencing things—a vague realization that a disturbing type of inner referent does exist. Sometimes the individual recognizes an experience only shortly after the inner experiencing event. (Stage 4)

As we move up the continuum feelings are sometimes experienced with immediacy; that is, the individual conceptualizes and expresses his experiencing at the moment it occurs. This is a frightening and disturbing thing because it involves being in an unknown flow rather than in a clear structure. The only comforting aspect is that there is, in the fact of experiencing, a referent which can be symbolized and checked or rechecked for its further meanings and symbolizations. There is a strong desire for exactness in these conceptualizations. There may be a dim realization that living in terms of these solid referents would be possible. There also may be the realization that most experiencing occurs with some postponement after the event. (Stage 5)

---

new phases of discovery and assimilation in psychology, and it is my prediction that the place of subjectivity and the human encounter with life will receive more attention than at present. For this reason the discussion by Gendlin of the relationship of subjective experiencing to the logical positivism of psychology is refreshing indeed.

Immediacy of experiencing, even of feelings previously denied, and an acceptance of being in process of experiencing, is characteristic of the next stage. The experiencing, in the immediate present, of feelings previously denied, is often vivid, dramatic, and releasing for the individual. There appear to be strong physiological concomitants. There is full acceptance now of experiencing as providing a clear and usable referent for getting at the implicit meanings of the individual's encounter with himself and with life. There is also the recognition that the self is now becoming this process of experiencing. (Stage 6)

In the final stage the individual lives comfortably in the changing flow of his experiencing. There is a trust in this process. The individual lives in terms of present experiencing, rather than interpreting the present in terms of the past. Differentiation between different experienced referents is sharp and basic. (Stage 7)

Thus in this strand we find a continuum beginning with a fixed situation in which the individual is very remote from his experiencing, unable to draw upon or symbolize its implicit meanings. Experiencing must be safely in the past before meanings can be drawn from it, and the present is interpreted in terms of these past meanings. From this remoteness in relation to his experiencing the individual moves toward the recognition of experiencing as a troubling process going on within him. Experiencing gradually becomes a more accepted inner referent to which he can turn for increasingly accurate meanings. Finally he becomes able to live freely and acceptantly in a fluid process of experiencing, using it comfortably as the major referent for his living. In the furthest aspect of the continuum experiencing with immediacy is the major characteristic of the process of therapy. In such moments feeling and cognition interpenetrate, self is simply the reflexive awareness of the experiencing, volition is the natural following of the meaning of this flow of internal referents. The individual in this portion of therapy is a flowing process of accepted, integrated experiencing.

The Degree of Incongruence

A third element which enters into the changing quality of the process of therapy is the change in the degree of incongruence. Incongruence is a concept which we have endeavored to define as the discrepancy which exists between what the individual is currently experiencing and the representation of this in his awareness, or in his communication (5). Such discrepancy cannot be directly known to the individual himself, but may be observed. Its opposite is a congruence between the experiencing of the individual and the symbolization or conceptualization of this in his awareness.

In the beginning end of our continuum of process, we find a very considerable discrepancy between experiencing and awareness. This is observable to the trained diagnostician, or evident on projective tests. There is no awareness whatever of such discrepancy on the part of the client. (Stage 1)

A slight change in this picture is indicated when the client voices contradictory statements about himself as an object, with little or no awareness that these represent contradictions. (Stage 2)

Further up the continuum these contradictory statements are recognized as such, and some dawning concern is felt about them. (Stage 3)

Still further these contradictions are clearly realized and a definite concern about them is experienced. (Stage 4)

As another step in the process the contradictions are recognized as not simply diverse attitudes, but attitudes existing at different levels or in different aspects of the personality. Such phrases as "one part of me wants this, but another wants that," or "my mind tells me this is so, but *I* don't seem to believe it," indicate this kind of recognition of the nature of incongruence. (Stage 5)

In what appear to be significant moments of movement in therapy, there is a vivid experiencing of some aspect of incongruence as it disappears into congruence. That is, the individual is vividly aware of the inaccuracy with which he has symbolized his experiencing of some feeling, as he symbolizes it more accurately in the moment of fully living it. (Stage 6)

In the final stage incongruence is minimal and temporary as the individual is able to live more fully and acceptantly in the process of experiencing, and to symbolize and conceptualize the meanings which are implicit in the immediate moment. (Stage 7)

The Communication of Self

Still another thread woven into this pattern of process involves the degree to which, and the manner in which, the individual communicates himself in a receptive climate.

At the frozen end of the continuum we find the individual unwilling to communicate self, even avoiding any expression which seems in any way revealing of self. Communication is about material entirely external to self. (Stage 1)

A bit further in the process expression begins to flow on topics which might seem related to the self, but which are handled as non-self material, e.g., "My education was good," "My parents were insecure." (Stage 2)

The next step which can be differentiated involves a freer flow of expression about the self as an object, and about self-related experiences as objects. There may also be communication about the self as a reflected object, existing primarily in others. Past self-related feelings are described. (Stage 3)

In the next discernible step there is considerable communication of present self-related feelings. There is some expression of self-responsibility for problems. (Stage 4)

Further up the continuum we find the client freely expressing present self-related feelings. There is increasing acceptance or ownership of self-feelings, and a desire to be these feelings, "to be the real me." There is a clear acceptance of self-responsibility for problems. As the self is expressed as present feelings, there is less evidence of the self as an object. (Stage 5)

In the following stage the self exists in the experiencing of feelings. There is little awareness of self as an object. At any given moment the self *is* the experiencing. There is only a reflexive awareness. The self *is*, subjectively, in the existential moment. (Stage 6)

In the final stage the self is primarily a reflexive awareness of the process of experiencing. It is not a perceived object, but something confidently felt in process. It is not a structure to be defended, but a rich and changing awareness of the internal experiencing. (Stage 7)

The Manner in Which Experience is Construed

There are three other strands in the web of process which will be described much more briefly, since refined discrimination of points in the continuum does not yet seem possible. They will be described simply in terms of endpoints, with the implication that these elements exist in degrees, but that we are not yet able clearly to state these degrees.

The first is the manner in which experience is construed—borrowing Kelly's thinking regarding personal constructs. At the fixed end of the continuum we find that personal constructs are extremely rigid, unrecognized as constructs, but thought of as external facts. Experience seems to *have* this meaning; the individual is quite unaware that he has construed experience as having this meaning.

In the process of therapy one can discern a gradual loosening of such constructs, a questioning of their validity, and an increasing discovery that experience has been construed as having such and such meaning rather than possessing this meaning inherently. Each such discovery naturally raises the question of the validity of such a construct.

In the moments of greatest movement in personality change, there is a dissolving of significant personal constructs in the vivid experiencing of feeling which runs counter to the construct. There is the realization that many personal constructs which have seemed to be solid guides are only ways of construing a moment of experiencing. The client often feels "shaky" or "cut loose" as his solid foundations are recognized as constructions taking place within himself.

In the flexible end of our continuum, experience is tentatively construed as having a certain meaning, but this meaning is always held loosely, and is checked and re-checked against further experiencing.

The Relationship to Problems

Another strand which may be briefly described is the way the individual relates to his problems. At the rigid end of the continuum, no problems are recognized and there is no desire to change. As there comes to be a recognition of problems, they are perceived as external to self, with no sense of responsibility for them. As the process continues there is increasing recognition that the problems exist inside the individual rather than externally, and that the individual has contributed to their existence. Increasingly there is a sense of self-responsibility for problems. In the peak moments of therapy there is the living of the problem, the experiencing of it. It is no longer an object in itself. In the final phase the word "problem" is no longer particularly meaningful in the ongoing experiencing.

The Manner of Relating

Though the manner of relating to another is undoubtedly an important element of the process, it is not so easy to discern separable stages on this continuum. Suffice it to say that at the beginning stage of the process close relationships are perceived as dangerous, and the individual avoids them. During the process the individual becomes increasingly willing to risk relating to others on a feeling basis, and that in the final stages the individual openly and freely relates to the therapist and to others on the basis of his immediate experiencing in the relationship.

THE USE OF THE PROCESS CONCEPT

Can the Scale be Made Operational?

What has been presented thus far is an organization of observations, the beginning of a theory of the process of therapeutic change. Can these observations be formed into a reliable operational scale in order to test the hypotheses implicit in the theory? It is too soon to say, but I would like to mention a beginning effort along this line.

With the help of Dr. Alan Walker, the discursive, observational account of the process of psychotherapy, contained in the initial paper, has been translated into a more orderly schedule of therapy stages, outlining different strands to be considered at each stage. At this point Mrs. Marsel Heisel planned and carried through a small pilot study, which indicated that we are dealing with some real continuum, and that samples of client behavior taken in a receptive climate can be reliably scaled along this continuum.

A Beginning Validation of the Scale

Following this pilot study, Walker and Rablen, together with the writer (1960), undertook a more crucial study with the scale of process.

From earlier transcribed cases on which we had research data as to outcomes as well as counselor judgments, I selected six cases to represent a considerable range of outcome, with three cases representing marked progress in therapy and three minimal. I endeavored to select mostly brief cases, because at the time I thought we might be making ratings of all of the material in each case. The cases and the order in which I ranked them as to progress in therapy, using all the evidence available, are as follows.

1. Vib—9 interviews. Rated first in degree of movement or change in 1949 study (Raskin, 1949) on objective evidence.
2. Oak—48 interviews. Showed marked objective progress in 1954 study (Rogers and Dymond, 1954).
3. Sar—4 interviews. Showed dramatic movement in four interviews.
4. Bebb—9 interviews. Showed objective progress in therapy, but decrement afterwards. Reported in 1954 study.
5. Sim—7 interviews. Ranked 7.5 out of 10 in progress in 1949 study.
6. Sketch—3 interviews. Ranked 9 out of 10 in progress in 1949 study.

From these cases single pages of the transcribed case were copied without any identifying information. Pages in the longer cases were taken from the second interview, the third interview, the third from the last, and the second from the last. In the three- and four-interview cases it was the first and second, and the next to the last and last interviews which were sampled. In the three-interview case two nonconsecutive pages from near the end of the second interview were assigned at random to early and late conditions. In all but this last instance it was the next to the last complete page in the interview which was copied. This avoided "closing remarks" but sampled the presumably more significant half of the therapeutic hour.

This method of sampling gave us two pages from early interviews, and two pages from late interviews with each client, selected in such a way as to preclude bias. There were thus twenty-four pages, each identified only by a code number. These were placed in random order for presentation to the judges.

The two judges worked together for a number of hours training themselves on interview material from other cases in order to learn to make the discriminations called for in the scale. They tried rating several interview samples independently, to determine whether they had achieved inter-judge reliability. They then turned to the randomly ordered twenty-four pages from these six cases. Working independently, with no knowledge of the case or its degree of success or failure, and without knowing which four pages came from the same case, they performed a number of discriminations. The most crucial were these.

1. They sorted the twenty-four pages into three equal groups representing lower, middle, and higher rating on the process scale.
2. They assigned to each page a rating as to its stage in the process of therapy, refined to the first decimal point. (Essentially a 70 point scale.)

The findings as to inter-judge reliability were as follows: When the twenty-four samples were sorted into low, medium, and high groups on the process scale there was 75% exact agreement, 25% one-step disagreement, and 0% two-step disagreement. When the twenty-four stage ratings made by the two judges independently were correlated, the Pearson r was .83, significant at the .01 level. This is a very satisfactory degree of reliability.

A measure of validity could now be obtained in the following manner. For each case the mean rating on the process scale was calculated for both the early sample and the late sample. The mean change was then calculated, and the cases ranked from greatest to least change on the process scale. This ranking was then compared with the ranking of the cases on external criteria, given above.

When this was done, a rho of .89 was found between the ranking based on rated movement on the process scale, and the ranking based upon external criteria. This figure was significant at the .02 level, though it must be interpreted with caution when the number of cases is so small.

Another way of considering the validity of the ratings is to compare the change on the process scale of the three cases selected as representing marked progress, with the change in the three cases selected as representing minimal progress. In the first group, the mean changes on the process scale were 2.3, 2.0, and 1.5, a mean of 1.93. In the second group, the changes were 1.15, .62, and .30, a mean of .69. It will be noted that there is no overlap between the two groups.

From this small study it seems clear that satisfactory inter-judge reliability can be obtained in using the scale. The preliminary test of validity indicates that using very small samples of transcribed interview material, the scale differentiates satisfactorily between the degree of process movement in more successful and less successful cases. It seems reasonable to suspect that a higher reliability and even more satisfactory validity would be obtained if the ratings were to be based upon auditory samples of recorded interviews, rather than upon transcriptions.

There are several research problems to which we hope to apply this scale. Could it be that the essence of movement in therapy is that the therapist responds at a process level just one shade higher than the client has expressed in his response? To put it in clinical terms, the client expresses something vaguely or in a descriptive phrase, and the therapist says, "I guess you feel annoyed about that." In terms of the process scale, that's a bit further up the scale than what the client has said. The client may welcome that and respond more in terms of expression of feeling. It has been suggested that perhaps we could make a very minute study of therapy on the hypothesis that in interviews or in cases where there was the greatest movement, you would find that the therapist's responses tend to be judged in each case a little higher than the preceding client response. You could have each response judged independently so that there would be no contamination of judgment. This is one kind of possibility we might explore.

Another hypothesis which I have put into the study we intend to make on therapy with schizophrenics, is that periods in which more rapid advance occurs on this process scale are likely to be followed by periods of disorganization, because I feel that if a person by any chance moves too fast for himself, then he must regress quite a bit before he can move forward again. That simply is one marked example of what is probably always true. In dealing with one area where there is not a great deal of incongruence, the individual might move up rapidly on the process scale. But when opening up another, more incongruent area of his life, he has to drop back and begin at a lower level.

It is quite possible that we may find that the most adequate therapy for a person who is at stage one or two is different from the most adequate therapy for a person who is at stage three or four. One factual reason for this observation is that Kirtner and Cartwright (1958) seem to indicate that we frequently fail, and I think probably all types of psychotherapy frequently fail, with people who would be classified in the lower stages of the process continuum. Yet, sometimes we succeed, so it isn't an impossible thing, but it does raise the very real question whether we may learn better ways of dealing with people who are very remote from their experiencing. I think one experience in this direction is that if a person so classified can be involved in group therapy where he doesn't have to speak up unless he wants to, where he can sense the atmosphere and let it soak in, then he may really begin to profit by it even to the point that he wants to use and can use individual therapy. But, if, when he is fairly low on the process scale, he is faced at once by individual therapy, our chance of success is probably slight.

A person in the lower stages of the process scale may not perceive the relationship elements which are being offered to him and this seems to me to be one of the practical perplexities at that level. How is a mute, withdrawn patient going to know that you have an unconditional, positive regard for him? He is not going to know it through the ordinary procedures that we have learned to use on an interview level. Yet, it is equally important that he perceive it, if any change is to take place. So, some therapists have worked with patients of that sort and have used physical affection, demonstrating in different ways: "I do care," and "I am willing to receive you as you are," and so on. But the language of communication in the relationship may have to be rather different at the lower levels than at the upper levels, to which we are more accustomed.

Implications of the Conceptual Scheme

At times I feel very much sobered by the bold prediction which is implicit in the development of this conception of the process of personality change. What I have been saying hints at the possibility that a brief sample of an individual's expressive behavior, taken in a situation in which he feels fully received, can be analyzed to give us knowledge of where he stands on the continuum of psychotherapy or even the more general continuum of personality development and flow; and that this analysis may be possible without knowledge of the individual's genetic history, social and personal background, personality type, psychological diagnosis, or length of time in therapy. If even a portion of this implicit prediction is fulfilled, it will be a startling development.

I have endeavored to give a streamlined, simplified picture of a process continuum of psychotherapy and personality change. I have suggested the nature of the theory of process which arises from these observations. I have not tried to provide illustrations of it as it is found in psychotherapy, nor have I described the irregular rather than smooth nature of this process. I have pointed out that on the basis of a preliminary pilot study, and other work now being undertaken, it appears possible to give this theory of the process of therapy a reliable operational meaning which will enable us to test a variety of hypotheses as to the quality and nature of personality change as it occurs in psychotherapy.

Psychotherapy in Reference to the Schizophrenic Reaction

by Otto Allen Will, Jr., M.D.

MY PURPOSE TODAY is to discuss the following: (1) some aspects of interpersonal theory, with particular reference to the work of Harry Stack Sullivan; (2) certain concepts of the schizophrenic process viewed as manifestations of interpersonal phenomena; and (3) selected aspects of psychotherapy relevant to the disorder and the theory.*

Sullivan emphasized the concept that the proper concern of the psychiatrist is the study of the interaction of one person with another. From this point of view, the psychiatrist does not study a disease "within a person," nor does he study a "diseased person" apart from the situation in which the person has his being. He suggested that the psychiatrist had available to him only what Gardner Murphy referred to as a "career line of interactions between individuals," and that the relationships, not the individuals, were more suitable for observation.

He later expanded his views in an effort to formulate a field theory

---

*Having no great enthusiasm for unduly elaborate "dedication" to schools or theories, I do not present these remarks as a "Sullivanian," but as a psychiatrist who has, within his personal limitations, an interest in psychiatric theory and in psychotherapeutic problems, as well as a considerable respect for the remarkably complex and influential involvement of man with his cultural and interpersonal environment. This brief presentation being grossly inadequate in terms of the requirements of the subject matter, no pretense is made to the effect that "interpersonal theory" is developed here other than superficially and from my "own" (to use an inaccurate locution) point of view. In other words, my aim is to discuss some phenomena of possible interest to a psychotherapist—not to "interpret" Sullivan or others.

of interpersonal relations, writing, for example, as follows: "People behave in interpersonal fields. The patterns of their performances reveal the field forces by virtue of the people's susceptibility to these forces. . . . These people who in their behaving reveal the interpersonal fields are to an extraordinary extent the result of their past experiences with interpersonal fields. . . . Past experience in interpersonal fields, and the time pattern of such experiences, may greatly affect one's susceptibility to interpersonal field forces and the resultant pattern of behavior in the fields in which one is participating." (Sullivan, 1947).

At another juncture he said: Psychiatry is "an expanding science concerned with the kinds of events and processes in which the psychiatrist participates while being an observant psychiatrist. . . . The actions or operations from which psychiatric information is derived are events in interpersonal fields which include the psychiatrist . . . events in which the psychiatrist participates." (Sullivan, 1953).

Mental disorder, as we have customarily referred to those behavior patterns which preoccupy the attention of psychiatrists, was thought of by Sullivan as being evidenced in interpersonal fields, as having its origin in such fields previously experienced, and as being therapeutically approachable through operations in a social field. From this point of view, the focus of our concern is not "a disorder," and it is not a person, or even two people together. All that can be observed, with any hope of accuracy, is the interaction between people, in which are involved not only those "really" there (that is, tangibly and visibly present), but also representations of their previous experience (eidetic personifications as Sullivan would have said), whose past influences in the lives of the present participants alter the participation of the actors in the current scene.

In a sense, a mental disorder may be looked upon as reflecting the development of cumbersome, expensive methods of interpersonal relatedness, which interfere with the formation of constructive integrations with other people. Such behavior enables some semblance of human relatedness to be maintained, but interferes with aspects of learning, distorts growth, and reduces the chances for self-realization of the organism. The person, growing to be sensitive to, and dependent upon, the approval of others important to him, molds his behavior, and thus his personality, in the service of being acceptable to these other people. In this way, largely through learning experience and the function of anxiety, the character (or personality) is formed. When certain distortions of the personality organization interfere with the satisfaction of biological necessities, or the gaining of adequate interpersonal security, a "mental," that is, an interpersonal, illness may be evidenced.

Again I quote Sullivan, who said: "If the term mental disorder is to be meaningful, it must cover like a tent the whole field of inadequate or inappropriate performances in interpersonal relations" (Sullivan, 1953).

Sullivan used the term "dynamism" in a way that becomes relevant to our interests here. By this term he meant, to use a rather formal and I think somewhat awkward definition, the following: The dynamism is "the relatively enduring pattern of energy transformations which recurrently characterize the organism in its duration as a living organism" (Sullivan, 1953). Of particular interest to psychiatrists are those patterns of behavior "which recurrently characterize the interpersonal relations—the functional interplay of persons and personifications, personal signs, personal abstractions, and personal attributions—which make up the distinctively human sort of being" (Sullivan, 1953). An extension of this concept is the definition of personality as "the relatively enduring pattern of interpersonal situations which characterize a human life" (Sullivan, 1953).

Of particular importance is the concept of "self-dynamism," which is a product of anxiety and interpersonal experience and makes use of all zones of interaction (the oral, tactile, and so on). This is an "organization of educative experience called into being by the necessity to avoid or minimize incidents of anxiety" (Sullivan, 1953). This system may block favorable chances in personality by limiting awareness, operating to reduce the impact of the feeling of anxiety. Such a system obviously can on occasion interfere with learning, requiring that a person become inattentive to many things which might be important in his life. That is, he must avoid matters which might cause him to feel anxious. The self-system also hinders *unfavorable* changes in the person; as anxiety is diminished through the operation of this self-dynamism, certain types of interpersonal contact are permitted to go on and through them learning can occur.

By anxiety, we refer to a transformation of energy characterized by a generalized and very considerable feeling of discomfort, insecurity, and tenseness. It is always preceded by, or as we sometimes say, it is set in motion by, certain events which are associated with or lead to a decrease in self-esteem. Human beings are brought up in such a fashion that when they feel that other people are going to be threatening to them, or are not going to think very highly of them, gross discomfort may occur and they may feel anxious. Anxiety being unpleasant, people do something about it and try to attenuate this experience. An extraordinarily uncomfortable experience, anxiety is very commonly transient, being replaced in awareness by some other sentiment more tolerable to experience. The anxiety with which we are now concerned is a state characterized by a diminution of the feeling of well-being, of the sense of security, the causes of this reduction usually being obscure to the one who experiences it. No one wants this experience; he will not seek it out; he will go to extremes to avoid it. So unpleasant is felt anxiety that elaborate defenses are built against it, and these usually operate so quickly, so effectively, and so automatically, that we are, for the most part, exposed to only fleeting contacts with anxiety. We often experience anger, boredom, contempt, depression, irritation or whatever, without recognizing that these feelings, so apparently rational and often readily explained, are defenses, or as Sullivan would have called them, "security operations" carefully structured through the years to shield us from the distress of anxiety, or to add to our feeling of security.

The origins of anxiety are found early in life. The infant is at times exposed inevitably to the anxiety of the one who mothers him. In those early months of life, concepts of the self, or the selves of others, are not developed, and the infant can only be aware of times of comfort with his mother when she is at ease, and times of increased tenseness and discomfort when she is anxious. The baby responds as if he and his mother, who is now very largely the total of his interpersonal world, were one unit. The infant-mother complex, as it were, experiences euphoria and peace, or great tension (anxiety) as a simple unit, and there are few gradations between these extremes; the world is either very satisfactory, indeed, or very much otherwise. This is a way of saying that the young human is acutely responsive in an empathic, non-verbal fashion to the emotional states of his mother.

As development proceeds, there is an increasing awareness in the infant of himself as a person distinct from others, and of his mother as an entity who is at times comforting and very useful in the fulfilling of certain satisfactions, such as supplying food, warmth, protection from loneliness, and so on. At the same time, the young human is developing a need which pertains more to the culture and is peculiarly related to interpersonal events. This last is the need for security, and has its origins in the baby's relationship with his mother. As his awareness of himself and of his mother as a person increases, he notices (although he has no words to formulate it in this fashion, and we are now talking of non-verbal concepts) that at times he feels at ease and secure with his mother, and at other times quite the contrary. Eventually, he may relate his mother's distress-provoking attitudes with "improper" or "wicked" behavior of his own, and vaguely identify what we might refer to as the "bad" or the anxious mother, with the concept of himself that might be labeled "bad me" or, to put it another way, "the me that does something that leads mother to be less comforting and makes me less secure."

For our purposes here we should notice that the infant experiences anxiety as unpleasant, as involving his total world, as being beyond his prediction or control, as being destructive to his greatly needed sense of comfort, and as creative of tension which he must in some way relieve. As he grows older, he defines the source of his discomfort as being somehow in his mother and somehow related to what he himself does. Although he cannot be at all clear as to what behavior of his may make his mother anxious, and he can have no knowledge of what else in mother's larger world may have been acting to disconcert her, he does evolve a concept of "good me"; that is, the good baby, is somehow related to the good and comforting mother. Without any appreciation of the multitude of factors that operate in the complicated field of his mother's life, he learns to adopt that behavior which seems most likely to produce in his environment the characteristics of the "good mother," a mother who is not anxious, who meets his need for satisfactions and his growing need for interpersonal security.

As he grows older and the development of the concept of himself elaborates, he conceives of his mother as approving or disapproving of his behavior. He learns techniques for inviting the one and avoiding the other reaction. He learns to be remarkably responsive to the approving and disapproving gestures of other people. It is necessary that he be responsive, or he will experience the anxiety which he felt as an infant in association with the anxious, non-comforting mother and which he has come to associate with anything resembling disapproval. If his experience with anxiety in his early months and years had been frequent and intense, the child will come to be exquisitely sensitive to any manifestations of disapprobation on the part of others, and will develop complicated and expensive devices to serve him in the automatic avoidance of felt anxiety. In a somewhat oversimplified way, anxiety may be said to arise in an interpersonal situation in which one member at least anticipates an unfavorable appraisal of his activity or status by another whose opinon is of importance to him.

In summary, anxiety is related to an actual or anticipated decrease in self-esteem. It has its origins in interpersonal situations, and it is developed and re-experienced exclusively, as I use the term, in human relationships. This experience is difficult to identify, or to observe, or to alter by the one who experiences it; being felt as intolerable, the events precipitating it often go quite unnoticed; its origins remain obscure, there is available no adequate method for dealing with it directly and its presence is not easy to detect because of the complexity of "security operations" (or defenses) which are erected in opposition to its function. Anxiety, as I understand the concept, is a disjunctive force in human relationships, serving to drive people away from each other, arising as a response to an interpersonal situation and giving warning that discomfort is to be anticipated and that one had best withdraw in some way from this threatening development.

The task of therapy is in part to help the patient to become aware of certain aspects of his living (his ways of relating to others) concerning which he is highly motivated to remain uninformed. This is one of the things that complicates therapy. We are concerned with leading our patient to become aware of certain great truths about the inadequacies of his living; at the same time, he is concerned with his efforts to reduce his feelings of anxiety, to keep such great truths consistently obscure. Around such doctor-patient integrations arise certain problems of therapy which get spoken of as technical complications—as "technique."

The following philosophical assumptions may be found in Sullivan's concept of therapy (Murphy and Cattell, 1952): (1) Sullivan frequently used the phrase, "We are all more human than otherwise." The essence of this remark is that we are all more simply human than otherwise, be we mentally disordered, criminally inclined, or whatever, we are more like each other than we are like anything else. There is an important implication in this statement—namely, that collaboration between humans is quite possible; that there is no adequate basis for feelings of contempt or of guilt in the interpersonal relationship. It is on this fundamental assumption that collaboration is possible, that the therapeutic situation is founded.

(2) The second assumption is: "Since social situations are reciprocal, they can be transformative." That is, both parties, particularly the therapist in this instance, may play a part in transforming the interpersonal situation in a corrective direction.

(3) The third concept is the recognition that reality is safer to live with than fantastic constructions (no matter how amusing) erected for short-term peace of mind. The therapist keeps it in his mind that no matter how comforting the fantastic elaborations of his patient may seem to be, painful reality is conceivably somewhat better for his long-term living.

(4) The fourth point is that destructiveness, which may be seen as verbal attack, indifference to anxiety on the part of another, or gross misunderstandings never fit the needs of a mutual interpersonal field.

Finally, (5) that ultimately in the course of therapy, and in the course of a human relationship that develops in the direction of increased communication, there are no requirements to accommodate to the special needs or handicaps of the participants, other than, for example, severe organic defect or the effects of gross immaturity. All that I am saying in this complicated fashion is that as the relationship between patient and therapist improves, each member of this relationship is increasingly asked, and hopefully is increasingly able, to collaborate fully in the exchange of views without compromise. To put this in another way, as the therapist goes on in intensive psychotherapy with someone, no matter how troubled, one of the indications of having come somewhat closer to the end of the work, is that each participates with the other freely, and often without direct reference to the roles which they play, so that patient and therapist can, at least on occasion, play fully collaborative and somewhat equal roles.

In this brief survey, I shall now comment on the various *developmental eras* through which the human animal passes en route to becoming a more fully human person. Of importance to note in this review is the idea that deviations of development resulting from experiential deficiencies or traumatic interferences with growth may continue from one era to the next, being unchanged or imperfectly corrected, leading to the warps of personality that then may become known as "mental illness." In the study of personality, in the interview with a person with the goal of making a psychiatric diagnosis, in the evaluation of an individual for a job, and so forth, and in the engaging in psychotherapy, I am interested in the experiences which have characterized that person's living in these various eras, to which I shall briefly refer.

I am concerned as I gather some of these data, in the appearance, or in the maturation of potentials for behavior, and in the opportunity which is presented at the appropriate time for the expression of that behavior. That is, I am concerned with the proper matching of potential and opportunity for experience, this matching being required for adequate growth.

We shall start by referring to infancy, defined as the time from birth to the maturation of the capacity for language behavior. I am not at the moment referring to influences on the prenatal organism, although starting with infancy does not mean that I attempt to rule out the possible prenatal influences in the creation of the state of tension which may make one vulnerable to anxiety. But since I know relatively nothing about such, I must eliminate it from my consideration now.

Of particular concern to us is the infant's vulnerability to his mother. The human infant requires the mother's care for a long period of time before he can be anything like self-sufficient in providing for his own needs. Experience during the early period of infancy was referred to by Sullivan as occurring in the "prototaxic" mode. "Proto" comes from the Greek "protos," meaning first in time, and "taxis" simply means division, arrangement, or order. Thus, the experience of the infant was referred to by Sullivan as prototaxic.

Experience for the infant (and for the disturbed schizophrenic patient) seems to occur in discrete series of momentary states, *i.e.*, there seems to be no clear connection between a past, a present, and a running on into the future. There is in the infant, so far as I know, no awareness of the self as a self, or of other people as entities distinct from the self of the infant. Felt experience is undifferentiated, there being no definite limit in space, or in time, or in person. Experience has, to use a term applied to it by adults, a certain "cosmic" quality.

This kind of experience, in accordance with Sullivan's views, is simply not describable in words. It is an experience which at times is found in certain of our dreamy processes, and quite frequently, I think, in the experience of schizophrenic people, though their efforts to transmit this to us in words are inadequate—that is, cannot be anything like precisely informative.

The infant, to move on to another point, experiences what we refer to as a *tension of needs*. Such needs pertain to communal existence with the physical-chemical universe, which is a rather roundabout way of saying that the infant needs such things as food, water, sleep, warmth, oxygen, and bodily integrity, some freedom for movement and the expression of his physiological processes. When these needs are met, tension subsides and something which we refer to as satisfaction occurs. The development of experience in the infant arises apparently from an alternation of these needs and their satisfaction, and leads gradually to the development of that something which we look for so hopefully in adults, and which we call *foresight*.

The sequence of events to which I refer here may be somewhat as follows: tension being felt, action is taken, leading to satisfaction and a decrease in discomfort. There then may be noted to be a connection between tension, the following event, and the resulting satisfaction—a formulation of concepts relative to the elaboration of predictions of the future.

Time for the infant is largely spent in sleep, shifting over into something we call awareness. What goes on in and out of awareness becomes a matter of great interest to the treatment of people who are labeled psychotic. The environment of the infant is identified apparently at first in terms of his own feeling, and then of external objects. We may speculate that the mother's nipple, in the process of nursing, may be perceived in various ways by the infant—ways not lending themselves readily to verbal description. The infant's tension, which we label "hunger," is temporarily relieved by milk from the mother's breast, for example. The nipple which provides milk easily, without an excess of flow, may be thought of as the "good and satisfactory" nipple. A nipple adequate in contour, but producing a slow flow of milk, might be referred to as a "good but unsatisfactory" nipple. The "wrong nipple" is one which has the proper size and shape but produces no flow of milk. Of particular importance to our interests in psychiatry is the concept of the "bad nipple." In this instance the nipple is adequate in regard to its size, shape, and flow of milk, but is presented by a mothering person who is at the time anxious. Those who have had experience in a nursery and have seen nurses care for small infants, or who have children of their own, may have noticed the infant's discomfort in the presence of anxiety in the nursing person. The infant, having as yet no clear concept of self and other, cannot identify his mother as a person distinct from him, who, at that particular time, is tense. For the infant there is no such fine discrimination. Instead, the infant-mother complex is marked by discomfort. To put this another way the nipple is experienced as "bad." Although milk is provided, tension is not reduced adequately, there being an interference with the course of hunger—nursing—satisfaction by the mother's anxiety transmitted to the infant—or felt in the infant-mother complex.

As the infant begins to identify differences in perceived objects, he slowly develops the ability to generalize experience. He elaborates something to which we can refer as *self-sentience, i.e.,* he discovers his body, gaining a concept of "me," and of "my body." Such learning may be distorted—for example, by parental anxiety. Parents may take pleasure in observing the baby's discovery of his nose, his ear, his fingers, and his toes. However, the persistent finger in the mouth may cause concern because of the possible danger of resulting interference with dental occlusion. Also, the sucking of the thumb may be worrisome to some parents if it is looked upon as evidence of their failure to bring adequate love to the child. The parental attitude influences the act of the infant—that is, the situation becomes interpersonal—so that putting the finger in the mouth may be experienced by the infant as having a markedly different—if not comprehended—significance than pulling the ear.

In some instance, should the child handle his genitals, deriving pleasure from the contact, the entire interpersonal environment might alter markedly. That is, some people feel quite differently about infants tugging on genitals than they do about infants tugging on ears. Thus, as one builds up a concept of the self, it is apparent (although not to oneself) that some aspects of the organism are not as readily available for inclusion into a general bodily scheme as are some others. The image of the body may be reasonably clear cut and comprehensible excepting for the region near the genitals. The person who has experienced anxiety relative to the peri-genital areas may remain simply unclear about that and related aspects of himself. This is seen strikingly in people who develop what Sullivan spoke of as a "primary genital phobia." We see it in quite a number of schizophrenic people and in many others, who can talk with the greatest of facility about the usefulness of the hand in making a model boat or something, but will have a great deal of difficulty in talking to you about the structure of the male genital which they happen to possess, or of its function.

The infant organizes a picture of his mother which we may describe in adult terms as "good" and "bad," behaving as if there were two people (the "good mother" and the "bad mother") rather than there being a single mother who acts in various ways. The mother is seen on some occasions as one whose presence leads to satisfaction, and on other occasions brings discomfort: it is as if—without explanation and beyond control—the infant might at times be confronted by a "good" (non-anxious and tender) person, and at others by a "bad" (anxious and frustrating) person. The reasons for the "goodness" or "badness" are not evident to the infant, and the distinction between himself and the other being in an early stage of formation, his vulnerability to the adult is impressive.

This sort of thing happens with schizophrenic patients. During the past year, in working with a very disturbed schizophrenic gentleman, I was quite impressed by the fact that on some days he received me with a mild degree of agreeableness, and on other days with anything but amiability. Finally he was able to comment on my wearing a certain sportcoat on some days; then it occurred to me that he actually treated me, and apparently experienced me as being quite different when I was dressed in one way from when I was dressed in another. As we progressed in our understanding, I became aware that he treated me differently when I was somewhat depressed and withdrawn from when I was more amiably inclined toward the human race. I would say to the patient, "I am the same man, in sportcoat, business suit, depressed, amiable, whatever, I am the same person." This is where the clinical significance of this "good" and "bad" mother is seen; that is, the patient sees me as "good" or "bad," not as possessing good and bad qualities.

The infant also develops a concept of the "good me." That is, he knows that under certain circumstances what he does wins approval. On other occasions, without knowing quite why, he doesn't gain approval from people, and so, though he doesn't use these terms, he may refer to himself as the "good me," or the "bad me"—something which children actually do.

In infancy there develops another concept to which Sullivan referred as the "not-me." The "not-me" is not readily available for discussion, happily being somewhat uncommon in the experience of most of us. On occasion the infant may be exposed to situations marked by such devastating anxiety that the perception and symbolic representations of the circumstances are dissociated and thus not readily available ·to awareness. Although such experience is included as an influential portion of the total personality, the individual may have only intermittent, transient, and ill-defined knowledge of these portions of the self. With such a fleeting awareness there is a feeling that the experience is foreign—is not truly a part of one—and is somehow "not-me."

In the dream, in the nightmare, in certain states of fatigue and drug intoxication, and in schizophrenic reactions such "not-me" experiences may intrude on awareness. The "not-me" refers to symbolic representation of previous interpersonal events marked by anxiety of such a degree that the comprehension of them was grossly disturbed. Events of that nature may be labeled as dreadful, and the invasion of awareness by their symbolic reflections may be attended by feelings of awe, dread, horror, or loathing—sentiments referred to by Sullivan as the "uncanny emotions."

The infant also learns something about fear early in his life. Fear is a felt aspect of tension arising from danger to the existence, or the biological integrity of the organism, *i.e.*, such things as anoxia, starvation, thirst, subcooling and molar injury. Fear can be dealt with to some extent, for example, by removing or destroying the cause of fear, escaping from it, neutralizing the cause, or in some interesting cases, simply ignoring it. Anxiety, however, is an interpersonal event. This tension (anxiety), when it is experienced in the mother, is *empathically* transmitted to the infant, which is to say that it is transmitted by all kinds of gestural components including tone of voice, which cannot be easily observed, but can be readily experienced. The infant cannot deal with anxiety as he did with fear. Unlike the sources of fear, the origins of anxiety are obscure; it simply "exists in" his mother. The infant has no ways available to him for changing that anxiety. For example, if the infant in response to anxiety begins to cry, there is a good chance that his mother will become more anxious and tense. As her anxiety and tension increases, he may cry more. Then the mother is in turn more anxious and tense, and so on. The only relief for this anxiety is for mother to become less anxious, and the infant is not yet skilled in techniques for reducing her anxiety. What he can do is go into what Sullivan described as a state of "somnolent detachment" which clinically looks like apathy, i.e., he simply withdraws from the situation; he acts as if he paid no attention to it. As he stops crying, the tension may be reduced and he may sleep for a while, and in the course of this, his mother's anxiety may subside, removing the cause of his own anxiety. If, however, these somnolent detachments persist in the presence of continuing anxiety and frustration, there may occur what we used to refer to years ago in pediatrics as a *marasmic state,* in which the individual infant is withdrawn and acts as if he had abandoned his life. He may very well die unless appropriate nursing care is brought to him, and by appropriate I mean a great deal of bodily contact and personal concern for his well-being.

In infancy there is another development of great importance. That is, the infant forms some relatedness to people in the area of tenderness. When the mother observes activity in the infant requiring her care, there is aroused in her a tension which leads her to offer the care. This tension and this offering of care has a pleasant component which may be experienced as tenderness, and adds further impetus for the mother to care for the infant. There is formed very beautifully in the reciprocal relationships of mother and infant the need for tenderness and the need on the part of the mother to give tenderness.

A general responsiveness to approval of others is formed in the infant, and there is thus developed in the small child, before the age of two, an increasing need for security. In addition to the infant having a need for the satisfaction of certain biological necessities, he now develops a strong need for approval or tenderness from other people. We shall not go into any details about the amazing development of facial expression and of early speech sounds, all of which are learned during the stage of infancy, along with increasingly effective muscular coordination and the patterning of movements after others in the environment.

During the first year the rudiments of the "self-dynamism" form. That is, increasingly complex forms of behavior are refined in the service of reducing the distress in the experience of anxiety. The range of techniques is at first not wide, but is greatly increased as learning is acquired from the family and the extended culture. Among the earliest of these ways, helpful in the attenuation of experience and the maintenance of needed relationships, are dissociation, denial, withdrawal, and the beginnings of selective inattention and sublimation.

During these months, an early bit of the self is formed. You might say an early *self-dynamism* forms. The child engages, for example, in what looks like, very definitely as I think of it, rudimentary movements of sublimation enabling him to adjust to the needs of others, and so in this (and other ways) forms techniques useful in relating to others.

I shall speak briefly of some of the other developmental periods. The period of *childhood* extends from the ability to begin to use communicative speech to the maturation of capacity for living with compeers, *i.e.,* with other people about the same age. This goes on from the age of roughly two to five or six years, though these eras are not measurable in definite fixed periods of time. During this time, a great deal of value is placed on verbal behavior, and a fusion takes place of those personifications of what we spoke of as the "good" and "bad" mother, and of the "good" and "bad" me, and so forth. The mother is now seen as a separate person, and the child has become a separate person himself. Sublimation is increased, and communicative language develops. The child develops a great deal of what we might refer to as required behavior. That is, the cultural prescriptions are interpreted to him by the family and he begins to learn something of cultural values. He also learns to deceive and to conceal when he becomes anxious, as he inevitably will at times, and he uses various verbalizations and rationalizations, and what Sullivan called "as-if performances." By this last is meant those dramatizations in which the child assumes various roles to avoid punishment, or to get tenderness, and those preoccupations in which the child loses himself in thought to ward off anxiety.

One of the unfortunate developments of childhood of great significance for our work with schizophrenic people, is what was referred to as the "malevolent transformation" by Sullivan. In such cases when the child manifests a need for tenderness, the response of tenderness is denied and instead of tenderness he receives anxiety or pain; thus the need for tenderness brings, instead of an expectation of tenderness, a foresight of anxiety and pain. The child begins quite properly in such cases to conceal his need for tenderness, and to exhibit, instead, what we call *malevolent* behavior. This may be seen as undue timidity, in which case the child, obviously well equipped to do certain jobs, mentally and otherwise, is too timid to do them; this reluctance to act may be very frustrating to those who stake some of their prestige on his performance. He may show mischievous behavior, may act as a bully, and so forth, at times when his real need is for tenderness. In other words, the child undergoes the malevolent transformation in which ineffective or hateful behavior conceals the desire for human warmth. I'm inclined to think that most people whom we see as schizophrenic have undergone this course in life; they act as if they lived amongst enemies in a kind of jungle where they must constantly be alert to the devilish operations of others around them.

By the end of childhood, if things have gone well, the child is able to distinguish reality from fantasy and to use what Sullivan referred to as the "syntaxic" mode—that is, speech becomes more simply communicative.

The *juvenile era* extends from childhood to the maturation of the capacity for intimacy with one other person; it is the time for becoming sociable. Here the individual has a great need for playing with people his own age, and begins to be sensitive to the threat of ostracism from groups. He knows that his security depends in part on being a member of the "proper" group. The limitations and peculiarities of the home environment have an opportunity for remedy now, as the child mixes with other people and compares his home and parents with the homes and parents of others. He develops some realistic view of his parents, and he learns a great deal about certain social techniques—competition, cooperation, and the ability to compromise. He learns to give and take according to rules.

He also learns something which may help him some in his adjustment to other people, but later on may be very troublesome to them. He picks up the use of stereotypes, crude classifications of people and behavior. These often reflect unhappy personifications of the self, so that he too readily begins to speak of people in a stereotyped fashion, a trick which is hard to overcome. In this period also, he will inevitably learn something of the great device of disparagement, often from his parents. There seems to be no end of teachers available for teaching this. The shortcomings of other people are very quickly noted, and an unhappy effort is made to maintain personal esteem by simply lowering the prestige of other people. This is a commonplace operation, but it can be expensive to the child, or the juvenile, as its continued practice leads to an inadequate appraisal of human worth; the worth of others always being felt as a threat, their useful qualities often go unnoted. One can only feel something like, "Well, I guess I am not quite as bad as the other swine," which is a good step on the route to developing loneliness and hating isolation.

In the period known as *pre-adolescence*, there develops the ability to find someone else as a close friend, someone of equal importance; this is the basis for mature love. At this time in life, which may come between the ages of nine and thirteen years or so, the need for interpersonal intimacy is manifest. Indeed, this is a time of great idealism in which one finally discovers, out of the ruck of his juvenile relationships with many people, with whom he has learned something of competition, and compromise, and the use of stereotypes and disparagement, etc., a friend, one other person with whom he can communicate with a freedom the like of which he has never known before. Such intimacy permits the validation of the private, and now implies, not cooperation as found in the juvenile period, but collaboration, in which the "I" becomes a "We." During this time in life, the two-group is dominant, but it may operate in a gang in which the person may learn patternings of leadership and so on. It is my opinion that a great deal of warp may be corrected by the chum and by the gang, and that many unfortunate moves toward later unhappy living experiences may be corrected in the pre-adolescent period, if one is fortunate in finding a friend.

At the time of pre-adolescence, one may experience also that which we know as loneliness. I shall briefly summarize the course of development in regard to this concept of relatedness and its corollary of loneliness. The infant has a great need for bodily contact, and in his experiences with his mother develops the ability to receive and to give tenderness. In childhood, he develops the need for adult participation in his play, which becomes very important to him in contrast to the rather commonplace parallel play of children. In the juvenile era, he learns to play with his group and to abide by the rules, finding that acceptance by other people near his own age is of great importance to him. In pre-adolescence, he discovers intimacy with one other person, and as he moves into the period of *adolescence*, having gone through the puberty change, he develops further the lust dynamism (the clearly expressed feeling of sexual interest and ability, in the male, for example, to have orgasm). In adolescence, if things have gone well, the drive towards intimacy and the drive towards lustful satisfaction may be adequately combined with the appropriate biological and social object —someone of the opposite sex.

Late adolescence continues from the patterning of genital activity to the establishment of a fully human or mature repertory of interpersonal relationships, this being dependent on the available opportunity, both cultural and personal.

Now, let us turn to a consideration of the schizophrenic disorder. What I have to say may have some relationship to the work of Sullivan, but it is so personalized by now that I am very largely speaking for myself. Preliminary to my later more detailed comments, there follows in outline form the principal features of this thesis.

First, the schizophrenic process may be looked on as being to a considerable extent the reflection of the social situation in which it is manifested, and as an expression of the vicissitudes of living in the earlier life of the patient. The schizophrenic person has become, partly as a result of anxious, painful contacts with his fellows, increasingly isolated and lonely. Such isolation and loneliness are not compatible with human growth, or even life. The reaction which we call psychotic may be looked upon, not only as an expression of the result of disorganization and desocialization, but as an attempt to communicate meaningfully with other people. In this sense, communication with one's kind may be looked upon as a vital necessity for human survival, and some aspects of schizophrenic behavior then appear as complicated, obscure communicative endeavors designed to preserve some semblance of necessary social living.

Second, the schizophrenic disorder does not appear suddenly without there having been for some time increasingly clear evidences of its development. There is a period of so-called *onset,* characterized by more or less commonplace social phenomena, preceding the appearance of that behavior which we call typically psychotic.

Third, the phenomena characterizing this onset have a certain utility, in that through their expression the human organism maintains some semblance of social consistency and stability at a time of marked decline in the sense of well-being and personal security experienced in relation to other people.

Fourth, this underlying insecurity, and the behavior developed to deal with it, may be comprehended in terms of the life of the person who displays them, and may not be looked upon as weird artifacts of biological diversity. In our attempts to learn more about the distress felt by our patients, it is quite proper, and often profitable, for us to seek enlightenment in the study of the family and of the culture of which the family is an expression, accepting the patient and ourselves as remarkably complex and subtle representations of the interrelatedness of that to which we refer as the organic, or the social creation which we call our culture.

Fifth, consideration of those events associated with the onset, of the historical perspective and of the current social scene, reveals a picture of the person who is labelled "schizophrenic." He is now observed as making some degree of sense in the situation in which he exists. It is fundamentally important in our work, as in any other, to consider the probability that human behavior makes sense if adequate data are available for its evaluation. It is also important to recognize that we may on occasion *be unable* to make any sense out of some performance. When such an instance occurs, we are not then required to explain this behavior by either obvious or obscure rationalizations or to label it as somehow non-human or un-psychological. We are advised, I think, simply to notice, and to record, our ignorance and to seek further serviceable data.

Sixth, in accordance with our understanding of the human who has become our patient, and of the behavior characteristic of him, we may be able to devise therapeutic procedures consistent with the personality structure, the historical events related to his development, and the needs of both the patient and his culture.

My point is that mental disorder may be comprehended as a reflection of the difficulties that people have relating with each other, and in turn that those relationships are expressions of difficulties extending back into earlier life. Many of these difficulties, having occurred before there was development of speech or a concept of the self, have not been readily formulated into communicable ideas, which makes their correction more complicated than it might be otherwise. Without at the moment getting myself involved as to what is precisely cause and effect, I may say that I look upon the schizophrenic reaction as being in part an expression of the personality of the person who displays the behavior or the disorder. Personality is simply the reflection of multiple interpersonal fields extending back into the past experience of the patient. From this point of view, the schizophrenic reaction, having arisen from difficulties in interpersonal situations, lends itself to observation in an interpersonal context, and to further understanding from that standpoint.

Next we note that psychotherapy itself is an interpersonal process, involving an interaction between two or more people. At the moment I refer to an interaction between two people, in which the only thing that can be observed is the interaction. If I talk about what happened yesterday, or about what I dreamed, or about what I remember that my father did to me some forty years ago, that is an account of great interest to which attention should be paid. However, it is an account grossly distorted by the passage of time, by the action of my own anxiety, and by my often overweening necessity to give a report which will in some way be satisfactory to a therapist (although I may never be quite clear what it is that he wants). Also, it is a report very much distorted by certain personal necessities of my prestige, by my memory defects, and so forth. Thus, it is an account of something, but that it is very accurate in representation of the experience which existed between me and my father some forty years ago seems grossly unlikely. What I am saying is that what can be observed (and by this I do not intend any devaluation of the genetic approach, or of getting data from the past, or of dealing with dream material, and so forth) is what goes on between you and another person *at that particular time*. The transaction is an interpersonal process, and is a fit subject for study. I wish to emphasize the view that personality development, the schizophrenic reaction, and the psychotherapeutic process, are all expressions of interpersonal situations, and thus may be studied, and to some extent understood from an interpersonal point of view.

To focus attention on the clinical data, I shall develop my remarks with reference to the course of several years of psychotherapy in which I participated as a therapist of a young woman who displayed a schizophrenic reaction.

Late one fall afternoon, in a large eastern city, a man returning from work heard emanating from the window of an apartment house the screams of a woman. He might have passed by, but he was deterred by the terror, the urgency, and the wildness of the outcry. He entered the building, located the apartment from which the sounds came, and rang the doorbell. No one came to the door. The cries ceased for a moment and were then renewed with such intensity that the man called for the police. When the police entered the apartment of Mrs. X, a woman then twenty-three years of age, she was found huddled in a corner, clad in a torn dressing gown, her long hair in disarray, her feet bare, and blood seeping from a number of deep scratches on her face. She seemed frightened, cringed at the approach of the police, and sobbed and screamed in a harsh voice when she was questioned. When the officer suggested that she accompany him to the hospital, she ran from him and attempted to crawl through a partly open window, breaking a pane of glass as she did so. Attempts were made to restrain her, and she responded to these by fighting, screaming, biting, kicking and scratching, while tears ran from her eyes, and mucous and saliva from her nose and mouth. She was subdued by force without physical injury to anyone, and was soon thereafter taken by ambulance to the psychiatric section of a local hospital.

At this hospital she was placed alone in a room, and continued to be agitated and at times assaultive, destructive of the furniture and her own clothing, and was obviously very fearful of anyone who came near her person. She struck her head against the wall, burned her face and arms with cigarettes, and said that she would kill herself. She was unable to give any sort of coherent account or history to the physician who attended her, saying only that she was filthy, that she was unworthy of her relatives, and that people talked about her in a most disgusting and unpleasant fashion. With the aid of a sedative, she slept fitfully, at times awaking screaming as if from a nightmare. At such a juncture she would again huddle in a corner of a room or beneath the bed and would scratch herself deeply with her long nails, would bite her forearm, or when possible, burn herself with a cigarette. During the following day, her panic continued; she ran against the wall, bruising herself; she wept and said that she was hopeless, and vigorously resisted anyone coming close to her. She seemed suspicious, often turned her head as if listening to sounds not audible to others, and whispered that she was being tested and watched. She refused to discuss the situation with people, giving no information about herself, and she turned her back on those relatives who came to visit her. This behavior continued for six days despite the use of sedatives and warm baths. Mrs. X was then transferred to a psychiatric hospital, the diagnosis of schizophrenia having been made.

I shall review excerpts from the patient's history, gathered bit by bit over several years of work with her.

The patient had been known to be a sensitive, very talented and good child. She was described as having been a quiet and passive baby who soon learned to get along well with adults, by whom she was described as being cute, happy, delightful and older than her years. Let me note one aspect of her personality relevant to the theory of malevolence. As Helen (as we shall call her) turned toward her mother for tenderness, she often met with what was experienced as rebuff or criticism. Thus, she came to associate the need for closeness, or tenderness, or affection, with that which often followed upon the expression of that need—anxiety, rebuff, or pain. Helen then developed that unhappy pattern by which the child who wants tenderness, but anticipates rebuff and stress, exhibits the hostile behavior which would seem appropriate to the anticipated anxiety, concealing those responses which would be more conventionally displayed in a secure, loving situation.

Helen had gone through a malevolent transformation, as Sullivan would call it, and exhibited mischievous, aggressive, or strangely inefficient behavior at those times when she needed tenderness. What she got in return for such "bad" behavior was further rejection or punishment, which served only to confirm her growing conviction that people always hurt one, and that they should therefore be avoided or attacked. She needed affection, but she was developing techniques that led to her getting anything but affection. She was often praised for her beauty, her talent, her accomplishments; such praise she accepted bitterly, or rejected as false, feeling that no one knew or loved her. The fact is that she was becoming increasingly correct in this opinion. That which she dreaded and wished to avoid, loneliness and lack of understanding, were becoming hers as if by her own action. She seemed to be isolating herself "deliberately."

Now, let me say a few things about the history which properly might be given in much more detailed fashion. Certain points abstracted from it emphasize the concept that the schizophrenic process involves a series of events in the life history of the person, early deviant developments leading, unless corrected, to further deviation, ending at last in what we finally recognize as mental illness. You recall that this girl was not secure as an infant, as far as we can tell. I came to know her father and mother reasonably well, and met one of the nurses who cared for her. She was cared for by a number of substitute mothers, with no one of whom she felt fully comfortable. In childhood, her insecurities continued, with the result that she was ill at ease with other children, avoided them, and thus failed to learn many important things from them. In order to protect herself, she used speech more for defensive purposes than for simply communicative ones, and hid her ideas from others. She feared to hear ideas of others, since these might provoke anxiety, and her language and thought processes therefore maintained a peculiarly private quality which was not corrected by the usual procedures of sharing them with other people.

As a juvenile, she avoided group play, and her failure to learn the arts of competition, cooperation, and compromise, created marked defects in her later living. Handicapped by her feeling of insecurity with people her own age, she missed finding a good friend, whom she could love—the truly significant experience of pre-adolescence. However, she covered her defects with pseudo-sophisticated performances, for example, being what is known as "popular" and going on many "dates." But she failed to love someone of the opposite sex. She was lonely, and she knew it. In terms of physical development, of education, and of many social skills, she was adult, but the deviation in infancy, the feeling of being unloved, unsuitable, and afraid of people, had not been corrected. She now felt "empty," as she put it, alone and incapable of relating to another human. Let me emphasize once again that I am not saying that this kind of behavior pattern in infancy is the "cause" of schizophrenia. We don't know enough about these infant behavioral patterns to say that they are the cause of any particular kind of personality development, except those that become so devastatingly severe that they lead to immediate or very early dissolution of all prospects for interpersonal relating, in which case the infant will not survive.

Also note that I am not maintaining that deviation from useful experience in infancy is not correctable by later experience. Although patterns of behavior can be set up and maintain themselves quite rigidly from infancy, childhood and so on, they are influenced by later, beneficial interpersonal experience, often other than the psychotherapeutic. (If we had to rely just on the professional psychotherapeutic experience, our chances for survival would be poor.) There are many people who, I think, have developed certain patterns of behavior which can be grossly destructive, but which have become corrected in the juvenile and particularly in the pre-adolescent era.

It is difficult to set a time for the *onset* of the schizophrenic disorder. Note that in this patient there is an account of long standing maladjustment, marked by difficulties in each of the developmental eras, the deficiency of the early period interfering with the acquisition of corrective experience in the next. The signs of failing adjustment in this patient (which I did not review in detail) were overlooked; they were explained away, or they were dealt with by manipulation of the environment, with no increase in understanding, or of durable benefit to the person. By manipulation of the environment I mean such as moving from one school or place to another. Getting into difficulties in one, she was shifted to another; one always found someone in the old school or place to blame, and the interpersonal difficulty itself was never clarified.

In the main, her behavior was consistent enough with tradition and convention to present a crude semblance of good health. If no one looked closely, and if the person on the way to becoming a patient moved rapidly enough from one imminent failure to another, and if the observers had little interest in the events (or possibly even had a certain stake in not noticing the implications of the behavior), the growing disorder was not identified.

For practical purposes, we may say that the appearance of the schizophrenic state occurred at the time when this woman heard a voice call her evil, whereupon, she became obviously disordered and experienced panic. What went on before, including the unhappy events which we have described, constituted a complicated series of restitutive movements designed to keep painful, anxiety laden concepts out of awareness by the process which we describe as repression, or dissociation. We think of the schizophrenic person as one who has suffered severe assaults on his sense of security prior to the development of skill in the use of language, and prior to the formation of a concept of his self, as a personality distinguishable from others. Being at such a period of life remarkably dependent upon others for the satisfaction of both his security and physical needs, the anxiety-filled aspects of important relationships, as with the mother, are then kept out of awareness.

In this woman difficulties in lustful integration in a situation of intimacy were kept from awareness. In her relationship to men, she was able to give accounts of somewhat satisfactory sexual relations with certain gentlemen. On the other hand, she could also give accounts of having known a number of gentlemen who were very pleasing to her as intellectual, companionable people, but were unsatisfactory as objects of sexual interest. If one spoke about this odd dichotomy—her inability to combine in one man her needs for intimacy and sexual satisfaction—she would manifest evidence of dissociated processes. That is, she became psychotic. She was unable to make this simple statement: "I love another person in whom I can find the resolution of my needs for intimacy and sexuality." The concept of such love was horribly anxiety laden, and its investigation with me during the first three years of therapy always was accompanied by considerable anxiety.

In the schizophrenic state, the effectiveness of techniques to keep anxiety-provoking concepts out of awareness is reduced, and the person finds himself increasingly unable to meet the more complicated requirements of his adult social life. He then discovers that his need for intimacy, or closeness to another person is kept from fulfillment by the very anxiety roused in him when he moves toward an intimate situation. His self-esteem declines in the face of his social inadequacy. In adolescence a person is required to declare himself and establish his identity in various ways; he must do something about his lustful needs, about finding a friend, about the concept of marriage, having children, finding a job, and so forth. All these matters are interpersonal—that is, they require a commitment to other people. It is around these problems, I think, that many of these youngsters have great difficulty. As the person's self-esteem declines in the face of his increasingly apparent inadequacies, dissociated processes come into awareness, and these poorly formulated, anxiety-tinged referential processes from early life are not well-defined; their significance is not then evident, the relationship of one idea to another is unclear, and meaning seems to spread from one event to another, accompanied by a sense of urgency and terror known to most of us only in the nightmare.

Prior to the appearance of this kind of psychotic episode, the personality makes use, as it were, of a series of maneuvers which may be referred to as *partial adjustments*—efforts to reduce stress in the organism's environment. Thus Mrs. X's behavior before she became grossly disturbed might be comprehended as a composite of methods of maintaining some sense of stability in the environment in which she was feeling increasingly alone and insecure.

The first of these *partial adjustments are the compensatory activities*—a substitution of simpler activities and fantasy for difficult, or seemingly impossible, social adjustments. In other words, action which involves some participation with other people, becomes dangerous, as it carries the threat of anxiety and humiliation. Action, therefore, is to some extent renounced for day-dreaming, for reading, for attendance at the theater, for the seeking of sympathy, and for thoughts about vague problems with one's fellows, who somehow or other do not seem to understand one. Minor discomfitures may be rationalized away, or dealt with by a sort of innocent "white lie," without clearly acknowledging the action as lie or evasion. In all cases, action and consequent possible failure are increasingly avoided, and the seemingly safer course of thinking is followed. None of these activities mentioned are in themselves unusual or abnormal, and youngsters exhibiting them are not necessarily thought of as ill.

There occurs also an increase in what I speak of as the *sublimatory activities*—more complex activities and fantasies, which are in conformity with certain public ideals, and are *unwittingly* substituted for the more direct adjustive processes. In other words, that in moving directly towards a certain goal one experiences anxiety, and then finds a somewhat more roundabout but socially approved way of behavior which provides him with some satisfaction. That is sublimation. I said *unwitting* as this kind of adjustment is quite outside of one's awareness.

As matters worsen, certain *defense reactions* appear—the third group of the partial adjustments. These are more complex activities and fantasies, which unlike these sublimatory formulations, are *not* in close conformity with the social standards. Among these are evasions, forgettings, rationalizations, transfers of blame, negativisms, and hypochondriacal incapacitations, none of which work well, and none of which can be fully approved of by one's fellows. Now the person, desperately dealing with his anxiety and attempting to maintain some human contact, is using methods of behavior which more and more attract attention to him and make him conspicuous, which fact in turn increases his anxiety and drives him toward greater isolation.

In the schizophrenic experience, the self-system, as we call that complex of defensive maneuvers which serves to reduce the tension of anxiety and keep disturbing matters from our attention, and which is carefully structured throughout the years from infancy, fails to restrict awareness to those more precise referential processes that can be validated with other people. Much of the time what one is aware of are things which one could put into words, and could report to others in a way that would make sense. But what I refer to now is the appearance in awareness of ideas which cannot be spoken of "sensibly," cannot be placed into words, or validated with others. There are illdefined, poorly understood concepts concerned with interpersonal relationships of earlier times in the life of the individual when concepts of the self and of others were unclear, which now come into awareness. Never having been comprehended well, these are not comprehended now, and they appear in strange forms as terrifying phenomena, as frightening and awesome generalities, the implications of which may be quite horrible and puzzling, but cannot be clearly grasped. At the same time as these phenomena appear in awareness, the more conventional thought processes are also present, with the result that the person who experiences this condition may exhibit speech which is at times quite simply communicative, and again is quite simply not, expressive in such cases of what seems to be autistic abstractions from a dream. The lady to whom we are referring first began to feel as if someone had taken advantage of her, as if people would reveal her weakness. At times she felt a feeling of awe, or dread, or horror when she was in contact with these people who were increasingly threatening to her. At other times she noted an odd feeling of fascination, as if somehow or other she were drawn toward an involvement with the people who seemed most troublesome to her. Again, on occasion she felt a revulsion which was accompanied by so much gastro-intestinal distress that she sought help from an internist.

She was aware at times of an awful suspicion that dreadful things somehow or other would occur without her being able to do anything about them. She suffered from an increase in jealousy, it being noticeable that the intrusion of dissociated matters into awareness increases the fantastic quality in jealous integrations. In other words, she became increasingly jealous of the supposed (but not actual) carryings on of her husband with various ladies in the community.

There then appeared in her mind something which has been labelled by a somewhat atrocious term, autochthonous ideas. These are ideas which appear rather startlingly in one's mind and seem to come from somewhere else. It is as if they are not part of one; one cannot connect them with that which has gone on before, and the experience can be quite startling.

You may have had some such experience in a dream. You wake up with a start, recalling only fragments of the troublesome dream which woke you and left you with such a feeling of fear and bewilderment. You try to reassure yourself by getting up, moving about the room, having a cigarette. Perhaps your wife awakens and asks, "What's the matter?" But you can't tell her; you don't clearly recall the dream, and you are embarrassed by your apprehension. You mumble something about its being "only a dream," and you go downstairs to look at the paper, being reluctant to go to bed—and perchance to experience again that which is hazily remembered as having been so unpleasant. In other words, in the dreams thoughts came into awareness—thoughts poorly understood, frightening, and now not clearly recalled. The dream was a nightmare marked by anxiety, and the dreamer is not clear as to what occurred, is unable to report it to someone else, and is somewhat ashamed of his apprehension. He stays up for a time, renouncing sleep, as he does not wish to re-experience the fright, and he wishes to get quite clear as to his concepts of himself. That is, the self he knew in the dream, and on first awakening, seemed strange to him. Now, as he sits, and smokes, and reads, he becomes as we put it, "more himself" again.

The patient who experiences the intrusion of dissociated matters into awareness (such as the autochthonous thought, the hallucination) is frightened as is the dreamer; he feels uncertain and "strange" to himself. He doesn't run and tell people about his experience. To do that would expose him to someone saying that he is crazy, an eventuality that no one welcomes. But the person does feel crazy, and he is frightened. His fear and his insecurity are increased by the fact that he cannot formulate or verbalize his experience, and cannot communicate it to anyone.

The autochthonous idea is one of the early indications of the development or the appearance in awareness of a dissociated motivational system. Then there may appear the hallucination, often followed by the panic state in which all past experience is dissolved and foresight is lost. There seems to be no adequate way to deal with the present, and there is a sense of tremendous urgency. The patient in panic is searching for an explanation of the confused and uncomprehended situation in which he finds himself. All people who experience a schizophrenic panic state express some paranoid views such as: "It must be his fault. It is not I; it is he," which is a very nice way of speaking of the "not-me" part of the personality. The dissociated events seem foreign, and the thoughts seem to belong to someone else. The "paranoid" expression is an effort to explain peculiar events as being the result of action by someone else.

The following quotation is taken from a recording of an occasion during which I saw Mrs. X when she was in panic. She sat in the corner of the room; at times she spoke in whispers and again in loud screaming tones. "I've cut off my hand, and I mailed it to you. Oh, I tried to do that years ago but then you went away. (She paused and looked around.) Oh, the babies are crying. Oh, I know they're crying because they're happy no one lied to them. Well, they didn't know how to lie, did they? (Then she screamed.) Oh, there's blood on the floor. Now stop him, he's coming through the window. Save me." She ran and threw herself onto the bed. She looked at her arms and screamed again, saying, "Go away! I am evil. Look at my arm; now smell my flesh; it's green; look at the bone shine through. It's rotting. I smell so bad." And she wept, "It's horrible!" Then she said to me, "Look, the walls are moving; it's getting smaller in here. Where's the air? I don't breathe now." She pounded at the wall, saying, "Something terrible is going to happen, I know you want to kill me. So, you let other people kill me, but I'm going to kill you first, Doctor." Suddenly she was quiet. "Why do you do all this, what's this nightmare? Oh, stop shouting, you are all so loud." There was silence for a little and then she whimpered, "Be quiet, let this graveyard die. Be still. Be careful now. They are going to kill you soon."

That which I have described in part occurs in what I think of as the essential schizophrenic reaction, the catatonic state, commonly preceded by panic. Such a condition may persist with fluctuations for some time, or may be resolved in several ways, as follows:

First, there may be, without our knowing often too clearly why, a major re-synthesis of experience with profit. That is, through fortunate circumstances, including always, I think, benign human contact, the personality becomes more stable, and the chances for developing interpersonal relatedness are increased. Some of our patients are able to integrate something resembling previously missed pre-adolescent experience. Sometimes, they experience such intimacy with a nurse, an attendant, or another patient. One may never know anything about such a relationship, but things get a bit better, and life isn't quite as threatening. If the relationship goes well, the patient is better in the sense that he can validate his ideas more appropriately with others in the future. He might never have another schizophrenic state again, I think, if this theory I'm talking about is at all useful.

Second, there may be further major dissociation of symbols of previously dissociated experience. Once again much of that which has been undergone is not readily available to awareness. Having known the terror of panic, upon recovery from the experience the person moves thereafter with a certain caution in his interpersonal dealings, avoiding as best he can any situation that might threaten the equilibrium that he has painfully learned is precarious. Such caution, while protective, interferes with the making of possibly useful relationships with others and is a handicap to learning.

Third, the person may withdraw from such meaningful human contact, and become preoccupied with less complex and less interpersonal aspects of himself, such as his body orifices, the function and the movement of the intestines, etc. In such case he becomes classified as hebephrenic, and is, indeed, an extremely difficult person with whom to establish a communicative relationship.

Fourth, there may be effected a massive transfer of blame, as we call it, with the development of that grandiose self-appraisal characteristic of what we eventually refer to as the paranoid person. These last, the hebephrenic and the paranoid reaction, may be looked upon as unhappy and expensive efforts to deal with the schizophrenic reaction, and the concomitant persistence of markedly reduced self-esteem. These resolutions are not in themselves schizophrenic. The paranoid state, the hebephrenic state, the undifferentiated chronic dementia praecox, and so forth, are very unhappy, persistent resolutions of the schizophrenic panic reaction.

In conclusion I shall say something first about the patient, and then the doctor. The patient, such as the one discussed here, is shy, frightened, and has been traumatized in his experience with other people. At times, he is in a panic, a state of extreme fear, wherein any factor in the situation may be frightening, and his ability to evaluate adequately the behavior of those around him is grossly reduced. This is the kind of person—with an acute schizophrenic reaction—to which I refer in terms of therapy. As a reflection of his fear and anxiety, he withdraws from social contact, this being shown in his verbal and other behavior, and he is remarkably susceptible to the actions of associates. Both his aggression and his withdrawal are, in part, ways of avoiding those contacts to which he is so vulnerable. He is seemingly at the mercy of anyone who can increase his anxiety. He is lonely, and he cannot live as a human without human contact; since such contact has provoked anxiety in him, he is thus handicapped in solving his problem of loneliness. He doubts the value of human relationships, which doubt is but an expression of his own lack of assurance that there is any value in himself. I quote Mrs. X, who said at one time, "I have no evidence that contact with another human has helped me. It has never helped me to talk with anyone." The patient is often quite puzzled because he cannot comprehend some of the thought processes that have come into his awareness, and he seeks for explanations, trying to make some sense of what goes on. Meaning seems to *spread,* as we put it, so that significances are attached to events quite unrelated, or not closely related, or related in a way different from that which the patient perceives it. The patient often does not feel like himself, his behavior is at times quite unpredictable to him. There are *shifts,* we say, in his levels of awareness, a rather crude locution, so that he seems to move without apparent cause from the normal waking state to something resembling the dream. He feels that he is dealing with magical forces, and quite properly, he may attempt to exert magical power, acting like a wizard, and exhibiting powerful gestures, as is beautifully demonstrated in the catatonic state. When one is involved with these "not-me" problems of which he cannot make any sense at all, he may exhibit magical gestures in an effort to resolve them. We ourselves may get involved in problems, the origins of which we don't know, concerning which we can predict nothing, that we can't explain well, and about which we feel we must do something immediately. In such cases, quite privately, we may use certain magical gestures. We may say, "Well, just for today I won't step on any cracks on the sidewalk. I know that it's all silly, but I won't do it anyhow. I won't tell anybody about it. Not that it will work, but. . . ." And so it's not surprising that our patients get involved in this sort of thing.

The patient cannot communicate readily with other people because he fears self-revelation. Dissociated matters disturb the organization of his awareness, and can't be put into words. Autistic thoughts cannot be explained easily to other people. He feels inadequate and he is ashamed of that. He may feel crazy, but he doesn't like the idea. He is among strangers, often in a hospital, when we first see him, and is not likely to talk freely to an unfamiliar person. He may experience a variety of physical sensations marked by a quality of oddness, so that when he speaks of them the doctor may look surprised and the patient fears that he is revealing his insanity. He feels evil, unwanted, and is troubled by disturbances of perception, and by phenomena called by others delusion and hallucination, which entitlement does not turn out to be particularly helpful or informative to him. At times he feels quite simply crazy, and this cheers him no more than it would you or me. If such troubles are continued, his morale is not very high. He very likely has not been greatly encouraged by his experience with previous attempts to help him. He has not failed to notice that despite these attempts he continues to be disturbed. There is little reason for him to think that his strange experiences should be presented to the ministrations of a physician. A magician might seem more appropriately concerned with what is happening to him. Thus, a psychiatrist who says too readily that he can help may seem to the patient to be speaking nonsense, to be uninformed, to be a charlatan, or possibly to be just simply stupid, and none of these ideas is helpful to the development of the therapeutic relationship.

Consider the therapist. I am talking about the therapeutic situation as being an interpersonal situation in which the tool of the therapist is himself, his personality. This is in the main what he has to use in the psychotherapeutic relationship. To use it well, he must know it, which means that he must possess some knowledge of himself, the acquisition of which may be discomforting, as well as enlightening. The patient is asked to expose himself, in the course of treatment, and it should be noted that the therapist will also be exposed, and in this procedure, marked by honesty and understanding, is afforded an opportunity for growth of *both* participants, differing from certain earlier pathogenic relationships distinguished by obscurity, hypocrisy, and persistent anxiety. The therapist of the schizophrenic patient need not pretend to know everything and a certain quality of humility can be quite helpful in dealing with people who doubt themselves so greatly. The therapist will, in the course of his work, learn from his patient, discovering that for the patient to be the teacher, and on occasion, in a sense the therapist, will not damage the self-esteem or the growth of either participant.

The therapist may not comprehend all aspects of his patient's behavior, but he can be expected *not* to look upon any behavior as beyond the realm of human experience. He can only differentiate clearly that which he does understand from that which he does not, letting his patient know where his (the patient's) behavior fails as a communicative instrument. The therapist will gain satisfaction in his work, but he cannot turn to the patient for the fulfillment of certain fundamental needs such as prestige. The patient, having experienced parents who may have used him to satisfy certain needs, does not respond well to similar behavior in the therapist. In the course of the work, the therapist will discover that he has within himself a delicate instrument, his self, responsive to the significant aspects of the patient's feelings as displayed in voice tone, facial expression, other gestures and words. As he notices his own feelings, he may determine that some of these reflect those of his patient, and reporting these to the patient, take the early steps in developing improved communication.

In the course of therapy, we will discover that he who has seemed crazy and incomprehensible to us appears so, in part, because his behavior is a reflection of those aspects of living common to all of us, but rejected or forgotten by most of us as we become adult and put behind us (often to our misfortune) the experiences and ways of behaving of our earlier years.

In our work we will learn that human contact is an absolute essential for human survival and growth, and that the personality is largely a reflection of such contact, as the family is a reflection of the larger social order. In our search for useful therapy we do well not to overlook the great potential that lies in each one of us for understanding both ourselves and other people. In psychotherapy, we are attempting to make use of this potential in structuring interpersonal situations marked by durability and by respect, in which anxiety is reduced, communication improved, and growth made possible.

Comments on the
Psychotherapeutic Intervention

by Otto Allen Will, Jr., M.D.

I SHALL SUMMARIZE, with considerable omission, the course of psychotherapy conducted by me with a young woman patient over a period of five years. I do not present this material as an example of ideal therapy, or a procedure which can (or which I think necessarily should) be applied in every case. It does, however, give a crude picture of the interrelationship that is part of any intensive psychotherapeutic program. These endeavors are not to be described simply as a doctor treating a patient, but as an interpersonal relationship, developed slowly, and marked by complexities which are, for the most part, not immediately recognized, and certainly not soon comprehended by those concerned, or even, by other observers should they be present. In the course of therapy the recurrent, yet ever changing nature, of the data may enable the therapist—and hopefully the patient—to identify patterns of behavior, reflective of the past and demonstrable in the present. As these are formulated and seen in relation one to another, understanding of the patient's (and, to some extent, the therapist's) modes of experience and living will increase.

By this, I simply mean that if you introduce into the psychotherapeutic field another observer (such as through the use of a recording apparatus) you soon discover that all does not become clear even to that somewhat more detached observer. If you sit and watch talking movies of therapeutic endeavors, as far as I am concerned from the little experience I have had, the field becomes so extraordinarily complicated that it is difficult to evaluate. The main point of my earlier remarks was that as one sits through a course of psychotherapy, certain patterns which appear again and again become somewhat more evident and may make increasing sense.

In my further remarks, I shall illustrate the appearance and course of certain distorted views of the other, held by each of the participants in the therapeutic endeavor. These distortions are not always readily observed by the therapist. Their recognition and further understanding come from a study of their repeated demonstration in the therapeutic situation. At the time of their greatest intensity, they may not appear as distortions at all, but are experienced as very painful reality. Through the study of such experiences, something may be learned of those difficulties which led the patient to require psychiatric help. Distortions, then, may be looked upon, not as objectionable interferences with the progress of treatment, but as potentially useful accompaniments of that procedure. Although they are often obscure, they are profitable forms of communication whereby the patient presents to his physician a representation of the gravest problems in his living.

The physician has the advantage of training, experience, and some detachment from his patient's living. Thus, he is able to observe this interpersonal relationship in a somewhat different manner than his patient. The patient has the advantage of having lived his experiences, of having the data more or less directly available to him. He has before him the task of increasing his ability to be an observer as well as a participant.

Although the physician and the patient will turn to the past for information to help illuminate current events, and although they will not ignore the development of foresight in dealing with the future, both will find that there is only one field which can be repeatedly observed by each of them with some slight hope of increasing accuracy.* This field is that of the interpersonal relationship occupied by therapist and patient. What can be observed are the day-by-day occur-

---

*The function of foresight is an interesting factor in any interpersonal relationship. Current behavior is not only reflective of past experience, but is somewhat influenced by the organization of what has been past experience into certain concepts which are predictive of the future. One operates in the present in terms of both his recall of the past and his anticipation of the future. Foresight is a reflection of what one has experienced in the past. Nonetheless, it is organized into something having a more or less predictive value. Its influence on the therapeutic situation is such that one is frequently concerned with aspects of communication that indicate the exercise of foresight by a patient.

rences which take place in their meetings, the pattern or patterns of their dealings with one another; in brief, "what goes on between them." It strikes me quite frequently that I as a therapist may engage in evasive operations to avoid dealing with something in the immediate interpersonal field. With the best intent in the world and with rational explanations, I may find that it comforts me as a person somewhat more to hear further dissertation about some event which occurred in some dreadful past, than it is to deal more directly with aspects of the relationship which exists between me and that patient now in the room with me. This does not mean that I think field theory might be completely disassociated from the past, and that therapy can be effective without reference to past events. However, it behooves the therapist to consider again and again the possibility that some of his preoccupations might serve to divert him from a consideration of that which is most available to him—the operation then going on between him and the patient.

The behavior displayed in the therapeutic situation will be a product of that which has gone before; it must be a representation of the interpersonal fields in which both patient and therapist have previously existed. This is just another way of saying that the personalities of therapist and patient are involved in this activity. The behavior in the therapeutic situation will be influenced also in some degree by an anticipation of future events. In viewing the therapeutic relationship, the participants can come to a greater comprehension of those events which led to the formation of current patterns of behavior. In the act of gaining this understanding, they can, each of them, gain greater security in their relationships with others, increase their knowledge of human behavior, and develop further respect for themselves and others.

Particular emphasis should be placed on *aspects of the interpersonal relationship which are called evidences of transference,* or, to use a term more suitable for my purposes, and relevant to the theories of Harry Stack Sullivan, of *parataxic distortions,* although the two terms are not exactly equivalent. The term parataxic distortion was not first used by Sullivan. I think that Thomas Verner Moore, a research psychologist at Catholic University, used the term prior to Sullivan. "Parataxic" refers to processes of thought which are not well organized in terms of cause and effect, and prediction of the future, and are frequently connected with interpersonal experience in one's past which has been marked by anxiety and has not been clearly comprehended. The behavior reflective of such experience is likely to seem unreal, being unduly influenced by the past in terms of the current situation.

Of transference, Freud (1948j) said, "They are new additions or facsimiles of the tendencies and fantasies which are aroused and made conscious in the progress of the analysis; but they have this peculiarity, which is characteristic of their species, that they replace some earlier person by the person of the physician. To put it another way: a whole series of psychological experiences are revived, not as belonging to the past, but as applying to the person of the physician at the present moment. Some of these transferences have a content which differs from that of their model in no respect whatever except for the substitution."* In the psychoanalytic theory transference phenomena are considered to be an inevitable, and potentially useful, accompaniment of the therapeutic process.

In the theory of analytic technique, transference phenomena are an inevitable necessity. "Parataxic distortion," Sullivan (1954) said, "as a term, may sound quite unusual; actually, the phenomena it describes are anything but unusual. The great complexity of the psychiatric interview is brought about by the interviewee's substituting for the psychiatrist a person or persons strikingly different in most significant respects from the psychiatrist. The interviewee addresses his behavior toward this fictitious person who is temporarily in ascendancy over the reality of the psychiatrist, and he interprets the psychiatrist's remarks and behavior on the basis of this same fictitious person. . . . Such phenomena are the basis for the really astonishing misunderstandings and misconceptions which characterize all human relations. . . . Parataxic distortion is also one way that the personality displays before another some of its gravest problems.

"In other words, a parataxic distortion may actually be an obscure attempt to communicate something that really needs to be grasped by the therapist, and perhaps finally to be grasped by the patient. Needless to say, if such distortions go unnoted . . . some of the most important things about the psychiatric interview simply go by default."

As I have suggested, the therapist must be alert to the appearance of transferences or parataxic distortions, the latter term having a broader meaning. At times, the therapist may be unhappy with the patient's continued presentation of what appears to be some distortion of his (the therapist's) conception of his personality, or as he thinks of his role in the community, and so on. But, one notices also, that although this distortion is evidence of the patient's difficulty, it is also one of the clearest ways of displaying, in the therapeutic situation, some of the things that are troublesome to the patient. For example, I may find that my therapist is extremely difficult, seeming to be a some-

---

*This kind of comment defies proof, I think. How would one know that there was no difference between a current concept of a person in the immediate scene, and a concept that one had of somebody in the remote past?

what authoritarian person. Let us say that this therapist is in many ways *not* terribly authoritarian; in time I may notice that my attitude towards him is slightly out of keeping with his actual role and position. I may also notice that although treating him as a harsh authority is a rather unhappy and expensive method of dealing with him, it also is a way of presenting before him one of my patterns of relating to people. That is, I show clearly in my behavior with him that I have trouble relating to people in authority, and that I tend to treat all such people alike—that I react more to a stereotype than to reality. The point is that my difficulty is thus presented in the immediate interpersonal situation in which therapy is done.

In the following condensed presentation of five years of intensive psychotherapy it can be observed that parataxic distortions are not always observed readily by the therapist—in this instance by me. Clarification comes as a result of their repeated demonstration in the therapeutic situation. Some disturbances of behavior may be presented by a patient over months of time and simply go unnoted by me. When noted, I sometimes may think of them simply as being obscure and troublesome, and privately wish that they would go away. But as they persist, and we wrestle with them through time, and the patient survives it all, one may finally notice a certain pattern from which some clarity emerges. Thus, one learns, often tediously, something of what has happened to the patient, and may say to him, "Well, it looks as if this way of dealing with me is an indication of thus and so, eh? And possibly this behavior relates to this tedious early experience with your father." You say all this with a somewhat pardonable feeling that this is a demonstration of your good technique and insight. But then your patient may say, "Sure!", as if you had said only the obvious. Now this is a demonstration of interest. The patient has gone over repeatedly with you the data which led you to make your interpretation; the experience has finally become available to his awareness; it is "part of him." Again and again, in therapy, the interpretations that one finally makes about these interpersonal difficulties have already become "old hat." The patient "knows" it all by the time you interpret, and then sometimes says to you rather wistfully, "Why don't you sometimes make a real bright interpretation which casts light on things the way other people's therapists do?" That is as it should be. All one can do is to hope that when your patient talks to other patients he may distort the situation enough so that the other patients think that you make bright interpretations as their own therapists allegedly do.

At the time of their greatest intensity, distortions may not appear as distortions to the patient, and they sometimes do not appear as such to the therapist; they simply appear as painful reality. For example, if one said to the patient, "Oh, well, you're angry at me as you were at your father," the patient might reply, "You're being the psycho-analyst again, rattling off those clichés of yours. My view of you has nothing to do with my father who was quite different from you. I simply find you tedious." On the other hand, the therapist may find himself entertaining the view that his patient has certain difficulties in living which he now thinks of as biologically determined, or organ-ically structured, so that nothing can be done about them. In such a situation he may say to one of his colleagues, "I think that fellow is something of a loss to humanity." The colleague may reply, "Maybe you were just anxious at the moment." To this you say, "No, not at all. I have simply discovered the relative hopelessness of this other person." That is what I mean by a "real" quality; to the patient—and on occasion the therapist—the parataxic distortion appears to be the clearest of truth.

Through the study and increased clarification of these distortions much is learned of those difficulties which led the patient to seek the psychiatrist. The distortions need not be looked upon as objectionable interferences with the progress of treatment, but as often obscure and frequently profitable forms of communication.

Now consider the patient. A young woman became an in-patient at Chestnut Lodge at the age of twenty, and was in treatment with me for about five years. For over three years we met four hours each week, and on occasion, as frequently as six or seven hours; by "hours" I mean meetings generally extending sixty minutes. For the next six-teen months we met about three hours a week, and for the following few months, a couple of times a week—a total of roughly 700 hours.

She was an in-patient at the hospital for fifteen months. Except for a couple of brief hospitalizations for a night or two, she was there-after an out-patient.

She was brought to Chestnut Lodge from another hospital by a nurse. At first, she would not discuss her difficulties with anyone—the admitting physician, nurse, or anyone else. She finally did say that she never had been happy with people her own age; that she was the only child in her family, and that in some ways her family life seemed troublesome.

Some of the behavior leading to her hospitalization can be outlined briefly. Although in retrospect it might seem that this lady's troubles began early in her life, she was not considered to be sick in the con-ventional sense until she was eighteen years of age, and in her first year of college.

During the period from her fourteenth to seventeenth year, she was known to be a good student. In the private high school that she attended, she took part in school activities, but she did not go out with boys when the other girls began to do so. She was always described, at least by my informants as being "sweet," unaggressive and shy with people her own age. During her high school period, she tended to read a great deal and this was looked upon as evidence of her studiousness. She stayed alone a considerable part of the time, particularly in her last high school year. At that time she often went to the movies alone. None of this behavior would be termed abnormal, but, in retrospect, there was some indication that this youngster was not finding group experience particularly gratifying, and that she had no person who was very close to her.

Between the ages of seventeen and eighteen, during her senior year in high school, she complained of some general physical troubles, such things as fatigue and headaches, which she could not describe accurately, except to say that they were "bad." At times, she was thought to be rather listless, and in retrospect, she noted that she often found it took a great deal of effort to continue school. She frequently found getting up in the morning a great task. Now that in itself may not be remarkable. As I came to know the young woman, I learned that she felt increasingly on awakening that "It's tough to face the world." This does not imply that everyone should leap out of bed with sheer delight at the idea of facing the pleasant world. There was a *shift* in this person's behavior; there was an increasing tendency to stay abed. If one (her mother, for example), said to her, "Come, get up, and get at it!", she responded with a vague comment to the effect that she was fatigued. Then her mother might say, "You ought to get to bed earlier. You need more rest." It was perfectly apparent, however, that she was getting enough rest, as she was staying in bed more than had been her custom. I think that we are noticing at this time, at the patient's age of seventeen, some beginning disturbances of the sleep process. This young woman actually experienced some slight intrusion into her awareness of phenomena ordinarily dissociated, a process occurring during sleep, but not clearly recalled as a dream or experienced as a nightmare. Sleep is becoming increasingly disturbed, but there is no recall of what went on in it. This is observed in some patients who tell you, for example, that they don't sleep at all. One wonders how they exist without sleep. If they are in a hospital, the nurse may report that they get what seemed like five or six hours of sleep during the night. Such sleep frequently has been interrupted, and the person has awakened recurrently for a while. Perhaps he got up for a cup of coffee, being restless; perhaps he didn't get to sleep until one in the morning, or slept profoundly from nine until eleven in the morning, and so on. If you yourself have experienced this sort of thing, you know that you often have the feeling that you didn't sleep at all, although you were sleeping, in an interrupted fashion a good portion of the night.

In the case at hand, the young woman was experiencing the intrusion upon her awareness of dissociated processes, and her behavior reflected the development of what we may call defenses against the anxiety attendant upon such alterations in perception. When one is asleep, he is vulnerable to the approach of dissociated processes. If one sleeps, he may dream, and into his dreams may appear matters suggestive of the unpleasant experiences of his earlier years. In this situation sleep is marked by an increase of a peripheral (to use inadequately a geographic term in the service of a psychological process) awareness. As anxiety continues, one becomes chronically alert even while sleeping, and attendant upon this form of awareness, there is an increase in fatigue. When questioned, he who experiences such phenomena may have no recall of dreaming, but reports only that he feels fatigued without knowledge of the source of his disability. He dreams and knows it not, except indirectly through his body's voice.

There was noticeable evidence of illness although it was not described as such by anybody at the time. During this last year of high school, somewhat to the gratification of her parents, this woman became more neat than she had previously been. Whereas at times in the past she had been rather helter-skelter in her activities, she now not only kept her room rather well, but she did it in such a meticulous fashion that on occasion her fussiness was troublesome to her associates. Her mother might say, "Let's move things around thus and so," and would discover that her daughter was opposed to such maneuvering of the furnishings in the room. At times, in fact, she was quite angry about any proposed changes, and would say, "Look, Mother, this is my room and I want it kept just this way. After all, I am grown up and I'll have things the way I want them." In itself this was not remarkable. But it was evident that she was exhibiting increasingly obsessional behavior—substitutive operations in the service of the reduction of anxiety. Some of her anger was an expression of the increase in anxiety when her mother interfered with behavior (such as compulsive neatness) designed to reduce the feeling of discomfort. The room arrangement had a magical significance, being an obscure (in terms of its referents) magical gesture in the service of the decrease of anxiety. The anxious girl felt more at ease when "things" (and people, also, if such could be arranged) were placed in a certain order marked by some degree of predictability.

Toward the end of her seventeenth year, our patient developed a persistent diarrhea. She told her mother, who said it was probably "nothing." This is not evidence of any particular unkindness on the part of the mother; but there was now manifest what became an increasingly severe physical complaint, and the mother tended to dismiss it as of no importance. As I came to know the mother and the patient, I regarded this response as an indication of the profound distance between these two people, and their gross inability to communicate with each other. One might say that our patient was expressing feelings of unrelatedness with the smooth musculature, leading to the appearance of the diarrhea. In effect she said, "Look! I don't know what's the matter with me. Isn't it odd, that one of the most distant aspects of my personality, which I can't formulate into words at all, namely the operation of the autonomic nervous system, is working in such a fashion now that I have what is called diarrhea?" The other person might then say, "You don't need to tell me about that in words. I can experience your feeling of tenseness somewhat. You are talking about isolation, aren't you?" The body language—the diarrhea —was presented to the mother, who was unable to deal with this kind of communication. Unable to comprehend, she said to her daughter, "It's probably nothing." The saying that something (the diarrhea) which was profoundly troublesome was "nothing" led to further isolation.

After completing high school, this patient was admitted to an excellent college. During the summer before going to college, she ate markedly less. She lost some weight, and the diarrhea continued. She was noticeably preoccupied and spent increasing amounts of time alone.

In the fall, at the age of eighteen, she went to a women's college where she lived in a dormitory, having expressed a wish to be away from her parents and to be independent. In the dormitory, she was unhappy and felt out of place. She didn't seem to fit in with her classmates. She then consulted an internist because of the increasingly severe diarrhea. An able person, he said that she did not have a colitis, which at first it was thought she had, and he recommended that she seek psychiatric help.

Despite her difficulties, she made the Dean's list in the first semester. Toward the end of this first semester, her isolating mechanisms were reflected in an increase of physical activity; she began to walk the streets at night, feeling, as she put it later, as if she were about to experience panic. But this comment was retrospective. At the time she felt as if "something," somehow or other quite dreadful, were going to happen, but she didn't know what this "something" was. It seemed as if whenever she sat in one spot for very long, the imminence of this dreadful thing became greater. She walked, often long hours, occasionally through the night, wandering around about the streets. On one occasion, she went to the infirmary, weeping and refusing to leave. To the doctor she presented a vague account, saying that she did not know what was the matter, but that perhaps her strange feelings had something to do with her upset intestinal tract. She was admitted to the infirmary for several days. She thought very highly of the doctor but during her few days there she was withdrawn. She wept a good deal and occasionally said that she didn't know what was the matter.

The doctor thought that it would be useful if the patient saw a psychiatrist. She accordingly left college after completing the first term of her freshman year, and continued to see the psychiatrist once or twice weekly for the next seventeen months.

During those seventeen months, she lived with some family friends, it being thought that it might be useful for her to live apart from her parents. She exhibited what looked like a great deal of anger and hostility towards her parents, saying that they did not understand her, and that they had not raised her in the right way. They were, in turn, apologetic and hurt, and said that she had always been a good and loving girl, and that her behavior seemed quite inexplicable, as well as being troublesome. They showed feelings of guilt about their daughter's accusations, which simply led her at times to feel quite guilty in turn, and at times to become even more accusatory. The patient did some volunteer hospital work for a few weeks, and then carried on a flirtation with a man of forty-five, some twenty-six years older than she. This was interesting because she had never had any heterosexual, or other sexual experience, aside from noticing her own genitals, occasional preoccupation with sensations from them, and fantasy regarding their manipulation. In other words, she had not developed any patterning of sexual behavior but suddenly was carrying on a flirtation with a man who was attracted to her. On one occasion, he responded to her obvious flirtatiousness by impulsively kissing her. She was startled, and withdrew with a great show of anger, which astonished and frightened him. She would see no more of him, and he willingly dropped their relationship, being affronted by her response.

She then left the home in which she had been living and went to the home of her uncle for about a month. While there, she awoke one night screaming, and came running down the hall in a state of obvious apprehension, saying that something terrible had happened. Perhaps she had had a dream, or a nightmare. She was not able to tell anyone about what had occurred, saying only that her experience had been terrible. She didn't sleep for the rest of that night. On the next night she appeared somewhat better. She went to bed, but the family awoke in the morning to find her gone. Perhaps she was in what might be called a fugue state, a dream-like wandering about the country. But the patient remembered nothing. She turned up in another day or so at her home, her clothing dirty and torn, unable to give an account of what had occurred. She was welcomed by her parents, and thereafter spent much time isolated in her room, at times locking herself in.

In the fall of that year, while in her room one day she began to scream, broke some things, and would not come out when asked to do so by her mother, and her father who came home from the office. They were frightened, called a physician, and she was admitted to a small hospital near her home. There, because of her violent behavior, she was placed in restraints. When she was removed from these, she was assaultive to the doctors and nurses, saying that they were laughing at her, and were trying to influence her. What the nature of this influence was, we don't know. Her disturbance rapidly subsided and after a few days she returned home.

Once home she again tried volunteer work at one of the hospitals, but worked only a day. She complained of increasing fatigue and general listlessness. She had been a good musician, but she no longer paid any attention to her music. She did not read, and often was found sitting alone in her room. Her parents noted with some pleasure that she seemed a little happier at the Christmas season. Again, she tried a few jobs, but was too tense with people to continue for long, always finding that somebody criticized her unduly, or that the working conditions were unsatisfactory. She was isolated, frightened, and on a number of occasions, had what were described as "hysterical" spells, during which she would suddenly scream, run into the night, or lock herself in her room, where she might stay for a day or more.

She had a difficult time with her psychiatrist. She seemed to be fond of him, but was extremely jealous of him. Often she was tearful after leaving him, and she frequently felt rejected by him. On many occasions she would stay away from her appointments, locking herself in her room, refusing food for four or five days.

Because of her isolation in her room and her refusal to eat, she was finally taken to a psychiatric hospital, approximately eighteen months after the onset of the disturbance which led her to be separated from school. She entered the hospital frightened and mute. I did not see her during this time, but the records show that on occasion she was extremely hostile, and at other times seemed to be bewildered, seductive, and silly. She finally spoke, and said that she had an atrophy of the brain, and was going to die. She ate very little, but was not tube fed. She was described as withdrawn, and as showing evidence of thought-disorganization, and she was repeatedly and violently assaultive. To quote from the records, "Retreat and disorganization were prominent features." She refused all social contact, seemed to be hallucinated, and talked as if her former psychiatrist (who now no longer visited her) were present. In some of her sessions with the hospital therapist, she became impulsively disturbed and struck him. She frequently attempted to choke fellow patients and had unexplained spells of screaming.

The patient received fifty deep insulin comas and about thirty-six electro-shocks without apparent benefit. She continued to attack patients, and threatened to kill them. She was hostile to physicians without exception, and insisted in response to their questions that there was nothing to discuss with them. She was restless, often quite manneristic, standing in the corner of her room only partially dressed, holding poses for long periods of time. On one occasion it was thought that she was completely disoriented and hallucinated. Once she ran away from the hospital for a few hours, but was brought back by some of the personnel; there followed three days of withdrawal and mutism.

Although she improved on some occasions, she would soon revert to being perplexed, bewildered, and withdrawn, lying abed mute. The diagnosis was *schizophrenia*. On being told that she would go to Chestnut Lodge, she said, "I don't want anyone else meddling in my life. I don't want anyone to get to know me well. I shall never change. I shall never talk to anybody."

At the risk of being somewhat repetitive, I shall speak briefly about some aspects of this onset. During this period, forms of behavior were used which enabled the patient to maintain a partial adjustment in what looked like an increasingly insecure interpersonal situation.

In the earlier stages of her difficulties, there occurred what we call *compensatory activities*. These refer to the substitution of *simpler* overt and covert activities and ideation in conformity with social standards, and in lieu of more complex behavior. In such case the person exhibits behavior which produces some satisfaction, which offers some rewards, which maintains some kind of human contact, which is passable enough in the community, but is not quite, if you look at it closely, as complex as other goal-directed behavior might be. Such behavior yields less satisfaction from active participation with people, and much less prospect of achieving a tangible goal. [There are exceptions to what I am saying, because some people *do* withdraw for a while in this way, and, to use a crudity of speech, act as if they somehow "caught their breath," as it were, and are able then to go back into the interpersonal arena, thereafter carrying on reasonably well. Some people become isolated, stay abed for long periods of time, have difficulty speaking freely, and obviously are dealing with dissociated matters; they have little to say, may read at intervals, many doze (slipping from sleep to a partially waking state), dream, and seem to be involved in the attempted solution of some poorly grasped problem. After some time they may totter to their feet again and go out into the world. It looks as if they had worked through some kind of restitution of their defenses against anxiety, as it were, and then were able to get about again with some satisfaction.]

Consider now the *compensatory activities*. It was "natural" that this young lady should have thought, as she did, that it would be pleasant to go on a date with a young man, because, in the first place, a lot of the other youngsters were doing so at this time of life, and in the second place, she noticed in herself some lustful interest. She found, however, that movements in the direction of making contact with a man were attended by anxiety, and she turned to an increased reading of romantic literature as an unhappy substitute. She attended the movies and speculated how things would be if one were older and Clark Gable only noticed one, and so forth. This kind of fantasy is certainly not unusual, in fact, it is almost inevitable. It is, it seems to me, a rather useful way of thinking about the future and making plans as to what one might do, not necessarily about Mr. Gable, but about someone else more available. But the patient's fantasy did not lead to that kind of action. This is why it was *compensatory* activity. Only limited satisfaction was derived from it, but action was not required. The possibilities of interpersonal rebuff did not have to be faced.

Included in this sort of behavior are bits of fantasy, going to the theater, reading, daydreaming with increased withdrawal, and (what may be noticed better in retrospect than at the time) an increasing attenuation of human contacts. If one should ask a person about his attenuation of human contacts, he would, of course, have a ready explanation to show why such withdrawal took place. The explanation in this young lady's case was an unhappy one, but it was fact; she had managed to gain weight and said that she was "too fat" to go out with the boys. She thought of herself as horribly obese. Also, she had braces on her teeth. Thus she was sure no one could find her attractive, and she could "explain" her growing isolation.

There was also the further development of *sublimatory reformulations*. These operations, as far as I know, begin in infancy and are more complex covert processes, which are in keeping with social requirements, whereas compensatory operations are *less* complex than the ordinary goal directed activities. Sublimatory reformulations are unconsciously substituted for more direct adjustive processes. Keeping the school store was some evidence of this in the patient. She sold candy and other articles to other children, and she received approval from her teachers because she was dependable in keeping the accounts. There was nothing wrong in doing this, of course, and it did win her approval, but it kept her out of other activities. Others didn't want this responsibility; they were engaging in all sorts of rewarding social performances. She was doing something very useful which brought some praise from her elders, and as far as we know, was unaware that she was sublimating. She conformed with social standards, but achieved little expression of her needs.

Sublimation, as I understand it, begins in infancy. The infant runs into what he experiences as "forbidding gestures." He encounters in another person behavior which indicates that this other may think less of him. (As a matter of fact, we all get so expert at observing forbidding gestures that we rarely notice our observation. We only note that somebody is a "difficult" person or "not quite suitable" for close contact, or belongs to the "wrong" racial group, or something of that nature; we then ignore his efforts to relate— as if they didn't occur. There are many subtle movements on the part of the other which we interpret, more or less accurately, as indications, not that he *is* making us anxious, but that he *might* make us anxious, if a relationship were permitted to develop.) Before the infant has developed any facility for speech, he is subject to experiences which produce in him an awareness of the "bad" instead of the "good" mother, the mother who is anxious instead of the one who is at ease. The infant quite automatically and with remarkable facility develops behavior patterns which he learns to associate with the appearance, in a magical way, of this good mother. That is, he learns to adopt patterns of behavior which are pleasing to the mother and which lead her to be less anxious—and this is the beginning of sublimation. This process goes on and on, becoming intensified in later childhood, where it serves a very useful function. Sublimation is one of the ways we learn to get along in our culture. If some activities are unsatisfactory, we "unconsciously" take on others. But sublimatory reformulation does not produce full satisfaction for the need involved.

One of the most obvious examples of this last is sublimated sexual interest. Instead of direct expression of genital interest, a person may engage in other, more socially acceptable, activities. For a time this works. However, the energy coincident to that part of the need being sublimated, is certainly not completely satisfied in this way. Sublimated behavior is not as simply goal directed as the more appropriate behavior would be. For example, becoming an excellent puller of weights at the YMCA, though dispelling certain energies, is not the same thing as experiencing direct expression of sexual interest, and hence can only partially satisfy this need.

But what about the so-called excessive need? This, we think, is taken care of by the development of an elaboration of fantasy. As fantasy is elaborated, a great deal of the need can then be dispensed with. Let us say a young man does not feel at a particular time that it is suitable to have much to do in an intimate, sexual way with a girl. Such contact would not fit in with his concepts of morality, perhaps. Then let us say that he engages in other activities which partly sublimate his needs. He is free, however, to think a lot about sexual matters, so that it occurs to him to picture himself with girls. This is fine, unless he develops the idea that the "thought is the deed." Then he is in a tough spot. He ordinarily could dispel a great deal of energy thinking about sexuality and could obtain pleasure in the obvious sensations from his genitalia, and so forth. However, should he feel not only that the thought is the deed (hence he shouldn't have the thought), but that the sensation from his genitals is also equivalent to evil, then he must do something about getting rid of the sensation and not having the thought. In order to handle this, he must elaborate substitutive thoughts. All kinds of thought processes are run through the mind in an effort to replace the troublesome thoughts. As he tries to sublimate some aspects of the sexual dynamism, or integrating tendencies, he may notice that sublimation doesn't completely meet certain needs, and that the excessive energy must be met by further sublimations, by discharge in fantasy, dreams, and what may look like purposeless physical movements. This obsessional substitutive thinking may work for a while. Then, in sleep, he may be betrayed by the appearance of not only dreams about sexual adventures, but by the awareness of physical sensations and activity of the genitals.

If the degree of dissociation is adequate, the dream will not seem to be a part of him, but only a wicked intrusion into his life. If he is clever at this business, he won't remember the dream, but will notice only that he was rather uncomfortable during sleep. He may have so-called nocturnal emissions. Something like that is a little more difficult to ignore, but he may be able to produce some verbal magic about it so that it becomes, not an indication of lustful interests, but a psychologically inexplicable physiological change.

All of this becomes a somewhat complicated structure. The young man lives in an environment which puts certain requirements on him. He may notice that other people do not have the same difficulties. That becomes troublesome. Because he is anxious about this sort of thing, he must avoid noticing sexual matters, sexual feelings, what others say about sex. This can be done through the operation of what we call *selective inattention.* He does not notice what other people say about sex, dating, and so forth, but explains it away, or does not extend the implications of what they say; that is, what they say doesn't seem to apply to him. An organization of thought processes and non-observances has been constructed which begins to put distance between him and other people. It becomes necessary for him to walk carefully in order to avoid some unkind citizen who might upset this organization and cause him great anxiety.

The dynamism of sublimation can be overloaded. For example, it will not carry the burden of sexuality, as far as I can see. Sublimation works beautifully through childhood, and very profitably in many ways. In pre-adolescence and in early adolescence, after the puberty change has occurred, and lustful integration is more manifest, sublimation does not handle matters very well. Fantasy becomes increasingly crowded, and a person may complain of being unable to study well, which is not very remarkable. He sits down to read a book, but a word suggests something. Then thoughts come into his mind to neutralize the "bad" thought that the word suggested. If this thinking leads into lustful feelings, then he must do something about that. Lust is our example but there are other sentiments—hostility, and so forth—that may be dealt with similarly. The remarkable thing is how some of these youngsters turn out really amazing intellectual performances when, as far as I can judge, they spend very little time at reading, or studying. Most of their time is involved in these peripheral processes. If asked about it, however, they have nothing to report, for if they do start noticing these processes within themselves, they approach the schizophrenic state.

This brings us back to the patient in the case study. She began to make greater use of obsessional substitutions such as I have suggested. She was obsessively neat, and she used magical compulsive gestures, one of which was the twirling of her hair when she was anxious, the significance of which I never understood. She spent a lot of time in repetitive and rather meaningless activity. She had idle thoughts which filled her mind, and a great many sexual ruminations which, however, seemed to lead nowhere. Then there developed more activities, more complex but not now so readily in conformity with social standards. These were the hypochondriacal preoccupations, which had an odd quality about them and which led her doctor to advise psychiatric care.

Let me pause here to discuss this a moment. As physicians, we see a great many people who come to us with all kinds of physical complaints. I have an old story which interests me in this regard. Some years ago, I served during a vacation period as a physician in a student health service. One morning, a young man presented himself to me and said that he feared he might have a hernia. I asked him why he had this fear, and he replied that he had been lifting and carrying some wood the night before to his third-floor apartment. He felt some pain in his groin, and he thought that he had a hernia. He knew that these things might occur, and he wanted me to take a look. I did, and he did not have a hernia. Since I had time and was in a more receptive mood than usual, I noticed that he seemed particularly unenthusiastic about this negative evaluation of his condition. As he looked rather down in the mouth, I suggested that he tell me more about his suspicion of a hernia. The story was a long one. Finally I learned that he wondered if he had a venereal disease. I said, "I think not. I didn't notice any signs of such. But you didn't ask me about that." And he said, "Well, I just thought maybe you'd find out in case I did." Now, it seemed apparent that he wasn't worried about the hernia; but he thought that if he was examined for a hernia, the doctor might look in the genital area, and perhaps remark, "By Jove, you don't have a hernia, and you don't have a venereal disease either." But I had said nothing. When I realized his fears, I said, "Well, let's have a look; have you been around with girls too much lately?" At this, he flushed a bit and appeared rather offended, which seemed odd, because if he had had no sexual contact, why did he worry about venereal disease? On examination, it was evident he had no disease. But I wondered about his continuing anxiety, because he still was obviously uncomfortable. Then he told me more of what had happened. On the previous night, he had been in his apartment, and the landlady, who was a rather attractive young woman, and who had managed to imbibe a fair amount of liquor and to become enamored of him, to his surprise had presented herself in his bedroom. She suggested that they get into bed together and he decided that this would be a fine idea. But when he had done so, he found himself troubled by great feelings that he was about to commit a sin. He really didn't know what to do and was rather inept about the whole business. His doubt was taken care of, however, because, before there was any genital contact, he had an ejaculation, and that was that. The lady remarked what a failure he was and that he didn't seem to like women or something, and he thereupon thought of her as a terrible person. He went up to his room and spent a restless and lonely night.

That isn't quite the end of the story. He puzzled about what had happened and his sleep was disturbed that night. Early in the morning hours, he wakened with the sudden thought that things were very bad indeed. He broke into a sweat and he walked on the street. He felt great guilt at having been with the lady. Soon there came the terrible thought, with striking clarity, that he was about to commit, or had committed, the unpardonable sin, and he felt impelled to speak to someone of this.

The point of my story is this: Had this young man come to me as a physician and presented his complaint as, "Doctor, I have committed the unpardonable sin," in saying this, and so exposing his feelings to me, he might (as he saw it) run the risk of my replying something as follows: "What are you doing consulting me? Perhaps you should consult a minister or a psychiatrist. I think that you may be crazy." He didn't wish to speak directly to the matter of his concern, fearing rebuff, and therefore approached his relationship with me in a devious manner, hoping to protect his pride and avoid excesses of anxiety.

In the early stages of these increasing anxieties, there are many physical symptoms, which have rather odd qualities. They are difficult to report to somebody else, because one doesn't want to be called crazy, and yet, going to the doctor establishes contact with someone. There is a hope that he will understand what the trouble is, and talk about it without increasing one's anxiety. That is what the young man was seeking when he complained of the hernia; he was near panic and required acceptance.

As mentioned earlier, in the course of the onset there may appear evasions—lying, forgetting, and various kinds of what are called hysterical amnesias—something of which our case study patient showed— and something resembling the so-called fugue state. There occur also the various "transfers of blame." This young lady demonstrated this by saying that other children were "at fault," and that no one understood her; she made references to such things as "my fate." ("It is my fate to be ugly; it my fate to be unattractive, unknown, unwanted," and so forth).

Withdrawal, negativism, and the development of so-called organic symptoms accompany this development.

With the decrease in the patient's feelings of relatedness, having by now withdrawn from her few girl friends, having no male friends, isolated from her parents, distant from her teachers, unable to relate with any degree of comfort to her fellow workers, and failing with the professionals (that is, the psychiatrist), she experienced a sense of isolation in which past, present, and future were not clearly connected, and in which she felt as if she had no self. Life seemed to have no meaning to her. She experienced then what we call panic, which reflected a marked increase in anxiety. Put in another way, panic seems to occur with the threat of the termination of human relatedness.

Throughout this development, there was an effort to use activities so that anxiety would not reach a level at which it could not be dealt with. This activity worked for a time. Despite increasing anxiety, and an increasing complexity and inefficiency of behavior, it was striking that the patient had been able to maintain some contact with other people. She did this by the use of sublimation; with physical complaints which brought her to the attention of others; and by obsessional maneuvers which in themselves help reduce anxiety, and on occasion brought her some needed praise, enabling her to do routine tasks in school, and in other situations. I am often amazed at the remarkable attempts made to maintain human contacts in the face of increasing anxiety. This patient worked in department stores as a clerk, although she frequently had to give up her job in a day or two; she worked as a receptionist in a hospital; she made attempts to attend school; she visited her uncle, she attempted to engage in a love affair with a man; and she made some attempts at psychotherapy, troublesome as they were. Despite her anxiety, some sort of human contact was maintained for a long period.

An interesting observation can be made about this. If there is a tension in the interpersonal field more troublesome than anxiety, then it is the tension of loneliness. Loneliness and unrelatedness are feelings about which people don't talk while they have the experience. I refer to the kind of loneliness, of increasing isolation, of inability to establish anything like a meaningful contact with somebody else, which seems at times to be a strong enough motivation to drive one toward the establishment of some integration with another *even in the face of anxiety*. This is what seems interesting about this young lady. All of these efforts to relate were painful. Why did she attempt them? That she was moving towards increased isolation seems evident because her course eventuated in the upset which we call a panic.

Notice the communicative aspects of this lady's behavior. The difficulties which we have described are not clearly recognized by her or by other people. She presents various complaints: diarrhea, headache, fatigue, a dislike of her music, unexplained anger, feelings of being a failure. All of these things were evidences of difficulty, and could be called "complaints." There were difficulties that she did not express openly: that she felt ugly, alone, unwanted, and hated. She was in the main reassured by people to whom she spoke on these matters. She was often told that she was "bright," and capable, and that things would be all right.

This can be troublesome to young people. They get to feeling—all patients do at times—that the other person, the psychotherapist or whoever, cannot bear to hear what is said. This is the kind of evidence they use to support such a view. The troubled person says to somebody, "I really am, I must admit to you, a mess." And the other person says, "Oh, no, you really aren't. Here's your school record, showing that you have five A's. You're really quite attractive," and so on. That's one way to call you a fool, and it's also one way not to hear you. The implication seems to be, "Don't reveal to me what may be behind these troublesome feelings. I can't bear to hear how awful you are."

On psychological tests, the patient was a bright young lady. The Wechsler Bellevue report indicated an IQ of 132. On the Rorschach, there was revealed a need to dissociate, and an extreme crippling of certain intellectual functions; her ability to integrate social experiences was very poor; her horizons were limited, and large areas of experience seemed to be "amputated." The patient seemed to focus on concrete aspects of experience and to see no more. A psychosis was being held in check by the limitation of growth to that which is safe, to the familiar, and to the non-committal. There was a threat of a schizophrenic outbreak. This test was made about three months after I began therapy with her, about fifteen months after her first hospitalization, and approximately three years after the clinical onset of the panic state.

I have summarized what I consider to be some of the dynamics of the onset. Her past was a troubled history, but must be omitted here.

Now let us discuss the therapy. In the first interview, the patient came into my office and was introduced by the nurse who accompanied her and then left. The patient nodded at me. She was a young woman, 5'6" tall, with a well-rounded, not fat body. She had bobbed black hair, a clear complexion, a youthful, rather attractive girlish appearance. Her clothes, which had been made by her mother, were of good quality and style, but seemed somewhat youthful for her. The girlish quality was accentuated by short white socks and low-heeled sandals. She was suspicious, tense, and curtly replied to my greeting. She quickly said that her main complaint was that she was in the hospital. I replied that I couldn't alter that. Then she snapped that there was no use in talking to me, that being there was a mistake, and that there was nothing more to say. All this was said with an odd little smile, in a somewhat contemptuous and mocking manner, which I found disconcerting, although she was conventionally fairly polite. I then remarked that she sounded to me like a good girl who had always been nice, and

I wondered why she smiled when she had to talk to me. So far as I could see, the situation was not amusing. I asked if she felt that she should be nice, and possibly resented this. To this she suddenly said, "Yes." She told me that she had often been pressured in a "nice" way to do things for others. I said that conceivably on some occasion she might not like this. She said she didn't. I observed then that she spoke as if she were supposed to come to the hospital for the sake of other people—her parents, for example. And she said, "Maybe." I said that, as far as I was concerned, treatment was for her and no one else, to which she said, "Bull!" I shrugged my shoulders and said that any improvement in her living, so far as I was concerned, would have to be by her and for her, and it wasn't going to be for me. As far as I could see, my life would go on all right whether or not she got better. At this point, she said to me rather sorrowfully that she liked her parents a great deal, and everyone in her life had been, and was now, just fine. At this, I expressed some annoyance, and said that this sounded like the comments of one who had of necessity to be polite and nice. I said that I thought she seemed to be very guarded in her remarks about her parents, and if her life had been so wonderful, I could see no reason for her talking with me.

At this point, she got up to leave. I said to her, "Oh, sit down! You've got nothing better to do and neither have I at the moment." So she sat down and said that she was uncomfortable when some of her statements were taken at face value. She felt that she was a sham and presented a "front" to others. She felt that other people tended to "fall" for this. I didn't comment on that. I told her that I planned to see her four times a week and that in our interviews I expected to get some understanding of what it was that interfered with the course of her life. At this she got quite angry. She said that nothing was wrong with her, and that in her previous contacts with psychiatrists, she had come to like the doctor pretty well, but that he would send her away or stop seeing her "for her own good." I said, "Well, I suppose this will happen again with me." She said that she certainly hoped so, because she didn't want to see me, and she did not like me. I said, "I don't know whether it will happen with me or not, but if it does, you are going to have to do something about it." She replied, "I don't want to get mixed up with a doctor. A doctor isn't going to do me any good and I have no hope of therapy being of any value to me. Can you help me?" I said, "I don't know. Help you? I don't know who you are, or anything about you. How could I say I could help you? I don't know. Just come and see me."

At this juncture, it was obvious that she was not psychotic but she was, at times, very sullen. In the interview, which lasted an hour and a half, she was silent for brief periods, and became very tense, holding herself rigidly, pulling at her hair, and giving sudden angry and explosive responses, which she attempted to cover by her formal and stereotyped smile.

We met for an hour four times a week during these months. At first, I directed our sessions by securing some history about which I took a few notes. I told her my memory was not good for some details (which is true), and said that I wanted to jot down a few dates, and this she accepted. I learned a little of her schooling, of her hospital experiences, and of her parents, and a fair amount in these first few months about her father. Finally she ran out of information. I suggested then that she say what was on her mind. At this she became extremely anxious, as one would expect. "Nothing" came to her mind, as she said, so that the invitation to do something called "free association" was an invitation only.

She no longer had any ideas in her mind. After some hours during which she was mostly silent, she said to me that she could never change; she felt that she had now discovered that I could never listen to her real troubles. She said that actually I was a very unpleasant person and a fraud. I would seem to be nice to her, but she knew that as our relationship continued, she would discover that I really hated her; people always "did her in" when they had a chance and she wasn't going to let down her barriers with me. She was glad that she had found my evil qualities so soon.

She put a great deal of emphasis on her hopelessness. This "hopeless" business went on drearily hour after hour. I found it very burdensome, and quite frequently would say to her, "Well, it's not so hopeless," or "How could you feel hopeless with me," or something like that. Such comments were of no profit to her. I began to notice that it was my own anxiety which required me to make such remarks; I was burdened by the accounts of despair. I noticed that I didn't want to hear about hopelessness. When she said, "You don't want to hear about me," she was, in effect, saying, "If you really did hear, you couldn't stand it." Though I always denied this, I began to question myself a little. "What is it that I can't stand?" I asked. One thing that I always think about in these instances is what it is that I *can* stand. If the patient says, "I hate you, Doctor," I am usually not greatly troubled. I can stand it less well if the patient says, "You're wonderful." I can stand it if the patient says that things were terrible with father or something like that. But can I tolerate the sort of non-specific, grinding, hopeless, unending, dull process in which nobody gets anywhere, and which leads only to some kind of human grave? That I find troublesome. I might say to the patient, "Oh, I can stand anything, just tell me something and I'll show you what I can stand." But if the patient says, in effect, "Well, I don't have anything to tell you at all, just nothing works for me," I often feel miserable. If I'm perfectly honest, I might say, "But this is what I can't stand. I can't endure unending accounts of feeling hopeless." Then the patient would say, "That is what ails me; I feel hopeless." Thus it is that the therapist must learn to deal with his own discomfort.

Although it is not in sequence, I would like next to talk about a period occurring in the seventh month of our work. There were many long silences. She was tense and preoccupied, and I often felt inept and uncomfortable. She sat and did nothing. Once in a while, she walked out of the office, leaving me alone. A colleague might say, "Where is your patient? Were you through early to-day?" and I would say, "Yes,—it seemed advisable." At such times one wonders if one is quite suited for such work. Frequently the patient told me that the treatment was no good, and that she felt I had contempt for her.

She began to say that I was a rather suave person; that I often was smiling, well groomed, and that I seemed to her to be a hypocrite. This new view of me had finally dawned on her. She was surprised that she hadn't noticed all of this more clearly earlier. She said she ought to have known that I was probably being a seductive hypocrite in order to manipulate her; I obviously talked too much; I chattered on and on. At times, she wanted to know all about me, and then would feel very guilty about this curiosity. Occasionally, I would tell her something about myself—simple things—where I had been for an hour, that I had gone down to get a cup of coffee, and so forth. Then I noticed that she would say, "Oh, don't tell me!" I would ask, "Why not tell you? I'm not ashamed of it. What are you talking about?" Then I learned that she had often wanted to know where her parents went, for example, and that there was a time in her life when she searched through the drawers in her mother's room when her father and mother were particularly unhappy with each other, and that she wanted to search through the drawers of my room, to look at the mail on my desk, and so forth. She had felt that her parents were going to get a divorce (which they came close to at one time), and it became apparent that she had felt her security was very much dependent upon the security of anyone to whom she was closely related. She wanted to know whether I was secure, whether I got upset, or carried on an unhappy life which would lead me away from her.

In brief, I seemed to be pictured as a seductive father. She had wanted a close relationship with him, but when she drew close, she had become afraid. She acted as if becoming close to me would get her into a trap, and this she had to avoid. Thus I was pictured as seducing her and wanting to hurt her. She responded by hating, by fighting, and by various attempts to hurt me.

This situation was resolved in about the tenth or eleventh month. She came into my office appearing calm, and saying that she no longer felt jealous, and that I was nothing to her now. She felt quite detached and insisted that she no longer had any thoughts about me. One by one she evaluated my other patients, some of whom she knew, and pointed out all of their bad qualities. She also pointed out that none of them were improving through contact with me. I was pictured as an old man who wanted to find his pleasures with young women, and who would try to take advantage of her. She felt contempt for any liking that I might have for her, saying that she wanted to seduce men and have them crawl to her as her father had done. His elaborate seductive relationship with her could be described in rather conventional Oedipal terms.

Now she began to engage in a great deal of acting out. I was troubled by this, and wondered if it reflected, in part, some difficulties with me, but was not able to resolve this. She threw things at the personnel, became assaultive, and was transferred to the disturbed ward of the hospital for a short time. There she was often grossly disturbed and I was anxious, feeling that I was in the role of the father, but being unable to clarify this concept with her. The relationship felt real to her, and did not seem like a "transference." When I made any interpretation about her feelings toward me being related to those about her father, she responded with ridicule, or by becoming upset. At the time much was not clear to me. It is easy enough to say that somebody is treating one like a father, but as yet there was relatively little data to support the view. I wondered if I were realistically contributing to her upsets, a possibility the therapist must consider. Was I taking an undue pleasure from her relationship? Was I accepting a certain sexual stimulation from the obvious gross upset of this young lady, who would be presenting me with variants of her emotional experiences? Was I, in other words, acting in some way which was provocative? Was I using her for my personal satisfactions, and was I in ways not clear to me, being seductive with her? Those are all good questions, which one has to consider, the raising of which may be associated with much anxiety.

I wish to point out that in the first year of the work with this patient, we identified some aspects of her relationship with me as being distorted by experiences in her past with her father. I seemed to be cast into a fairly consistent male role. In the first year or more, we dealt with material which seemed mainly to do with the father. She talked about her relationship with him, and felt that I was like a father. As time went on, she noted ways in which I was different from her father, and he finally became somebody we could talk about more freely. During all of that time, we rarely discussed her mother. Once in a while, I would ask, "You do have a mother?" "Yes, she was a very nice person," would be the reply, but the subject was not elaborated.

In this first part of our work the hours were often marked by her silence. She would, on occasion, denounce me for my stupidity, or my lack of understanding. Once, she suddenly attacked me, leaping out of her chair, striking me in the face, pulling, kicking, and biting. As she quieted, she said that she had felt so alone that she had to break through the barrier which stood between us—a simple description of something not at all simple. She had jumped at me on a number of occasions before, moving very quickly and ably but never managing to hurt me. Although, in theory, I knew that something had happened to make her increasingly anxious, I was not able to put my finger on it in most instances. Thus I was faced by recurrent, extreme assaultiveness, and was unable to deal with it to my satisfaction. On one occasion, she hit me, grabbed at me, bit at my hand, and wrestled a little. We both got short of breath, and when the struggle ended, after a few flower pots in my office had been broken, and a window had been shattered, she sat down in her chair. After we caught our breath, I said, "What the hell was it about?" She said that there was a barrier between us, and that she needed to get some response from me. She felt detached, and it seemed to her as if I were simply not living, and that she must have some sort of physical response. I asked her if she felt some lustful feelings at this particular time, because I had noticed in wrestling that some sexual feelings stirred in me. She said yes, that she had felt something of this. We agreed that the relationship which was developing between us might have at times a physical quality which, on this occasion, had to be expressed in hitting, and which should be expressed further in words. The entrance into awareness of lustful feelings was recognized as not inappropriate to a relationship of developing intimacy. Thereafter she talked a great deal more freely about herself. The months were marked, for a while, by recurrent assaultiveness, and at times I experienced fear of her. This was rather remarkable for me because she actually did not hurt me. Nonetheless, I became increasingly afraid of her. Often I saw her early in the morning, and as I would go to the hour, my pulse rate would increase. I would be preoccupied with what kind of a man I was to be so afraid. This apprehension was the only clue that I had to the increasing intensity of her anxiety and the coming assaultiveness. I spoke to her about my feeling, but much of what I was able to verbalize simply led to further upsets, and I was often silent through this period.

In the second period of our work, we began to discuss her mother. There was then a change in our relationship. We experienced, after having developed a great deal about the concept of her father, what I would describe as a relatively peaceful period of several months. During this time interpretations about various aspects of her life furthered, I think, some consolidation of gain in her living. She took part in activities with other patients, and lived outside the hospital.

Then the quiet period ended. Her dreams began to take on a grotesque and bloody quality. She noticed that her feelings about me were changing, and spoke of this in an odd fashion, marked by a quality of the uncanny. She finally said that she was through with me. She felt she could no longer trust me, and she noted that she had an awful suspicion of me, doubting everything that I said. Having a vague sense of something horrible in me, she began to hate me. She felt as if she wanted to kill everyone, and her anger mounted to such an intensity that I felt it transmitted to me. She described herself as inferior, worthless, impotent, enraged, and like a child. One day, she talked of her worthlessness and again she violently attacked me, reaching for a heavy ashstand which was nearby, saying that she wanted to knock me out. I held her arms, and she relaxed, wept, and said that she had a terrible fantasy of wanting to kill me, to keep my body in her apartment, and in this way make sure that she would not be deserted. A variant of this odd bit of fantasy about human living is described in William Faulkner's "A Rose for Miss Emily."

Her continued disturbance was increased by any reference to her mother. Finally she was able to speak of her mother in more detail, and this topic, too, bit by bit, began to develop. During this time she also referred to feelings too horrible to speak about. She was now reading some of Franz Kafka, saying that he expressed her feelings, and that she felt that she was like him. She was going to school some of this time, but rather hesitantly, occasionally having to spend a night in the hospital. One day she came in, saying that she had a horrible feeling she could not describe. (The diarrhea, incidentally, had continued through all of this part of therapy and she was in treatment with an internist colleague of mine. Frequently she left the sessions because of the persistent diarrhea.) She felt as if she were about to vomit, and said there was nothing that she could describe to me. I asked her to tell me a little bit more about her feelings, and finally she said that she had noticed something when she had gone to the cafeteria. While there she suddenly had the feeling that she would like to take the pudding and smear it into the face of the waitress. She said this with a feeling of horror. I said, "Well, what about it?", and I heard more. With great difficulty she spoke— leaving on a couple of occasions because of diarrhea and vomiting; she was a very sick-looking person. Finally she said that she had felt impelled to smear feces and vomit over me, and had a horrible picture of something very dreadful happening should she do that. She was disgusted, and thought that I would recoil from her. This was a touching moment. There was much more feeling than I can convey to you. We talked about her fear that her awful thoughts would never be acceptable and she said to me, at the end of the session, rather shakily, "You don't know how filthy I am, and I don't want you to ever guess." I replied in a somewhat conventional manner; but at least my comment was spontaneous, and I was moved. I said, "You don't know how human you are." My remarks appeared to be useful, because she suddenly was more relaxed. On leaving, she came over to me (I was still sitting in my chair), threw her arms around me, and briefly hugged me. I put my arm around her, patted her shoulder, and said nothing. She then went on her way and we did not discuss this episode further. Later she had a dream which was of interest and which I shall briefly mention as we draw this to a close.

I have not discussed the patient's presentation of dreams. Early in the work I suggested that she report what she recalled of dreams as well as telling me as best she could what she observed of her thoughts. In general, I made few interpretations, encouraging her to comment on a dream, to notice its possible reflection of previous events, and to pay attention to the course of her remarks after the dream had been recounted to me. When the subject of her mother was beginning to be dealt with in our discussions, the dreams became more fragmented and disturbing. To these I listened, often saying that I did not comprehend the content but was aware of their reflecting an increase of anxiety. As the relationship with the mother could be discussed more openly the dreams were better organized and communicable, and their references to me could be commented on without undue anxiety. In one long dream, not to be reported here, the patient reviewed our relationship, observing that her early fear and dislike of me were in considerable degree a reflection of a disturbed relationship with her parents; as our own relationship grew more secure and understanding of that with her parents increased, a more direct and anxiety-free expression of her affection for me appeared in the dreams—and later in our conversations.

Much of the horrible, distorted, "not-me" feeling referent to the mother, had now been brought into a more clearly interpersonal context, where the two of us could deal with each other more as Dr. Will and Miss Ethel, two people more clearly known to each other, as anxiety diminished. The patient was now more independent, could deal more openly and directly with me, and could see me more clearly as therapist and person.

As treatment continued, this woman experienced activities more consistent with living in the juvenile and the pre-adolescent eras of life. I haven't seen her professionally for several years. She is married, has some children, and is at times unhappy and anxious, so I hear, but is not psychotic.

I wish to emphasize the patient's frequently feeling as if he must take care of the doctor. The relationship which is formed so intensely between the two of them is such that not only will the patient be unable to tolerate separation but he may feel that the doctor will be unable to tolerate it. This has very important so-called transference aspects because, to my way of thinking, one thing that every schizophrenic person (and many other patients) must discover, is that those dear and close to him, such as his parents, can tolerate his becoming grown up, mature, and independent. Frequently parents cannot tolerate this very well. In this case, the patient was an only child, to whom the parents were "devoted," as the saying goes. They frequently said, "There is no other life but with her." Her father would say, "If she doesn't get well, I'll be dead." I often felt that if she *did* get well and independent, he might die, being unable to tolerate her growth. But, both of these people had professional help. The father consulted with a minister who had had some experience with general psychiatric work and was very supporting to him. The mother spoke with a psychologist whom she liked very well personally. This help for the parents was a useful aspect of the therapeutic work with the child. The parents had to endure long periods of time in isolation from the child during which she would have nothing to do with them. Often they felt rejected by her, and needed help in clarifying their own feelings. Toward the end of treatment, patient and parents established a relationship with each other that was mutually gratifying and allowed increased freedom and growth for all concerned.

This is obviously a very short summary of a great deal of work. Let me now briefly review certain goals which I wish to accomplish in the course of therapy. I don't mean that I shall accomplish all of these, nor do I mean that they should be set up as goals without regard to the patient's needs or the practical aspects of the work. The outline follows:

First: the identification of anxiety, and the gaining of some ideas as to its origin, its functions, the patient's methods of dealing with it, and its way of operating in the therapist-patient relationship.

Second: a clarification of historical data, whereby the patient comes to have a verifiable picture of himself, his family and its relationship to the community, and to the culture. This furthers the development of a sense of identity, with some realization and acceptance of those matters which can be controlled or altered, and those which are at present seeming manifestations of fate. In this way, man comes to know his current and usable power, and locates himself in his personal universe.

Third: the identification and clarification of certain major distortions of the self, the therapist, and others. I have presented examples of that.

Fourth: the recognition that not all unhappy observations are parataxic, and that no distortion can occur without stimulus and perception. The patient and the therapist learn the encouraging fact that all that is painful and wicked cannot be explained away as transference. When my patient observed that I was cruel, vindictive, dependent, and so forth, it was useful for her to note that although there may have been some distortion of me, she certainly did have a somewhat real perception of me, and that it was well for us both to investigate the reality aspects of her observations, as well as the distorted aspects of them.

Fifth: the exposure of intense emotion, and the mutual and reciprocal experience of it. Both participants will be strongly moved on occasion by emotion roused in their interaction.

Sixth: the recognition of there being at times irreparable loss, or deficiency in experience, and the acceptance of such loss, with grief and regret, but without denial or defensive distortion. Some potentialities of human behavior are not developed in certain cultures or through certain life experiences, and will not be anything like fully developed as the result of psychotherapeutic intervention. One becomes aware of some of these deficiencies, considers their origins, and simply faces them, instead of withdrawing into sadness about one's unhappy state.

Seventh: there should be participation by the patient in areas of experience which have been inadequate in his development, with at least some resulting correction of the defects. For example, this young woman had inadequate experience in the juvenile era, and never learned how to deal well with problems of competition, and so forth. I was glad that in the course of our work she could work out some of these problems of competition by participation in groups. She needed that kind of experience in addition to the individual therapeutic study of the problem.

Eighth: the use of some theoretical framework to which the work is oriented. Every therapist operates with some theoretical framework in mind. Even the person who says, "I am eclectic," is operating with, so far as I am concerned, a secret framework. It is better that we know what our theoretical framework is, that we have some allegiance to it, and that we have considerable clarity about it. We must also observe the recurrent demonstration during the course of therapy of both the adequacy and inadequacy of this framework. Unless the patient and the therapist can accept repeated demonstrations of certain inadequacies of the theory, then they are required, I think, constantly to alter, misconstrue, or guide the communications that arise in defense of the theoretical preconceptions. If a therapist maintains that everything which comes over the desk, or from the couch, is in support of his theory, he is presenting a beautiful example of selective inattention.

Ninth: the recognition of, understanding of, and correction of problems of communication; there must be an acceptance of the non-verbal as well as the verbal, in which the past, as in infancy, in childhood, and in the dream, becomes better integrated into the concept of the person, the comprehension of the present, and the prediction of the future. The patient runs into situations in which he cannot express to you in clear verbal terms what goes on, but makes some effort to do so, and in this attempt becomes a little more comfortable with the idea that much about his living lies in obscurity, and cannot be communicated readily to another. Otherwise, much time can be wasted in trying to verbalize concepts which simply do not fit words. Sometimes, one attempts to make precise verbal statements about matters which cannot be put into words because they relate to preverbal experience.

Tenth: the exposure, acceptance and recognition of dissociated matters without their being made a requirement of understanding. Thus one learns to accept his personal limitations and lack of knowledge. The sharing of such experiences through the therapist's non-verbal responses leads to a reduction of the necessity to maintain dissociation. That is, such things as hallucinations and obscure dreams may be accepted as simply human phenomena that may defy precise translation, but need not be denied or feared. The patient is able to express in action, and more in the vocal quality of his voice than in words, many aspects about his living to which the therapist can do little more than listen, and perhaps say, "Well, I don't quite know what you're talking about, and so be it, and here I am." I think that through such acceptance there is an increase in the opportunity for further associations, and a decrease in dissociation.

Eleventh: a relationship marked at times by something which I put into quotes, "a full exposure of the self." At such times, the two people meet without reference to role, without reference to duty, without reference to outcome, and without reference to mutual prestige requirements.

A year ago I had the great pleasure of participating in a seminar conducted by Martin Buber. Buber distinguished between guilt feelings (reflecting, consciously and unconsciously, life experience) and guilt (of an ontic nature), saying that the psychotherapist dealt with the former but not the latter (Buber, 1957). I am concerned, on occasion, with what I think of as the guilt that man may feel as a reflection of his denial of his relatedness to others. He engages in acts of self-concealment, denying himself to others and curtailing the possibilities of his own growth. This guilt, associated I think with the often only dim awareness of a state of unrelatedness, may not be approached if the therapist is bound too closely to rigid concepts of man in general, and of himself and his patient in particular, or is "devoted" to a particular theoretical frame of reference. At times the unyielding concept of self and others and the preoccupation with theory may stand between the therapist and the patient, even as my use of the two terms (therapist and patient) implies a separation of man from man. There are situations in which one may deal with his patient without regard for theory, becoming for the moment—and my words are inadequate (as may be the clarity of my concept)—a person fully responsive, available, and open to the other. I am not referring to "acting out" with the patient in the ordinary sense. I am talking about matters more basic—an openness of communication making possible a revelation of self to self and to other. There are brief moments during which therapist and patient may meet each other with an unusual lack of regard for those conventionalities which bind them within their ordinary defenses. In such meeting—not in itself to be set up as a goal of therapy, but not to be feared or denied—lies something of the healing potential.*

Twelfth: the discovery by the patient that his fear of being related is in part a fear of being controlled, ("engulfed," schizophrenic patients say, "used," "dominated"). In the course of therapy the patient must dare to become related and risk his fear. Then he may discover that relatedness, love, growth, and freedom are not necessarily inconsistent with one another.

Thirteenth: there must be increasing revelation to the patient that the therapist is a real person, and a growing ability on the patient's part to accept the therapist as less powerful, or less wonderful, or whatever; and the same may be said for the doctor's view of the patient. There occurs a dropping away of the doctor-patient relationship with an increasing mutuality of expression.

Fourteenth: the acceptance of family relatedness with a gaining of independence. By this I mean that the patient, becoming more independent and more secure, develops a relationship with his family, integrated in a way different from that of the past.

Fifteenth: the recognition that in the therapeutic process both doctor and patient give and receive, that growth is mutual, and that it could not be otherwise.

Sixteenth: the awareness by both participants that each derives certain satisfactions from the therapeutic process and that each may on occasion take proper pleasure in being both patient and therapist.

Seventeenth: the recognition that patient and therapist to some extent use each other as models, and that each may do so without necessarily fearing loss of his own integrity.

Eighteenth: the recognition that patient and therapist are alike and unlike, and that being alike is not necessarily equated with love, or control, or hate, and being unlike is compatible with acceptance and affection.

Nineteenth: a growing recognition that the process of what we call cure is simply at this time not clear; that cure cannot presently be adequately described in any system; that the concept of human relatedness is probably basic in psychiatric healing, and that this concept, unclear as it may be, need not be feared. That is, one

---

*Related to such comments Buber writes: "With all this . . . the psychotherapist in his medical intercourse with his patients has nothing directly to do, not even when he ventures in a particular case to set for himself the goal of an existential healing. The utmost that can be expected of him . . . is only this: that reaching out beyond his familiar methods, he conduct the patient, whose existential guilt he has recognized, to where an existential help of the self can begin" (Buber, 1957).

learns that in human relatedness lies both man's bedevilment and salvation, and that with the one, man must accept the other.

Twentieth: an awareness of the fact that each participant has certain values from which he cannot entirely free himself. That is, each of us judges a situation in terms of his own values. Patient and therapist must then recognize his own and the other's values, and gain some knowledge of how these operate in the therapeutic field which they share.

A Transactional Model
for Psychotherapy

by Roy R. Grinker, M.D.

THIS IS AN ERA of intense interest in therapies of all kinds which are oriented toward making psychiatric patients better—or among the incurably optimistic, curing them. Operations, drugs, milieu attitudes, induced regressions for the patients and sometimes the therapist, and various forms of psychotherapy are credited with curative powers in the same identical, magical, percentage ranges. The mad rush for statistical criteria of improvement has resulted in a rash of rating scales based on observations of behavior, on value systems involving social and work adjustment, personal happiness and creativity, and on a consensus between patient and therapist.

However, some psychoanalysts contend that only their reconstructive method cures if continued long enough, and that psychotherapy, although harder for the therapist, only gives an illusion of significant and permanent change. Recently, Harrower (1958) has published a very interesting piece of work, in which she reports the retesting of patients, whom she had tested some years before, when they first presented themselves for treatment. Among her patients were also people who had been advised to go into treatment but did not do so. The personality structure, both of the untreated and the treated patients, seemed to have changed. Those that were treated seemed to have changed more, but none changed as much as the therapist, from his clinical point of view, had anticipated.

Frieda Fromm-Reichmann (1950), one of the pioneers in the field of psychotherapy, contends that all therapy must be based on psychoanalytic principles. She said, "The goal of intensive psychotherapy is reached by gaining insight into and understanding of the unconscious roots of the patient's problems, the genetics and dynamics, to promote changes in the dynamic structure of the patient's personality." This meant to her that there is no valid intensive psychotherapy other than psychoanalysis or that based on psychoanalytic principles.

Actually, as a result of all our therapies, we are to various degrees successfully helping, curing, and failing in accordance with our own theoretical biases, and sparked by our immature enthusiasms which are dampened by age, experience, and receding libido. The percentage of improvements reported by any method is within that same range of seventy to eighty per cent, which is the magical range of all medical statistics. I recall, many years ago, reading a presentation of various forms of psychotherapy then extant, which indicated that the results of any psychotherapy are dependent upon the enthusiastic conviction of the therapist in what he is doing. How or why we achieve, or fail to reach our goals is by no means clear. Only one writer has proposed a scientific criterion of change, although it is not yet operationally feasible. In a little known lecture, David Rioch (1957) states that psychological alterations should be formulated by the nature of durable change in the functional organization of the central nervous system. This is not very easy to determine in the intact human being.

In the field of psychotherapy, whose practitioners contend it now constitutes a scientific discipline, tremendous activity has been stimulated recently. Recipients of fresh financial support are frantically observing and recording words, gestures, pulse rates, etc., of therapists and patients. Observers are observing observers and hoping that an interested statistician will some day find a method and several years' time to analyze the mountains of stored records.

These skeptical remarks, and they are intended to be skeptical, are an introduction to a preliminary presentation of our own experiments with therapeutic problems. I shall not present statistical accounts of results because I don't know what they are; in fact, I don't know if I am going to describe a therapy, or, if therapy it be, what dimensions it takes. I shall simply describe what I consider to be the current dilemma of psychotherapy and how I think it might be resolved by methods which enable therapist and patient to understand and to learn from each other.

Following World War II, public acceptance of psychiatry created a great demand for psychotherapists in clinics, hospitals, and private offices. The number of available psychiatrists was pitifully small to handle these demands, much less the population's needs, which were yet to be defined. As a result, educational institutions began turning out psychiatrists, psychologists, and psychiatric social workers as therapists whose training was more or less similar in almost every hospital or clinic. American psychotherapy has imitated and closely approached the psychoanalytic model with only a few exceptions. And these exceptions perhaps may be stated roughly as: the Rosen (1953) technique, which is assaultive and coercive in addition to demanding that with the false promise of love the patient must give up his psychosis; the Whitaker and Malone (1953) technique, wherein both therapist and patient sit and quietly regress together into a psychosis, and on recovery, seem to be all the better for it; and the Rogers (Rogers and Dymond, 1954) technique of non-directive therapy.

If we ignore the personal and economic motives behind every student of psychiatry wishing to become a psychoanalyst, we still have the fundamental fact that of all the theoretical systems in psychiatry, psychoanalytic psychodynamics yields most satisfaction because of its completeness, its sense of closure, and its analogical fit. In the United States, what we euphemistically call psychodynamics, is for the most part psychoanalytic theory. One can safely say that almost every systematic presentation of dynamic processes is based fundamentally on psychoanalytic theory, sometimes with additions or modifications, or even distortions. The basic core of our pedagogical processes in psychiatric training is the psychodynamics of Freudian psychoanalysis.

This theoretical system, in general, I also consider to be the essence of the best modern psychodynamic theory. However, I contend that the theory has a minor place in the operational procedures of psychotherapy. I am convinced that if we were to have truthful information about what goes on in the inviolate relationship between psychoanalyst and patient, we would find here, too, that the operations are not direct expressions of psychoanalytic theory. Strupp (1958), however, contends that there is a close relationship between theoretical bias and therapeutic operation. I might interpose a remark that, as I have criticized and will continue to criticize certain psychoanalytic operations, it is from the position of being within the field, in the sense that I am also a psychoanalyst, and thus have a right to criticize.

Actually, psychoanalytic theory, laudable as it may be as a system fruitful for viewing the psychological processes of humans, places a heavy load of interference on the psychotherapist who attempts to understand and to help a sick person through psychotherapy. This interference is greatest in those therapeutic procedures most closely related to theoretical conceptions. For example, Strupp states that the therapist pays close attention to the connotative or symbolic content of communications which he understands in terms of certain theoretical conceptions. Sooner or later the therapist communicates to the patient some part of this understanding. It does no good if he keeps it to himself. He may verbalize the feelings he thinks are expressed by the patient, or he may conjecture concerning the implicit meaning of the patient's message. In either event the therapist states an hypothesis or an inference commonly called an interpretation. The function of this activity is to increase the patient's self-awareness and to point out to him dynamic relationships which apparently have a bearing on his central emotional conflict or on one of its derivatives. Which aspects of the patient's communication are singled out for interpretive activity depends on the therapist's theoretical leanings, his objectivity, and the techniques considered most appropriate to achieve a desired therapeutic result. It is exactly in this operation where understanding is preconceived, rather than learned in the therapeutic situation, that psychoanalytic theory enters into the interpretation of symbolic content of communications and the choice of therapeutic interferences. These are loaded operations and in an *a priori* manner determine the contents of communications between patient and therapist.

Let me give you an example which occurred in supervising a resident psychiatrist. The resident was treating a man who, although competitive with his fellow workers and extremely active in asserting himself in his work, nevertheless, was extremely complaining and bitter about his wife's inactivity in the house and her tendency to partake of alcohol. The description that he gave of his wife seemed to a great extent distorted, and the therapist was advised to see the wife herself. When he did so, he found a very nice little girl who was trying her best to take care of the house, overburdened by too many children and without much income. He was satisfied that she was doing the best she could. When the wife went home, she told her husband that she liked the therapist very much, that he seemed to be a nice man, and that she was very happy about her visit. At the next session with the patient, the therapist did not discuss the wife's visit, and from that time on he had a great deal of difficulty over the patient's keeping appointments. Finally, the psychiatrist was instructed to open the subject of what the patient felt about his wife's coming to see the therapist. The patient responded with some sentences which made obvious that he felt his wife was interested in maintaining a dependent relationship on the therapist through some form of communication, and that the patient was somewhat jealous of this. However, the therapist said, "You are trying to compete with me, in that you think that we are in competition for your wife." I asked the resident why he made this statement on the basis of what he had heard in the therapeutic session. He answered that that really was the patient's basic personality. Therefore, the interpretation, despite the patient's communications, was directed back to an *a priori* theoretical notion of how the personality of this patient would lead the therapist to expect him to react.

For the past six years, I have been engaged in studies of the communications between psychotherapist and patient. I wish to indicate by this phrase that I am not sure that I am dealing with an effective psychotherapeutic process. However, the assumption is that we will eventually learn something about the psychotherapeutic process by studying its effectiveness on a wide variety of patients with individual problems. I have gone about these investigations by holding seminars in which fragments of psychotherapeutic processes were studied and discussed, other seminars which considered a single patient during an entire year, and in individual supervision with beginning therapists.

In all of these experiences, I have had to struggle against the deep impression made by the psychoanalytic model on youngsters barely beginning their training in psychotherapy. I had thought that this was characteristic of our particular hospital institute since its staff is largely composed of psychoanalysts or people striving to become psychoanalysts. Recently, however, I gave a talk at a state hospital in the Middle West, the staff of which was composed of psychiatrists who were not analysts: nevertheless, the attack I received for talking in non-analytic language was as great, if not greater, than within an analytic institution.

It is easily observed that these young people's goals included uncovering significant dynamic processes during long-term treatment with the desire for cure, or so-called "complete reorganization of the personality" which they also hold out for themselves in their future personal analyses. If you don't continue to believe in that, of course, you can't expect it for your own life. In the young therapist, this involved long periods of passivity and listening to the patient, hoping that at some time a significant dynamic process would pop up and be recognized. The passivity and length of relationship often induced a serious regression on the part of the patient, or the development of a transference neurosis, and serious counter-transference problems. In imitation of the psychoanalytic model, youngsters called for and encouraged the recounting of dreams, which they could not understand or interpret. Lack of understanding forced them to defend themselves against anxieties stimulated by communications from their patients and by frustrations of their failures to understand or to make progress, thereby further handicapping their therapeutic effectiveness. They tried to imitate the analytic imperturbability but instead achieved attitudes of coldness and objectivity, concentrating entirely on the content of the patient's productions. Some of them, without attempting to understand the patient's needs of the moment, developed notions of furnishing a "corrective emotional experience" by playing artificial roles which were easily penetrated as play-acting by anyone with a modicum of intelligence. Even though many of these students were shortly out of their internship, they very quickly and easily forgot their roles as doctors seeking to help their patients. They lost the human capacity of helping patients in serious life situations when these required temporarily stepping out of the therapeutic chamber.

For example, with a patient who has mounting ideas of committing suicide, according to the notion of some of these youngsters, one does not talk to anybody but the patient. But, somebody has to be notified; somebody has to take the responsibility; some care has to be taken. Very frequently it is with a great deal of shock that they receive the advice: "Why don't you notify the husband? Call the husband. Tell him about the situation. Ask him to come in and talk about it." The amazing thing is that the young psychiatrist, who should know the role of the doctor, often less frequently plays that role than the non-medical therapist, who is willing to talk to members of the family. I have never ceased to marvel at how quickly the seed of the psychoanalytic model sprouts and how difficult it is to uproot once it has gained a footing.

Can we set up a model of treatment based on an operational theory of psychotherapy, not on a theory of psychodynamics or diagnosis? If so, it should be derived from the empirical operations involved in psychotherapy. At the present time, our existing knowledge encompasses nothing new, different, or apart from what is involved in the communications between two people. Its variables must be defined in terms of the setting, of the persons involved, and what goes on between them. Abstractly, the relationships among field theory, role theory, and communications theory may be epitomized as transactional in its broadest sense, involving non-dimensional space bounded by people enacting a variety of roles and traversed by verbal, non-verbal, and paralingual communications. Now let us look at these various phases.

Translating the setting into practical considerations, we find its narrow and immediate range is the field of therapeutic action in the interviewing room in which the therapist and patient converse. Yet beyond this is the total clinic or institutional setting and its explicit and implicit meaning to both the therapist and the patient. Still larger are the social, cultural, economic, and ethnic environments of the past and present of both persons. All of these extensions have important influences on the behavior of therapist and patient as they relate to each other, and all influence the type, degree, and success in their communications.

Both persons are human beings with somatic organ systems, differently conditioned and in various degrees of harmonic integration. Each one has internal psychodynamics or personality structures. They both belong to and believe in various social groups, and subscribe to somewhat different hopes and expectations. Although this total field of interaction has considerable extension beyond the interviewing room, what one observes and hears depends on one's frame of reference at the time. For all practical purposes each one of the two persons views each other, understands, and communicates with the other not as a conglomeration of instincts, needs, defenses, and reaction formations but as persons involved in the enactment of a limited number of social roles.

Role theory, developed by social scientists, is advantageous in dealing with a small group of two persons in interaction within the therapeutic system. Parsons and Shils (1951) consider personality as a system of action, in contrast to psychatrists, who, by the very nature of their interests, usually focus on the internal psychological aspects of personality. Personality within a social structure or a cultural system is not reducible to a triad of topological psychological entities such as id, ego, and superego, nor is it a composite of conflicts and defenses. Personalities within the social system behave in action in relation to other personalities. For the sake of description, Parsons applies the term "ego" to the subject considered in any process of interaction, and the object with which the subject interacts is termed "alter." Thus, ego and alter constitute a two-person system, although there are many alters with which the ego interacts at various times. The personality or ego assumes various types of roles with various people, at various times for a variety of purposes. Thus, social role theory indicates a way to study and describe the interaction of two members of a social group as they adjust to each other within a social system. "A role is a goal-directed pattern or sequence of acts tailored by the cultural process for the transactions a person may carry out in a social group or situation...." (Spiegel, 1954).

Any small social group, of which the nuclear family is only one example, achieves some level of stability or equilibrium. Each actor-person in the group has his allocated roles in relation to each other member of the group. Complementarity—that is, the fit of the roles of the ego and alter—is desirable and comfortable. For every speaker there should be a listener, for every parent a child, for every teacher a pupil. Complementarity of roles means that each personality automatically acts in conformity with the role that he is expected to play, and, since few decisions are made, there is little strain.

Often the equilibrium maintained by role complementarity is disturbed and disequilibrium occurs. People's expectations from others are disappointed, and tension, anxiety, and self-consciousness develop. The result may be disruptions of interpersonal relations and breakdowns in group living, which in essence is the definition of neurosis. There are many reasons why role complementarity becomes disturbed, but they all lead to more or less shorter or longer periods of disequilibrium followed by attempts at re-equilibrium. I must emphasize again that when I talk about role playing, I do not imply artificiality such as that of actors playing their parts on the stage. Roles are automatic, learned behaviors, learned through the influence of persons who represent society and who teach the developing child a repertoire of expected behavior patterns.

These roles are largely explicit. They are conscious, describable in general terms, communicable by rational verbalizations and standard behavioral performances. They are explicit because they refer to consciously motivated behavior; and insofar as they are concerned and contribute to solving problems, they are instrumental. Explicit roles are conscious and exposed to observation and awareness of both participants.

Implicit roles are more remote from awareness and consciousness and, hence, may not be recognized either by the actor or the alter in their transactions. They usually express complicated aspects of the actor's personality and constitute such a wide range of variation that they cannot be easily classified. They express personality attributes characteristic of a wide variety of internalizations or identifications, which quickly shift in and out of the focus of expression.

Identifications that determine characteristics of the component parts of personality and delineate the self are expressed not only in role performance—that is, in the dimension of words or action—but also internally in communication among the various processes in the mental apparatus. Some are then expressed in whatever social ways are available after filtering functions have been passed through. Others, in conflict with each other, are neutralized, or locked in, or delayed for later expression. The formalized content of social roles represents but a small part of the internal action system, much of which is antagonistic or at least not in conformity with the main or observable stream of the self. I may point out that implicit roles, which after filtering through what we call the ego or boundary functions, express identifications which represent early transactions between mother and child, child and teacher, and so on, and their conflicts. Hence, when one grasps hold of implicit roles, one also grasps hold of some aspect of early identifications.

Explicit roles are like the hat one wears, visible to all; but the richness of human relationships is implicit and subtle. In therapy, the explicit roles of the patient and therapist structure that process and define its boundaries clearly; but for a therapeutic effect, the to-and-fro play of implicit roles furnishes the content of the relationship derived from each actor's personality, healthy or sick. Thus the explicit roles structure the relationship; the content it furnished by the implicit roles. The implicit roles are the unknowns in therapeutic transaction. We normally search for them in social communications and seriously attempt to follow their movements in an effort to achieve or modify complementarity.

In the relationship between therapist and patient regarded as a system of transactions between ego and alter, we may consider that the therapy involves behavior of a person in terms of his role in transaction with the therapist. Complementarity of roles when established represents stability and harmony and is conducive to the communication of information. Disequilibrium because of non-complementarity results in re-equilibrium, eventually, which represents the disruption of an old repetitive process and the establishment of a new system. When this is attained by modification mutually achieved, a learning process has occurred.

Activities within a transactional process, although they deal with current reality and start with well-defined explicit roles, expose the repetitive nature of the patient's unadaptive behavior and stimulate his recall of past experiences. Some of these are preconscious, and some are unconscious, but the orientation of the therapist remains in the present transaction within the field in which both members of the transaction find themselves. It can be stated quite certainly that this transactional approach evokes implicit expressive or emotional roles and incites repetition of old transactions and illuminates the genetic source of the current behavior. However, it does not require focusing on and interpretation of a vast, uncharted area of unconscious. On the contrary, it enables the therapist to orient himself in a special situation with a specific person in a transactional relationship which can be understood by common-sense evaluation of ordinary modes of communication.

This brings us to communication theory. Although psychotherapy has been defined by several investigators, especially Moreno (1951), Sullivan (1952), and Frieda Fromm-Reichmann as essentially a process of communication, it was Ruesch and Bateson (1951) who viewed communication as the social matrix of psychiatry. Recently Ruesch (1957) has defined disturbed communications as quantitative alterations or as forms of exchange not fitting a social situation. Conglomerations of instinctual forces and defenses are all contained in communicated messages which express the total person with his memories of the past and anticipations of the future. The psychiatrist as a participant in the communication process, as well as an observer, dealing with verbal and non-verbal communication, needs to be an expert in understanding language as it is related to thinking and behavior. He is, therefore, facilitated or handicapped by the language which he thinks, speaks, and understands. And perhaps this is the basic essence of Redlich's (1958) statement that for effective therapy the class positions of the therapist and his patient should fit fairly well. Certainly it is conducive to understanding the basic language; and we, who seem immobile in a single class struggle structure, find ourselves greatly handicapped, particularly when we try to work with adolescents and young adults. We seem barely successful in learning the language of adolescents one year, only to find that the words mean something entirely different the next year.

As we view the operational and philosophical concepts of transactions among people within a specific setting, we must be struck by the awkwardness of our linguistic expression. The Dewey and Bentley (1949) multi-hyphenated words and strange systems of communication are difficult to understand, although they express the wholeness of transaction. About thirty years ago, Whorf (1956) developed a new concept of linguistics which for him expresses modes of thinking and corresponds with psychological processes. We think according to the ways we have learned to speak. And here, I think, resides the difficulty for people who have been brought up in another therapeutic language in understanding transactional language. They want to translate it into their own language, which would mean that they would not learn. They have to use the language of the system in order to really understand it. Behavioral manifestations are associated with different language phenomena. Thus, the relation of behavior and thought to language is the science of linguistic relativity.

Unfortunately, the standard average European languages, of which English is one, lack the special symbols for processes occurring between objects, extensions of self and time relationships, requiring instead the use of analogies, metaphors, and terms referrable to physical relationships. This language refers directly or indirectly to aspects of physical contact indicating a continuity with infantile feeling, closeness, or warmth, which we hope to renounce in favor of maturer expressive communications through space without contact. This is an extremely valuable index to the degree of maturity of the person. How capable is he of accepting the satisfaction of relationships that occur through space and without contact? Yet we have very few words that specifically indicate emotional relationships through space which do not have to lean on physical words such as warmth and closeness.

Now, finally, we must consider transactional, as opposed to self-actional or interactional, as an implication of a relationship of two or more individuals within a specified environment. Both are included, not as distinct and separate entities or individuals, but only as they are in relatedness with each other within a specific setting. Each has an effect on each other that is specific to the situation in which they exist. One acts on the other, whose response in turn feeds back on the first. The process is reciprocal and cyclical. The setting of the system in which the transacting persons or foci exist determines and is determined by the processes going on. The specific life situation of patient and therapist in the therapeutic setting determines in the current time the nature of those transactions which are reciprocal, cyclical, and ever changing.

In summary, I envisage a model for psychotherapy that encompasses aspects of several major theories of human behavior. To begin with, we adopt field theory to emphasize the extent of influences surrounding the two-person system of therapist and patient. The field may be formally termed the matrix or the environment; actually, however, it is never neutral but constantly impinging in part or in total on, and is determined by, the two-person group. Thus, the setting of the clinic, the home environment of the patient, and life situations actively influence the relationship as constantly changing in potent influences. Here, of course, is one of the great errors in most psychotherapeutic systems. Not only do they not pay enough attention to the environmental influences, sometimes not even listening to a report, but they refuse to obtain an objective view of what actually goes on in the life situation. The therapist and patient communicate with each other verbally, non-verbally, and paralingually with various forms and degrees of distortion. Yet each tries to understand the other. Messages are received, acknowledged, and corrected in a cyclical transaction, which changes in time by virtue of the communications within the transaction that express forms of role performance, the role performance forms having explicit and implicit meanings, which indicate past learning and identifications, as well as current relearnings which we term therapy. Roles are expressed by the forms of communication which vary with the nature of the current transaction. Thus, the therapeutic field consists of the mutual understanding of transactions in which role processes, their antecedents, and patterned identifications are communicated and changed.

Let us take the beginning of the therapeutic situation. The patient is sick, and thus, highly motivated for change. His explicit role is that of a person who comes for help, although, as is frequently the case in all forms of therapy, when he begins to know more clearly what his implicit feelings really mean, he resists help, clarification, insight, or change quite forcibly and wishes to maintain dependency. However, through the intake interview or the diagnostic evaluation it has been or should have been clearly established that there is sufficient motivation to receive help because of the patient's suffering or difficulties in performance in social groups, in work, or in family relations. The therapist explicitly has a desire to help people who are suffering and has a particular attitude by virtue of the role which he has chosen for his professional life. If people do not have this, then they are lacking in integrity if they continue to function as therapists. This attitude, however, as Strupp (1958) has shown, cuts across all theoretical orientations. The therapist feels that his patient is a human being: he is worthwhile working with, and the therapist has the optimism that respect for another human being would instill in him. He hopes that his patient will change, feel better, or perform better and that he has certain inherent capacities for being different and for growing. The therapist's confidence is easily and almost directly communicated to the patient in the therapist's explicit role attitudes toward him. This positive feeling is the first maneuver which helps the patient begin to override his feeling of a nuclear core of badness. This applies to all persons who eventually become able to understand, after giving up their security operations, that much of their anxiety is based on their self-concept of badness, what the religionists a long time ago called original sin.

Most people are frightened of uncovering their innermost secrets, having defended themselves violently against their exposure because of this notion of badness. It is worst, of course, in the schizophrenic.

Respect for the patient also involves honesty on the part of the therapist in admitting his positive and negative feelings as they develop within the therapeutic situation. Particularly is this true with a schizophrenic, who is able to observe the slightest cues in paralingual and motor behavior indicating annoyances and irritations on the part of his therapist. To deny the existence of these, if the therapist has sufficient insight into himself, is to block or to distort the communication process. For example: A female patient of mine, who had been acting out her prostitution fantasies in identification with her mother, was about to begin a new sexual relationship but had been thoroughly warned about the results. There were indications that her acting out was an outburst against understanding, she was fighting against understanding her tremendous rage against her mother, which she could defend against by being like her mother: "I am like mother; therefore, there is no communication of anger between us." She, however, went into the relationship; and the next day when she came to see me, I was very stern and firm and disapproving. I had indicated my opinion of her behavior. She had betrayed me, and I expressed this to her in no uncertain terms. Nevertheless, after she left the room, she came back and said: "Are you angry at me, Dr. Grinker?" And I said: "Certainly I am." Now, if I should have said: "No," or "We'll discuss this another time," in the typical bland psychotherapeutic voice, there would have been a complete distortion of future communications, because I had already communicated that I was angry at her.

The therapist establishes permissiveness for his patient which encourages him to achieve his desire to return, belong, and adjust to the group. He helps the patient to communicate about himself by substituting verbalizations for neurotic acting out or visceral symptoms. This is indeed a difficult process.

The therapist's admission of his own feelings to the patient and his striving for permissiveness are not contradictory behaviors. The therapist has to establish permissiveness so that the patient can express anything that comes to his mind and feel free to recall whatever past memories might come to the surface, but, at the same time, he has to face the reality of reactions in life situations. This notion that you permit the patient to do anything, to act out anything, is a caricature of psychotherapy. I am sure there have been cartoons of the patient saying in the midst of her associations: "I think tonight when I get home, I am going to kill my husband." And the therapist saying: "Hmmm, and what else?" Permissiveness in expression is desirable; but you do not necessarily include in that the permission of acting out behavior. One can indicate to the patient one's disapproval of her behavior before it occurs, a warning that it might occur, and indicate disapproval after it occurs. There is, obviously, a reality in life which this patient must learn. She can't continue to be a prostitute and suffer the consequences afterwards, and cry and be comforted, which is the motivation for coming into treatment, unless she wishes to remain sick. If she wants to get well, she has to give up the acting out; and she can be as firm about that as possible. Sometimes it is necessary to adopt in complementarity of the expressive role, something that is an expression of concern, interest, but associated with firmness. For example, a woman who was depressed and in the hospital had given a fairly clear indication that she was running away from the recognition of a bad marriage that could not be dissolved because of young children, and could not be changed because the husband was such a weak and immature person, five years younger than she. She came into the interviewing room crying and complaining and whining. I said to her: "Stop that at once. You don't have to whine and cry and crawl on the floor like this. I expect you to stand on your two feet and face this problem. I have more respect for you than to permit you to do this." She stopped crying: she began to talk about her problem. When she left the interviewing room she said: "I have never had anybody talk to me like that in my whole life. I have never felt better." She had demanded, from her history, a strong man; her husband was a weak man. She wanted someone in complementarity with her expectations of what a man should be; and under the aegis of such strength, she could be permitted then to divulge her feelings about her husband, which she did. She complained and complained about him, but in a rational tone and mode which indicated there might be some compromise solution.

Since the patient cannot achieve insight into his own neurotic processes, he depends upon information from the therapist in the two-person system as to how he seeks out stimuli to elicit old-learned responses and, hence, perpetuate his neurotic behavior. This, I think, is one of the essences of the neurotic process. The neurotic is habituated in certain ways of living, certain patterns. They may be uncomfortable; they may be anxiety and depression provoking. Nevertheless, these are the behavioral modes that he has learned. One must be continually aware of the fact that he seeks out, even creates, stimuli which evoke these patterns that he knows how to use, and therefore, perpetuate his neurotic behavior. It is a struggle to give the patient the notion of how his implicit role is constantly oriented to evoke his old patterns. The neurotic, and especially the schizophrenic, forces others to assume roles which enable them to repeat compulsively time-worn and habitual pathological patterns.

Therapy is a learning process and its operations are concerned with facilitating that process. To do that, there has to be a certain attitude of permissiveness, and receptivity on the part of the therapist in relation to another human being who is sick, the therapist taking the role of the helper. Within that explicit framework, which is the structure of the therapeutic situation, communications will expose the implicit roles that the patient would like the therapist to take in complementarity with him. These roles, the therapist declines to assume, but instead interprets to the patient and points out to the patient that through the facade of the explicit role relationship, the patient really wishes another kind of relationship; and in that sense, the intelligent patient will generalize from that statement to other situations in which similar behaviors were used, and will learn. This will complete that particular therapeutic focus and the process begins again on another focus. The patient learns; this is the process of treatment.

Preparatory to beginning psychotherapy, we have been accustomed to making plans for specific goals over a long term. In doing this, we establish a theoretical bias and usually permit the diagnosis and formulated psychodynamics to influence our therapy of the patient. His communications are, therefore, made to fit a preconceived theoretical plan. Those of you who are members of clinical teams know that in almost every clinic or hospital dealing with psychiatric patients, there are formal exercises of presenting patients' problems. Patients are staffed, it is said. And after they are staffed, in the sense that their complaints, their backgrounds, and their informants' statements are divulged in the conference, then we ask the psychiatrist or psychologist or social worker: "Now, will you formulate the case?" Then the next question is: "What is your goal in therapy, and what procedures are you going to use?" We ask the therapist to decide right there and then.

It becomes exceedingly difficult to define goals without taking into consideration the criteria of the illness. If a person is ill, defined legitimately so by his culture, then the goal of psychotherapy is to bring him back to health. Unfortunately, this is not always possible in terms of rigid standards of health, as Jahoda (1958) points out in her recent book, nor do we have a strict discrimination between health and illness. The goals are dependent upon the patient's motivation, the therapist's capacity, skill, experience, the tools he has available, and the desires of the social group to which the patient belongs. There are many families who are only in equilibrium if the patient remains sick. There are many families who either fear or resist the therapy of the individual patient because then disequilibrium results. Unfortunately, too many psychotherapists set goals of an absolute nature, based on their own value systems; they are unconcerned with only betterment and speak in nineteenth century terms of *cure*, a term which all of medicine has abandoned. Even a setting of limited goals implies a prejudgment on the part of the therapist. It seems then that goals, although many authorities advise that they should be set before therapy begins, are a *result* of the transactional experiences between the therapist and patient. Slowly but surely, the motivation, the degree of illness, the capacity to endure the suffering of therapy, the ability to learn, as well as the special efficacy of the therapist, in a particular case, becomes clear. Thus, goals can only be determined in the general sense that both the therapist and the patient will continue just as long as the transaction moves satisfactorily in a progressive manner. In our experiments, we do not establish global plans but deal with the patient in successive short spans which involve specific therapeutic foci. We move from focus to focus. This gives us an opportunity to stop, continue, or change—in other words, to be flexible. We can determine the next therapeutic focus only on the basis of what the previous one had led into.

In our procedures, we are considerably more active than those individuals who model their therapy after the psychoanalytic pattern. Strupp (1957) has shown that the most experienced therapists are much more active, whereas the younger, less experienced ones are passive, as if they await the patient's insight and his communication to the therapist of what should be interpreted. We are active in that we choose the focus; we communicate adequately with the patient; we avoid long silences and the impassivity of a non-participant. These silences in psychotherapy are deadly, deadly to the patient and deadly to the therapist, and are great stimulants to sleep. Not only do we choose the focus for the subject of communication, but we decide when a transaction should be dropped and a new one adopted.

We do not invite dreams, nor when they are recounted, do we interpret them. Dreams are communicated to us as messages which we use along with other information, but we do not respond to them with specific interpretations. As a result of the absence of emphasis on dream material, the patient soon learns not to use the dream as a means of avoiding direct communication. He does not practice remembering them, nor does he assume that without them communication is not possible.

Let me give you an example, however, of what a manifest content of a dream can communicate. Here is a patient, who has been extremely infantile and dependent, and has broken down because his wife had a child and he could not share his wife's motherliness with the child. However, he decided to go to work; and during the course of his therapy, when the retreat from adult competition was being pointed out to him, he became more aggressive in his job, spoke to the office manager about a promised pay raise, which had never been given to him, and about certain work conditions in the office which were unsatisfactory, in a quite aggressive and mature manner. As a result of this, he got his pay raise and certain things were corrected. But the way in which he communicated with the therapist during the next session indicated his longings to give up this job and stay at home. He reported the following dream: He was walking through the city and he saw a museum. He wanted to go into this museum, and he barged right past the guard at the gate. After viewing the pictures, he was about to make his exit, when he saw a woman sitting there, and he immediately became quite frightened of being caught and crawled on the floor along the wall so that he could get out without being seen.

Here is a dream which indicates clearly the message that had been communicated in terms of his life experiences, but indicates perhaps in greater intensity the pull-back to the frightened guilty feeling of the implicit childhood roles, which he had otherwise communicated but not as clearly.

Since so many aspects of the person's difficulties are symptoms that are derived from defenses or security operations against anxiety, it is only logical to assume that in every therapeutic relationship anxiety will occur. The patient will require much time before he has confidence that strength to master anxiety increases with growth, that the anxiety of the past is now endurable, and that the therapist is a staunch agent for support. The therapist must estimate degree of disorganization in the patient's communication that his anxiety produces. Although he wishes to understand the nature and cause of the anxiety, he recognizes that this cannot be done as if one were demolishing a building with a bulldozer. He must be prepared, therefore, to gauge the degree of anxiety and to issue supportive and reassuring statements indicating that he understands, and he must learn how to remove or sometimes to avoid anxiety-producing pressures. The people who know how to do this best of all are not the psychiatrists; they are the psychiatric social workers. As one listens to the clichés of sweet and sympathetic understanding that they give their patients, one can see the anxiety reducing statements, which it behooves us to take over in lesser degree.

Although we do not invite, and we certainly avoid, the development of a transference neurosis whenever possible, we are obviously still dealing with transference phenomena, which is another way of saying that we are dealing with back-and-forth implicit communications between therapist and patient in which the present is colored by the past. We don't induce a transference neurosis, which is facilitated by the frequent sessions, by the steady appearance of the same room or the patient lying on the couch, by a regression which evokes a patterned response of early infantile conflicts in which the therapist plays the central role. We do not induce these transference neuroses. They are dangerous in psychotherapy where we see a patient only infrequently and cannot handle the explosiveness of the affects as they burgeon up from the past. Certainly, the patient, by virtue of his role, develops a dependent feeling, for he needs help; and we as therapists, once we have committed ourselves to him, have a positive helping attitude. In our wish to help him, we express a respect for his capacity to grow and to develop. We assume the role of a supporting figure, which, however, has within it the price of renunciation of immature forms of communication when they are no longer necessary or helpful. Here, of course, is one thing that is important; we try to encourage the subject to renounce childish, immature forms of communication, and hence, behavior, by interpreting the regressions as retreats from the painfulness or anxiety of the present. We do not attempt, in other words, to communicate or to deal with the past experiences of dissatisfaction. These form the neurotic core of the personality and will persist.

We attempt to avoid as far as possible what has been called the symmetrical relationship which especially occurs in treating schizophrenics. Their loss of self-esteem prevents them from daring to relate in complementarity. They avoid knowing themselves by assuming various roles as if they were other people, or defend themselves by learning by imitation or by becoming like the therapist. Thus, we try to avoid permitting the patient to become anonymous or intellectualizing, or to talk persistently about others. We persist in expecting that the patient will accept our attitude of respect and consider himself fit to enter a complementary relationship with us.

In the therapeutic process, we start out with the here and now— that is, the current real life which involves the communications between patient and therapist about their relationship. Although the time element is not restricted to the immediate relationship but will always bring in memories and communications about the recent or distant past, we do not emphasize the so-called genetic processes or the past experience of childhood; nor do we attempt to evoke early memories or feel particularly successful when we have been able to recapture childhood feelings. The patient himself will bring into communication as much of the past that is significant for the particular focus under discussion. Granted a modicum of intelligence, he will see, when he understands the implicit nature of the current transaction, that other experiences in different periods of his life conform and correspond to a category. We are content to work with what the psychoanalysts call derivative conflicts and we are not especially interested in his uncovering the so-called primary conflicts. Also in relation to the real life of the patient, we encourage him to experiment in relationships outside of the therapeutic situation, accepting whatever failures or successes may be reported as part of the learning process.

As the patient and therapist approach each other, it is as if they each are represented by arcs of two incomplete circles, across which distorted, misunderstood, and incomplete messages traverse in both directions. As they come closer together and finally unite, complementarity of explicit roles is achieved. Then there is no gap and messages are not distorted. Information moves rapidly around the circle, gradually accelerating, while at the same time the circle narrows by spiraling until a peak is reached. In this phase mutual understanding is complete, and ego and alter have a feeling of well-being. Patterns of information then become repetitive although the contents include present and recent and distant past.

At the point at which mutual understanding of explicit roles has been achieved and pattern information becomes repetitive, the therapist then communicates his understanding of the patient's implicit role, and also the role the patient is attempting to ascribe or induce in him, which he rejects, avoiding complementarity. By recognizing and rejecting these implicit role relationships, the therapist turns the patient toward reality and exerts pressure for understanding in the search for meaning. There usually is resentment, anger, or rage at frustration; anxiety may mount; subterfuges develop; and manipulations occur; but, if the therapist is firm, new solutions are sought. Some of these ways may be equally unrealistic; but finally a fit between implicit and explicit roles is achieved, repeated in form with different contents in working through; and learning is consolidated. The therapist then has a sense of closure and decides that the therapeutic unit has been concluded.

As the transaction develops, the therapist is then often under pressure by the patient to leave the field and talk about anything else, or the patient may say, "There is nothing more to say." Maintenance on the focus should be under the therapist's control. This controls the continuity, when to move on, when to choose a new focus—not passively in terms of "let's see what comes next," but by a logical decision based on questions remaining unanswered in the previous therapeutic unit.

In the process of communication the therapist becomes an instrument. He has knowledge of the three forms of the language of communication—the verbal, non-verbal, and paralingual. He is aware of the effects of the patient's communications on himself and observes the patient's responses for indications of what effect his communications have had on the patient. Thus, the therapist is engaged, as he participates with the patient in a back-and-forth series of communications, in observing both responses in the patient and in himself. In that sense he becomes an observer. The effective nature of his communications on the patient is determined by the patient's responses. The implicit aspects of the patient's responses are revealed by the impact on the therapist. Obviously this therapist instrument is never completely accurate. Supervision and training broaden the range of the therapist's awareness. This never can be complete but expands step by step as the therapist becomes more skilled in sensing implicit roles in the patient and in himself. Furthermore, as supervision occurs, the therapist gradually learns to avoid the use of analytic terms or technical devices and alters his way of thinking so that he may become more sensitive to his own and his patient's implicit roles.

The therapist and patient approach each other with explicit roles and come together with messages which are explicitly clear, but those that are not clear emanate from the implicit roles of each one of the participants. It is the implicit roles that carry with them the emotional and expressive and neurotic behavior. The therapist cannot assume complete complementarity with the patient's implicit roles but has as a task the function of making explicit by communication to the patient what his implicit roles really are. Thus, the therapist primarily searches for information; and his interventions consist of making clear to the patient the information he has obtained about his implicit roles.

The therapist's implicit roles often represent his own failures in consciously understanding and in communication. These, too, are only understood by observing their effects on his patient which are different from his expectations. A patient, let us say a schizophrenic, comes in and begins to talk, but stops soon, because, she says: "You're angry at me. You're disturbed about something." I don't feel angry; I am very much interested in the patient's communication, yet she has obtained some feeling from my implicit behavior that I have some anger; and I cannot deny it because as long as she felt it, it must be there, not perhaps in the quantity to which she experiencies it; but the cue is there. So I sit and think; and begin to recognize that I am not angry with the patient; but some member of the psychology department has come in and wanted more money for a project and it has annoyed me. I have to realize that she has understood.

These misunderstandings are what have been called "counter-transference difficulties." If the therapist does not recognize this difficulty he must rely on his supervisor or some non-participant observer to understand what disturbs communication with his patient. With experience and supervision he may begin to recognize more and more of his distorted implicit responses, but never entirely. Nobody can, entirely. However, this is a learning process for the therapist resulting in more accurate perceptions of the patient's communication and less distortion of his own. His instrument becomes more refined.

I would like to give you an example of two sessions of the therapeutic procedure: Our patient is an unmarried, nineteen-year-old doctor's office assistant, formerly a student nurse who had been in treatment for eight months because of uncontrolled crying and dissociative episodes after beginning her second year of nurse's training. These were precipitated by calls from a boyfriend whom the patient did not want to see but who was the choice of her parents. She stated that the problem involved a struggle between her needs to become independent versus doing what her parents wished. She was the second of three siblings, the others male, of a Midwestern Presbyterian family. The father was a civil engineer, a critical person with all of his family, but one whom the patient saw as depreciating to her mother and all women generally. Mother was an attractive, aggressive woman who treated the patient as a potential competitor and who made the patient feel that she should not grow up; that is, she censored the patient's reading material, and implicitly presented to the patient the maxim: "Do as I say, not as I do."

This is the sixty-second session: On the previous weekend, the patient's parents had visited her, and father had criticized her for not getting a job where she could get ahead. Mother had agreed with father. The patient had got angry at them because she had just asked for a pay raise and felt proud about getting it.

Patient [after short silence]—I'm still a little upset by something about my parents' visit [short silence].

Therapist—Did you ask them to come visit you?

Patient—Yes, I asked them up; I just wanted to have them come see me. Why do they have to be so contrary? It seems as if they can never agree with me. Oh! I've been thinking—I want to move away from where I am living now. The woman I live with is kind of balmy. She's always asking me to come and watch TV with her to find out what I'm doing. I tell her: "Right away." But I'm not interested in talking to her. She tells me about her sons-in-law, whom she doesn't like. I have my own things to think about. I would like to move into an apartment with a girl friend. She's coming to school in Chicago this fall.

Therapist—Seems as if your concern about your parents' visit and your desire to move are related.

Patient—My parents might make a fuss or they might not, but it wouldn't make me change my mind.

Therapist—Your concern about their visit might be related to what happened Saturday [when patient asked for and got raise in pay].

Patient—What?—Oh! [smiles] About the job—surprised by that myself.

Therapist—And then father comes along and says it's not enough, and suggests a change that might not even interest you. Nothing can please him.

Patient—What did you say? [long silence] I think my father might be the way he is because he was never around much—he missed the boat about having children and now wants his children to be like they were when he was gone. Do you think that might be right?

Therapist—Do you mean that you think your father wants to relive what he missed previously in relation to you and your brothers?

Patient—Yes.

Therapist—In the past you were angry at your father for not being around when he was needed and because when he was around all he did was criticize. He asked more than you were able to give, and things that you might not have wanted for yourself. Now he comes up on Sunday and is critical and demanding again. You're angry, but I wonder if part of this is because you wonder what my response will be to your moving—whether I will be too critical?

Patient [silence]—I'm not sure if you were right or wrong in the past.

Therapist—About what?

Patient—Well, last year I wanted to move, but could not afford it financially. Remember? But you said it was running away.

Therapist—And now?

Patient—I don't think so. Then I thought you were criticizing me.

Therapist—I asked you to think before you acted—so you could know what you were doing. It seems as if you've thought this move through.

Patient—Oh! [smiling] yes, [silence]. You know, I'm not sure that I can say it—how I feel; but now I can see for the first time that I can be happy about living—that I can enjoy things.

Remember this exchange; the next session:

Patient—Maybe it's a phase I'm going through—not meeting any young man—well, not the right kind.

Therapist—Are you looking?

Patient—Don't know.

Therapist—I don't understand.

Patient—Well, I've been thinking of Dr. C. again. [I want to call your attention to the fact that this session opens directly into a consideration of relationship with men], and I would like to have him return my feelings. He has a number of fine qualities. I know that he doesn't go out with anyone else.

Therapist—Is this the Dr. C. that you told me about before?

Patient—Yes. He seems to be burying himself in his work [short silence]. I guess I don't have the stuff. Then there's a pharmacist who works upstairs in the building where I am. The other girl said that he was going to ask me out a week ago—said something about it recently too. He probably won't because maybe he doesn't see anything in me. Guess part of it is my fault; I don't smile; I don't respond to greetings by young men; I always seem to be thinking.

Therapist—About what?

Patient—Things I have to do—have done—have not done. But the good part of this is that it protects me.

Therapist—From what?

Patient [Sighing—brings hands up to face—tearful—silent].

Therapist—Both of us know this is an old pattern of yours—falling back on not knowing; being helpless as a child. [He won't put up with this regression, he says: "We have to settle this problem here."] You really do know what you need to protect yourself from.

Patient—I feel like a failure [cries] and I have to protect myself against this feeling of being a failure. I don't want to be hurt.

Therapist—You failed once—so do all girls—what do you expect now?

Patient—All right, so I failed once, twice, three or four times; but I feel that I can do nothing but fail all of the time.

Therapist—What if you succeeded?

Patient—I'd be surprised. I couldn't believe it.

Therapist—Maybe you have more concern with success than you think.

Patient [silence]—You make me so angry—you act as if you don't know what I'm telling you. [He did act that way.]

Therapist—Yes, what?

Patient—I want to have a man to return my feelings for him.

Therapist—You've been talking about wanting to be accepted as a woman. You've made some moves in that direction. I think you're concerned now whether I will accept that—whether I will like you and accept you as a woman.

Patient—I haven't been aware of that.

Therapist—I wonder what makes you feel that I don't accept you?

Patient—I feel that you think of me as a failure, that I am not moving toward being a woman fast enough.

Therapist—Last week you spoke of your father being critical of you, of your not being good enough for him, and his criticizing whatever progress you made. You seem to interpret what I say or don't say as criticism of your being a woman as if your father were saying it.

Now, let me comment on these two interviews. In these two sessions, which are typical of the patient's transactions with the therapist, her explicit role is that of a young adult working and striving toward independence from controlling and directing parents and current parental figures. Her mother and the old lady where she lives play the same roles but are of different time relations. Implicitly, she longs for the child-like dependent role with its praise and affection from father, easily collapsing with tears and helplessness at criticism, and conversely bubbling with joy and happiness at praise and approval. That was evident, I assume, when the therapist said: "Well, I think you can move now." Approval was implicit; she became so joyful; she said: "I feel I can live again." Implicit in the transaction were her fascination with the therapist and its accompanying guilt with the expectation that with him, as with father and all men, she is doomed to fail.

From the therapist's standpoint, he explicitly wanted his patient to move away from her dependence, but earlier, as indicated in the first session in the patient's response, his implicit role was pushing and ambitious for her, while at the same time controlling. He wanted her to grow up, but he said she couldn't move and live by herself—the same thing that her father had done. His implicit role fell into complementarity. He wanted her to be independent but accused her of running away, making her more ashamed and helpless. Correcting this resulted in the patient's temporary joy. Then, feeling less a child, her sexual feelings for the therapist increase, and she expects rejection and failure. At once the therapist dissociates himself from the father and makes clear the difference between himself and the patient's expectation that he will be like her father. The transaction, however, is being pushed vigorously by the therapist's therapeutic ambitions and by his implicit acceptance of her affection—despite his words—as being specific and personal, for his own gratification; he was a young resident. This dooms the patient to another future failure. There is no question about that failure with the father and failure with the therapist. Thus, around the axes of both dependency and sexuality, the therapist has sent contradictory messages. As a result, there is a rapid movement by the patient, oscillating between the two axes, which has to be resolved to avoid her giving up hope completely and becoming deeply depressed and/or substituting her own fantasy solutions as a substitute for a contradictory reality.

In summary, what I have proposed is a method of psychotherapy based on the operations derived from field, role, and communication theories rather than on a theory of personality. This facilitates a vivid, current understanding of the patient without recourse to reified variables of unconscious, transference, counter-transference, resistance, topological foci, processes involving energy, or any part functions of the human being in behavior. Here, I will make a very dogmatic statement: The more we understand theoretical psychodynamics and the less we are influenced by it operationally, the better we may understand our patients and ourselves.

This model remains to be tested for its applicability to various pathological entities involving thinking, feeling, and behavior. Many technical problems require much more understanding to be developed from future experimentation. The model's effectiveness, by whatever criterion, needs to be proven, but I think it offers promise.

A Demonstration of the
Transactional Model

by Roy R. Grinker, M.D.

IN THIS PAPER, I would like first to summarize what I've been able to cull from the literature about the methods of psychotherapy. Secondly, I shall present two sessions of a single therapeutic relationship, demonstrating the theoretical orientation of the previous paper.

To review the literature pertaining to methods of treatment is a difficult task. Writers tend to use clichés in describing their therapy, or stereotyped words, such as persuasion, suggestion, conversation, psychological analysis, and synthesis. These words are never really defined. Other persons write about support, clarification, ego-strengthening, re-education, corrective emotional experience, etc. However, few writers actually ever state their specific operations in specific detail or through examples. As a result, the reader doesn't know what has been done. Very few detailed case presentations are published in full. They are either summarized or only the patient's side is given without the actual words of the therapist. This is, of course, the traditional procedure in the supervisory sessions of all disciplines; the therapist himself doesn't want to divulge what he said, to commit himself to having spoken specific words.

Often the contents of the case presentation are in contradiction to the theoretical framework within which the therapist says he works. The sophisticated therapist concludes that he can only learn or teach through long continued supervision. The beginner experiences depres-

sion from frustration until, by trial and error, he develops his own therapeutic style. I am going to give you some examples of what I have been able to obtain from the literature.

Whitehorn (1955), in attempting to understand psychotherapy and psychotherapists, makes a contrast between patterns. In the first, there is a tendency to learn about the causes of the patient's difficulties and undo them by insightful disclosures. This is the traditional uncovering technique, which is based on the psychoanalytic model. This pattern is currently very popular.

The second pattern is to concentrate on the patient's "bad" reactions in order to evaluate his assets and potentiality. There is an attempt to evoke the constructive use of the patient's potentialities, helping him better handle his unresolved problems which are significantly representative of his morbid reaction patterns. This kind of attitude in psychotherapy is more superficial and somewhat cynical in regard to the possibilities of personality reconstruction. In the hands of persons whose personalities enable them to operate within this pattern, the results with many patients seem to be quite beneficial.

Strupp (1958) has done considerable research regarding attitudes of psychiatrists toward their patients. He finds that the therapist's initial attitude toward his patient is the most important determinant of the prognosis, treatment plans, and the diagnosis. The more experienced therapists tend to interpret more, they take more initiative, they behave more as individuals. They are not afraid to be people, or to use their particular style of communication with other people. Whereas, those who have been analyzed are more sound, their interventions are inferential and they exhibit, perhaps, greater warmth. He finds that there are common elements in all forms of psychotherapy, regardless of the theoretical school, and that even therapists from the same school may differ quite widely in their attitudes.

Ingham and Love (1954) discuss psychotherapy in relation to the culture of the place and time and indicate that these factors result in quite different kinds of psychotherapy. Nevertheless, despite the various theories, the practices of psychotherapy are more alike than would seem apparent. The period of change in therapy usually results in anxiety, which can be dealt with, providing the therapist respects his patient, is honest with him, and assumes a position somewhere between the authoritative and permissive in his role. Imagine this as a crucial issue which has to be written about, that is, to respect your patient and to be honest with him! This is the essence of all relationships and communication. Ingham and Love utilize transference as a means of effecting insight, but also use emotional support and discuss both insight and resistance. They are active when they attempt to instill

value judgments. It is difficult to follow their case reports, since the therapist's role and his communications are not well enough stated. However, they basically describe a modified form of psychoanalytic treatment, with, however, considerable activity, many interventions and interpretations.

The psychobiologists represent a school, beginning with Adolph Meyer and lately interpreted by Diethelm (1950), which has caught hold among various people, but which has always been difficult for me to understand. Diethelm explains what he means by distributive analysis and synthesis, according to the school of Adolph Meyer, of which he is the most prominent representative. He investigates thoroughly through anamnesis the past and the present. Then the therapist, in a plastic way, focusses actively on a particular problem and guides the patient with a constructive and positive manner. In the therapist's conversation, he utilizes examples traced from the past and maintains considerable activity as he questions the patient. He suggests to the patient problem areas to think about, and critically reviews the patient's statements in light of reality. Frequently, during the course of therapy, psychological tests are carried out in order to pick from the patient's responses, specific topics on which to concentrate.

Muncie (1943) is also a representative of the school of psychobiology; he exposes and clarifies the patient's view of his problem through discussion. He does not intrude on the privacy of his patient; he does not attempt to teach him everything. His attitude is one of interest in the patient and he attempts to awaken a latent interest in the patient about his problems. There are no predetermined set goals, but growth is encouraged. There is a maximum of individual participation and self-determination on the patient's part. The question arises: How is this done? It is very hard to get hold of the essence of this treatment. There are no data really available from which to draw conclusions.

I hesitate to speak about Carl Rogers (Rogers and Dymond, 1954) here at the University of Chicago, but one could not review even briefly the subject of psychotherapy without including him. He has been a great exponent of psychotherapy called non-directive, and his students in college constitute a large following of psychologists who do psychotherapy as counselors. This, of course, is the term that psychologists use when they are doing psychotherapy. But as far as I am concerned, their so-called counseling is psychotherapy, just as when a psychiatric social worker says she is doing case work; within the interviewing room, she does psychotherapy.

The technique is apparently adapted to all emotionally or mentally ill persons, as there is no preliminary diagnostic evaluation. At least, in

my experience, having seen fugitives from this kind of therapy, there have been all categories of patients. It seems that many patients may seek help from the counselor. The basic personality change desired is considered to be an alternation in perception and concept of self. The patient is considered to have latent capacities in himself which are released by the psychological climate created by the therapist. There is acceptance, a sensitive attempt at understanding, with no effort to diagnose or alter feelings. There is a continuing attempt at gaining empathic understanding of the patient, called "client." The therapist provides an atmosphere of caring and safe warmth. In this environment, the patient changes his emphasis from reality to internal problems through experiencing. The patient recognizes his own feelings in the immediate present without inhibition. They bubble through to consciousness as never before. These new channels of thought are experienced as physical alterations. It is not the content but the recognizing of the experience for what it is that becomes important. Experiences felt in the therapy become generalized, especially when the patient finds that the core of his personality is really non-destructive. Thus, he becomes more confident in himself, cares for others more, and takes an increased amount of self-responsibility.

When we look at the descriptions of the operational procedure, which are given in considerable detail, we find a great deal of difficulty in determining, however, the essence of the technique. As Mowrer (1953) points out in his book, there seems to be a reflection of the feelings of the patient by the therapist stating in other words what the patient has already said. In addition to such phrases as "I see," "I understand," "So, you thought this," etc., are processes of echoing what the patient said with a warm, caring attitude of the interested therapist. This is the kind of therapy that Rogers states helps his patients.

Whitaker and Malone (1953) present an unusual form of psychotherapy. It is related to an acceleration of growth of the human being as a person. Emotional maturity is accomplished through adequacy derived from social experience, and this is acquired by both patient and therapist interacting in a real and symbolic relationship. They develop a constant dynamic equilibrium and communicate through non-verbal means. The patient and therapist, as much as possible, exist through the therapeutic sessions in a symbolic stage, which maximally goes into the psychotic level or core of the patient's personality. The patient emerges needing psychotherapy less and returns to the real world with a repression of his psychotic function. The therapist also takes the same form of regression and often prolongs the therapy because he himself is reluctant to return to the real world. Both patient and therapist dip in and out of the child-parent relationship again through the method of regression, and both are equally anxious during the process. Since this is done together, both act as patient and therapist to each other. There are long periods of silence, and even sleep, by one or another of the transacting persons. The use of aggression and physical contact and joint fantasy is recommended. There are some "don'ts" expressed by these authors. They indicate that diagnosis is not necessary. Acute anxiety should not be considered as an emergency and serve to slow the process. There should be no socialization in real life, no verbalizations without affect and no constant interpretation. Thus, the main therapeutic procedure consists of a deep bilateral regression in the transference and counter-transference process with mutual fantasies bordering on a psychotic experience.

It is quite apparent that this is the most irrational type of therapy yet known to man. It seems to be quite dangerous, and probably requires the therapist to be as ill or as nearly psychotic as the patient.

John Dollard (Dollard and Miller, 1950) states that psychotherapy deals with the immediate problems of the patient. The therapeutic situation is a learning experience facilitated by the prestige of the therapist, the warm, permissive atmosphere which he creates, and within which the patient has free expression. The therapist does not judge, and, therefore, helps to extinguish, according to Pavlovian theory, the patient's fears. Finally, the transference relationships, if properly managed, also facilitate therapy. Dollard states that brief psychotherapy deals with everyday life; conflicts are exposed in the present situation, although knowledge of past events are necessary. The therapist focusses on a single conflict and indicates the necessary points in time for the patient to change his area of communication. If the therapist is puzzled and requests clarification, this leads to the patient's re-evaluation. Dollard points out that that movement of the focus of therapy is from the outside to the inside, from the environment to the psychological structure, and from rejection to self-blame.

Despite the general impression from Dollard's theoretical discussion that he deals with a combination of learning theory, conditioned reflexes and psychoanalysis, actually in his operational procedure, he used a modified form of psychoanalysis. He utilizes transference and genetic interpretations associated with intense activity on the part of the therapist in a brief period. For example, he reports a case treated in seventeen sessions, held twice weekly. In this case, there was much defensive sparring and resistance and much intellectually forced interpretation that took the form of labelling of attitudes. Actually, operationally the procedure was a form of psychoanalysis, translated in terms of other disciplines, understandable in other languages.

Deutsch and Murphy (1955), in the second volume of their series devoted to therapy, state that all other therapies other than psychoanalysis can evaluate therapy only in a limited sector. They contend that their so-called sector psychotherapy is goal-limited treatment based on psychoanalytic principles. In this, the patient is given to understand the present in relation to the past. However, they induce a positive transference and the patient's thoughts are continually guided into past relationships from which they are reintegrated into the present. Not only do these authors encourage a positive transference, but deliberately play roles, even to a point of speaking like the patient, mimicking him. In this sense, they express a gross contradiction in that they contend that role-taking is artificial, and is inadvisable. Yet, they actually do it.

They talk about treatment weaving the past and the present together, especially in the latter part of the therapy and they indicate that confrontation of the patient with his behavior is associated with encouragement for growth. Again, there is a contradiction in their statements when they indicate that supportive therapy is uncovering. Their sector therapy uses both insight and transference on a vacillating level of regression and ego-control.

Goldman (1956) talks about reparative psychotherapy. Repair is considered in the sense of building up weakened defenses. There seem to be four goals in this form of therapy: 1) alleviation or elimination of symptoms; 2) the improved level of adaptive functions; 3) the stabilization of improvement; and 4) further growth and development. The indications for reparative therapy are mild neuroses, neuroses too serious for psychoanalysis, or when psychoanalysis is unavailable and for the purposes of exploration with the possibility of later psychoanalysis in mind. The therapist first attempts to manage the patient's dependent needs. He evaluates all emotional reactions with a positive frame of mind. He attempts to take an objective view of the stress situations which precipitated the difficulties and helps the patient to establish an emotional decompression. He attempts then to reinforce the ego defenses, particularly by educational processes. He reaches out into the environment and helps the patient to make an effective change in his life situations and modify them whenever possible. An effort is made to modify the patient's goals and demands of life and to decrease the patient's need for omnipotence and magic. During all this, the dosing and management of transference is carried out.

Gill, Newman, Redlich and Sommers (1954) report verbatim initial interviews in psychiatric practice and rightfully state that the older methods which involve the systematic elicitation of facts should not continue to be separated as in other medical specialties. This is by now generally accepted; one does not really get a complete history from the patient and then move into therapy, separating diagnosis from therapy. Rather, an initial diagnostic evaluation is made, and the details of the anamnesis are part of the revelations during the therapeutic process. History taking, examination and treatment constitute a combined operation.

They contend that although psychoanalysts have made the transition from separate steps in preparing treatment, many psychiatrists obtain a prior history before they start psychotherapy in order to allay their own anxiety. In my feeling, one has to know something about the patient, certainly enough to have some idea of the dynamic processes, before one decides to treat the patient. They enumerate four determinants for the structure of the psychotherapeutic process: The first has to do with the personality attributes of the two participants, that is, the patient and psychiatrist. The second is the way in which they view their own and each other's roles. The third, the conscious and unconscious purposes each is pursuing. And the fourth are the special techniques used by the therapist. In general outline form this is similar to what I was talking about in my previous lecture.

Alexander and French (1946) have talked about psychotherapy as a corrective emotional experience, conducive to a discriminating learning process. Their preliminary psychodynamic formulations are the basis of planning for therapeutic roles. These are artificial roles, played or pretended, which help develop a favorable emotional climate. Thus, if the patient's spontaneous emotional responses are based on past experiences with a harsh father, the therapist plays the role of the kind father. If the patient can learn from this one experience, that such a person exists, his neurotic expectations are replaced by more realistic ones and characteristically less stereotyped behavior ensues.

The therapist maintains the intensity of the patient's emotional participation at an optimal level, preventing excessive dependency by decreasing the frequency of sessions and interrupting at the necessary times. The patient is permitted extra-therapeutic experiences and experimentation. Although fixation on a particular infantile mode of behavior may be based on excessive gratification, during that period of development, it is more likely to represent a regressive flight from a painful present reality. Therefore, the therapist works on the problems of the present derivative conflict, removing the necessity for regression. However, in this procedure the revival of infantile memories results from successful understanding of the current reaction.

I shall dismiss those therapists who work by intuition and cannot explain how they come to make the necessary communications or interventions, because they and I don't understand them.

I should like now to present two sessions from the therapy of a single patient to demonstrate transactional therapy.

The patient is a twenty-eight-year-old single female teacher and ceramic artist who has had much advice to obtain treatment but also is herself aware that she needs help. She wants to get married but associates only with men who have no such intention, especially Paul, an overt homosexual. Like her mother, who was promiscuous after being divorced, my patient also has had many affairs. Her father has remarried twice and is confusingly contradictory in his attitude toward her. She associates with a semi-delinquent "bohemian" group but is extremely sensitive, handling her severely distorted background by denying her dependency needs and living a rich fantasy life.

There follows the second session of her therapy.

The patient was five minutes late and began the interview by apologizing, saying that she had misjudged the time. She commented, "I thought about your remark that I am hurt by Paul, but I don't feel anything, I'm just numb." When I [although I was not the therapist, I am using the first person pronoun here] indicate interest, she says, "Maybe he did want to hurt me, but I'm just not conscious of it." This bland attitude of being agreeable but not involved was characteristic of the whole session. The patient continued to say that just this was the trouble with her, that she didn't know where she stood, or whether what she thought was right or wrong. She knows that she is very insecure.

She began telling me about her ceramics job, saying that she did not know her position in this field. This is in contrast to the previous interview, during which the patient was able to state her thinking quite clearly. Throughout this discussion she characteristically presented one aspect, then would deny it by advancing a different idea, each time seeming to dodge any report that indicated her emotional involvement.

The patient has an evening ceramics class which pays her as much as $150 per month, from which she saved the money to go to Europe, using the salary from her daytime job for living expenses. She has educational theories of how to teach her students, who are primarily working girls interested in an evening hobby. Before she went to Europe, she told the director of the workshop that she did not expect him to hold the job for her as she had no idea how long she would be away. He assured her that she would always have a job with him as her classes had always been very popular.

She returned from Europe, was told that she could continue working, and found herself in the position of being the second ceramist. She has only two or three in her class "but they really enjoy it," while the other ceramist has a large class, "but she already has lost most of my students from last year." The department has gone $500 in debt, whereas before it always showed a profit. When the director spoke to her about it, she suggested that he talk to the other girl. She and the other girl have been planning to send out publicity notices for the class, but she has not done so. She denies any emotional reaction to all this. The therapist thinks that the patient is quite competitive toward the other girl but has no understanding of it. She, on the other hand, is quite open in saying that it would do no good to clarify her status with the director because he is insincere and does not mean what he says. She actually has accepted the status quo with no questions, although recently she has been earning only $11 per month. She is content because she uses the facilities of the workshop two days a week to do her own ceramic work.

On her regular job in a toy shop, she has spoken up to the manager about pay for holidays, etc. The boss, who makes a big fuss and often gives vent to his anger, is really quite easily managed—"I have his number." The other salesgirl at the toy shop has been there much longer than she has but has not been paid as well. She does not understand why this girl does not complain, thinking it is because she is Negro and is compensated by the status of working in this particular shop.

When I stated that the patient had said that she felt insecure and I was trying to understand this, she denied insecurity but laughed in a somewhat anxious way.

Let me comment on this second session. The patient entered the session explicitly as a person who presented no feelings, as when she stated, "I don't feel anything—I'm just numb." This external blandness seemed to be a defense against participation in emotional relationships, but beneath this surface attitude there seemed to be some genuine interest in her teaching and her creative work. This side of the patient's personality seemed to have integrity, was positively directed and not self-depreciatory.

The therapist assumed the explicit role of being interested in the patient's work, particularly as it related to her association with women. It seemed as if the emotional significance of women in the patient's life was negated. In this area she seemed to be rational and logical, although the therapist saw the competitiveness beneath the surface. By assuming the explicit role of interest with understanding attention, the therapist remained passive while the patient discussed work and feminine relationships about which she could see no problems. The therapist assiduously avoided any exposure of the underlying feelings.

Thus, the therapist assumed the explicit attitude of hoping that the patient would settle down and accept the treatment as an experience in human relationships. Her acceptance was calculated to elicit trust and to indicate that the treatment would not interfere with her whole life. Thus, the second part of the interview seemed to be structured toward the patient's statement of her assets and involved a discussion of her security operations.

As the patient continued to talk about her work and her relationship with women, she seemed to become more intent on denying what she had said in the first part of the interview. At that time she made the explicit statement that she knows she is very insecure. As she went on, she bragged more and more, denying her insecurity and indicating her sense of victory over men, such as the boss. In this manner the transaction spiraled. The therapist accepted the role of an understanding listener to the patient's increasing expressions of confidence.

At this point the therapist shifted to the implicit level of transaction by indicating to the patient that she herself had stated that she was insecure. Here the technique was not to interpret the patient's security operations, not to weaken her defenses and denials as in a traditional interpretation, but simply to call attention to the patient's implicit role in the transaction as it spiraled to a point, and to indicate the patient's own admission of insecurity. She reacted by denial, but her laugh indicated anxiety and the therapist ended the interview with this unresolved.

That the anxiety had been implicit all the time was evidenced by the fact that the patient entered the interview by talking about the therapist's interpretation that she had been hurt by Paul. Actually, in the previous interview the therapist had only said that apparently Paul wanted to hurt her. Also prior statements of the patient's inherent sensitivity were expressed in the intake interview when she talked about her feeling of rejection in Europe. In the previous interview she had also attempted to project the blame for the hurt in her experience with Paul, although she herself had contrived the situation, for she asked, "Why did he hurt *me?*" In this interview she states defensively, "But I'm *not* hurt." Thus, the explicit role in this bit transaction was, "Why did *he* hurt me?"; the implicit notion was, "Why do I *want* to get hurt?"; and this, in turn, is denied by an explicit statement, "I am *not* hurt."

The interview ended in a mild disagreement between the therapist and the patient which is a necessary part of the process of therapy. If complete complementarity were maintained, no work would be done.

But the therapist shifted the transaction, and by evoking a disagreement, indicated the focus of the therapeutic interest.

In sum, then, this interview seems to have four parts. In the first part, the patient indicates her disturbance concerning her feeling of wishing to be hurt, denies it by projecting the blame, is curious regarding Paul's wish to hurt her, while at the same time admitting some insecurity. The second part consists in a gradual building up of security operations, ending in a braggadocio. But implicit in this is a mistrust even of the boss, whom she states she can handle very well. The third part of the interview reaches a spiral of bragging and victorious denial by an exaggerated statement of constructive and positive elements in her life. The fourth period in the interview develops from the therapist's interruption of the explicit role relationship which has spiraled to a peak and is no longer productive, and the transaction is turned back to the essence of the patient's insecurity.

Let us now consider the fourth session with this patient. She is friendly but says that she really has nothing to say. "It is strange, but, now that I really have someone to talk to, I don't have anything to say." There have been times when she felt upset, that she had to have someone to talk to, but there was no one. I ask if she has to feel very upset about something in order to talk about it. "No"—she had been thinking about Paul and thinks she really could have been sympathetic —but she did not feel that way at the time. She really would not have been true to herself if she hadn't acted the way she felt. One thing she did think about last week—she is too critical. She tells of a boy—"I mean a man"—who told her that he wanted to be with her any time it was convenient for her. She thought to herself, "Ugh," but controlled her reaction and was nice to him.

I ask why she feels she was too critical. She thinks that she used to be very unkind and would say what she thought. She has been able to change herself in this, and feels it is possible to change and help her. Do I agree? I say that I do. For the last several years she has been able to control her reactions and she feels that she has changed herself a great deal in this respect. I inquire if she feels that her reactions were wrong. She immediately becomes specific. "Not about this boy, because I know I didn't want to go out with him or encourage him."

She begins to talk about Paul. Paul was always telling her that she was selfish. He was critical of her reactions. When she first went out with him, they traveled on the streetcar. Paul would bring a book, open it, and completely ignore her. This sort of thing often happened on dates. He told her there was something wrong with her when she objected. I ask for her opinion. She is very hesitant and circumlocutious. I point this out and ask again for her opinion. She is finally able to say that she does not feel this is the right way for him to act toward her on a date. I agree and wonder why she has had so much difficulty in saying it.

She brings out that she always has to doubt and to weigh her reasons before she decides what she thinks. When I say that she feels very much in doubt when she has a critical opinion, she is uncomfortable. She tells me of three parties to which she had gone as Paul's date. In each instance he "just didn't feel like taking her home." He told her to go home by herself and she did. She is able to say that she felt humiliated, that she is very sensitive and wouldn't let any other man treat her that way. "I didn't even question it." She tells of another party that Paul gave at which he "lay down on the floor like a baby" because he didn't feel in the mood for entertaining his guests.

She then appears anxious, and I question if she is not anxious because she is telling me some critical thoughts about Paul. She immediately denies this but feels she does not have the right to be critical, that she should be understanding. I point out that she is afraid of her critical thoughts, that she is afraid of her reactions, that she tries to stand off at a distance and keeps doubting how she feels. She begins to understand what I mean and tells me in some detail the extent to which she is always doubting and weighing her attitudes. She knows very well that she was constantly being humiliated by Paul but could not stop herself. She has to be sure of the truth. Why is this bad? I say that one can become emotionally crippled by having to stay at such a distance and doubt all one's reactions. She is startled. I say that I have made too strong a statement for her, that I mean to help her understand what she is doing to herself at times. She asks me "is there no place for doubt?" and I reply, "Of course there is," but that we are trying to help her understand when she uses it against herself.

She tells me that yesterday she bought two tickets to a show for her brother and his wife. She then became confused. Was she really buying them because she wanted them to enjoy it, or did she have some ulterior motive? Was she selfish, thinking that they would consider her a wonderful person for doing something like this for them? If so, she doesn't want any part of it. She wants to leave herself entirely out of something like this, because it is wrong to think of oneself. I tell her that I do not think it is possible to leave oneself out but that one is directly involved in one's own life. She understands this and says, "But how can I know what my motives really are?" I say that she is worrying about her hostile thoughts again and that we can try to help her with this.

The patient says that she doesn't like to think about the past, but that she has felt this way for a long time. Her mother was always nice, but for years she never knew what to expect from her father. It wasn't this way when she was little. She can remember sitting on her father's lap and enjoying it. Something terrible happened to her brother and he turned to her for help. She didn't know how to help him. The patient then tells how her brother's young wife had an affair with another man and how very upset her brother had been. Eventually things worked out between them. Her parents do not know about this.

To comment, the patient begins the interview indicating her insight into her need for a dependent relationship which she cannot utilize. The therapist responds to this with an indication that one can establish a safe, dependent relationship without being under pressure or without being dramatic. The patient reacts by discussing her true feelings versus what is expected of her, and reveals significant information concerning some past behavior. Apparently at an earlier point in life, she was considered too aggressive and too critical. About the age of eighteen and nineteen, at the beginning of the Paul period, she seemed to have been put under control by his neglectful, critical attitude. At the present time, she is able to control her aggressiveness, but she has continual doubts about her motivation. Critical thoughts about others incite anxiety. Compulsive doubts seem to dominate the patient's conscious and external behavior.

When the therapist evokes a startled reaction in the patient by pointing out her compulsive doubts, he becomes doubtful too, and reacts very much like the patient—retreating and indicating that perhaps this statement was too strong. Here we see feedback operating: what the patient said; what the therapist said; the feedback to the therapist; and again the therapist reacting to her own anxiety, feeding back again. Yet, a very short time thereafter, the therapist indicates that the patient is worrying not about critical thoughts, but about hostile ones. This is a much more direct interpretation than the one in which the therapist attempted to ameliorate and, in subsequent sessions, such an interpretation evokes a significant response. This comes home to roost again.

The communications in this session illuminate the differences between a modified psychoanalytic and transactional approach. One could, for example, consider that everything that the subject says has reference, in a disguised symbolic way, to her relationship with the therapist. The man who said she could be with him any time it was convenient for her was as permissive as the therapist. Paul, who would bring a book, open it, and completely ignore her, would be as intellectual as the therapist about her unconscious feelings and doubts about their relationship.

However, the transactional concept utilizes the relationship between therapist and patient for the purpose of facilitating and permitting the patient to ventilate her feelings regarding all relationships. Thus, the therapist was permissive and attempted to judge the degree of anxiety, which the patient experienced from the feedback obtained through her communications. When she asked why her doubts were bad, the therapist felt that her anxiety had become too strong and attempted to modify the statement, because he realized that the patient was potentially a person whose emotions could lead to or threaten an explosion. Later in the interview, the therapist recognized that the patient had sufficiently developed her defenses and had made a more direct interpretation regarding critical attitudes toward hostile thoughts.

Thus, the actual transaction involved a relationship which centered only around the anxiety axis to which the therapist was sensitive. The therapist acted by encouraging or decreasing the amount of anxiety, depending on what he thought the patient could experience with safety. As this transaction maintained itself, more and more material was remembered regarding past relationships, so that suddenly in the last portion of the interview there was a jump from the recent past involving Paul, to that of the more distant past involving the patient's family. Here again, although the implicit material had to do with the mother who was "nice" but actually gave nothing in satisfaction, the explicit material had to do with the father and brother. Here it is clear that not only Paul, but also father and brother, were unpredictable, and toward all of them the patient had to assume a giving role. She had to do what they wanted, to sit on one's lap, to help in the other's domestic difficulties; but at least through the concession of compliance, the patient seemed to obtain something real, as contrasted with her completely empty relationship with the promiscuous mother.

Thus, although the transaction with the therapist was not made explicit, nevertheless, as it continued on a level at which anxiety was held to an optimum, memories were revealed regarding past transactions. In this sense, the transaction was productive and will continue at this level until it is stalemated. This will occur when content becomes stereotyped and repetitious. Then, of course, the implicit role of the helpless and dependent child continually disappointed in the absence of a reliable and consistent mother will gradually emerge.

As the memory of transactions outside of the therapeutic relationship was revived, the patient truly ventilated the intense, painful humiliations that she endured from men. Her final statements indicated almost a nonsequential jump into the far distant past, which indicates to us the effectiveness of this technique in evoking not only intellectual memories, but also in reviving emotional experiences.

Emergence of Family Psychotherapy on the Present Scene

by Nathan W. Ackerman, M.D.

I WOULD LIKE to talk about a branch of psychotherapy in which I have been interested for some time, namely, a psychotherapeutic approach to the family as a unit. The psychotherapy of family as family is surely a most recent development; therefore, it is possible at present only to formulate this concept in relatively crude form. In this paper, I am going to try to clarify some basic principles and procedures relating to family diagnosis and family treatment.

Let me indicate at the outset what we're doing right now at the Family Mental Health Clinic which is a new facility in New York. It is a clinic run under the auspices of the Jewish Family Service of New York City, which is a large social agency with high professional standards. It sees 15,000 families a year. For some time there was within the organization a licensed psychiatric clinic. When I joined the agency it was agreed that the psychiatric clinic would be dissolved and in its place we would organize a Family Mental Health Clinic. This is a clinic established expressly for the purpose of conducting investigative procedures into the dynamic processes of family life, insofar as these processes are related to issues of emotional illness and health. The clinic carries a case load of about 50 families, all of which undergo systematic study. Our goal is to use these studies to refine the principles of diagnosis and therapy of disturbed family relationships.

Our main point of reference is the inter-relation between illness in one person and the functioning and mental health potential of the family as a whole. In gathering these data, we are mainly concerned with two broad aims: to work toward the construction of a family typology, a system of classification of family patterns according to their potentials for different kinds and degrees of mental health; and, to observe and record the processes of change in behavior while the family is being evaluated and treated. By means of this empirically-oriented investigation, we hope to conceptualize more accurately the processes which are relevant to the emotional health of family relationships. We hope to evolve concepts and to design testable hypotheses. This stage of the research does not make use of statistical method; it is oriented mainly to the finding of hypotheses; such hypotheses may later be put to a variety of tests. They may also be controlled by other partial studies that may make use of statistical means.

We have a clinical staff of psychiatrists and case workers, and then we have a smaller multi-disciplinary research unit, which concentrates on the analysis of the clinical observations. The research team is composed of psychiatrists, case workers, social scientists, and a specialist in research methods. To pursue our work, the personnel had to be prepared in a special way. They had first to become comfortable with this kind of approach to human problems within the setting of the family as a whole, in place of the traditional pattern of dealing with one individual at a time. There was an initial teaching and training job to be done. Therefore, for more than a year, the entire staff participated in sessions in which I interviewed family groups fresh, in order to elucidate some principles of diagnosis. Recently, we changed the procedure. I interviewed family groups once a week for about an hour and a half, in a unit of 6 sequential sessions, so that we could consider the relations between the principles of family diagnosis and at least the beginning stages of family psychotherapy.

In this undertaking, we make use of organized methods of study. We employ a systematic outline so that we can get comparable data on a range of different family types. Also, we have a tentative set of indices by which to judge change in behavior from one point in time to another point in time. In addition, we make use of sound moving picture recordings of the family interview process. This is primarily for research purposes but we also find it useful for teaching. We are designing a specific method for the analysis of these sound pictures with the use of multiple observers. We also play back the records of such interviews to the families themselves and record their responses to seeing and hearing themselves.

This present project does not arise *de novo*. It is based on previous work in other organizations which I describe in *The Psychodynamics of Family Life* (Ackerman, 1958). This evolved out of a long period of clinical study, mainly, the results of analysis of experience with 50 families. Thirty-five of these were studied at the Child Development Center in New York with a special concern for tracing the dynamic inter-relations of an emotionally disturbed pre-school child and the life of his family group. At the Hunter College Educational Clinic, when I was consultant there for 3 years, we studied a series of families where the presenting problem was a school-age child with behavior disorders and a critical learning block. We attempted there to inter-relate the child's disturbance, both in social adaptation and in learning, with the family structure and family function. Another source of observation were families seen in private psychiatric practice, over a period of years, from a different social class.

The Child Development Center itself was established in 1946, pre-cisely for the reason that certain dissatisfactions were felt with previ-ous child guidance practices, in which the child was viewed as an individual and studied in relative isolation from the family group. There were unsolved problems in the procedure of "separate treat-ment," that is, separate treatment of child and mother. In those days one hardly knew that there was a father, let alone taking a look at the rest of the family. When we re-examined some of the implications of this individualized approach to one person, in particular, the child patient, and thought through the limitations of this conceptual isola-tion of the individual child from the family, we then moved over to examine practices with adult patients. We asked ourselves, are there analogous difficulties that emerge from the exclusive approach in psy-chotherapy with an individual adult patient, where one has no contact whatever with his family group? We arrived at some tentative con-clusions. The life problems and personality functioning of an adult patient are distinct from those of the child. If we take fully into account the different bio-social matrix for the operations of personality in child and adult, there are advantages nevertheless, in correlating the psychiatric disorders of adult patients with the processes of emotional integration into the intimate face-to-face relations of the family group.

In my book (Ackerman, 1958) you will find a more extended consideration of the rationale for this approach, the conceptual back-ground, specific considerations of the limitations of traditional indi-vidual psychotherapy, pursued entirely apart from the phenomena of family life. But I can only sketch here some of the more important concepts which are pertinent to the family approach to diagnosis and therapy.

As we all know, the family is the unit of living, the unit of experi-ence. This is a platitude, but we ought to pay attention to it. The family is the strategic center for understanding of emotional disturbances and also for intervention on those psychic forces in human relations that have to do both with health and illness. In other words, the family group can make or break mental health. It has this power, insofar as it influences every aspect of human development, and of human relations. It shapes the adaptation of personality to the more important roles within the family, and outside the family. These effects can be traced in a range of interrelated processes: the psychic interplay of one person with his family group plays a central part in channeling the path of expression of emotion, in the control of conflict and anxiety, in the subjective perception of threats, in the choice of fight or flight, and other defensive reactions to anxiety. Also, the interactional experience with the family influences the patterns of reality testing, the training for the acceptance of social responsibility. It structures certain models for successful or failing performance in life. In essence, then, the dynamics of the family group affect the assertion of individual needs, the quest for security, pleasure, and self-fulfillment, and also the patterns of belongingness through identification. In these varied ways, the family is a powerful force in the organization of behavior. This, of course, is a two-way influence. The family group reinforces in the individual member patterns of adaptation which the group requires for its survival and further development, and the individual, in turn, holds the power actively to influence the changing vicissitudes of family process.

The question of stability is very much involved, as the homeostasis of personality and the dynamic equilibrium of family processes are intimately connected. A failure of the individual to integrate into one or several of his more important family roles may be the harbinger of breakdown and mental illness. When we concern ourselves with these questions, we recognize that we are confronted in our day with particular kinds of family phenomena, that the family structure in our time is in a very high state of flux. It has already become deeply transformed from what was primarily a work organization to a companionship group. Burgess (1957) calls it the "companionship family," and Eric Fromm (1941) speaks of the family as the "psychic agent" of society. In any case, many traditional family functions have been removed through evolutionary change. The home as a place of work, as a place for education and religious worship, and care and nursing of the sick has changed. These functions have to a great extent been taken from the family and assumed by the larger community. Therefore, what remains for the family is more significantly a social and psychological function, but a very vital one, the safeguarding of the psychic integrity of the growing child and the protection of the emotional stability of the adult member. When we appreciate that, we become very much concerned with the way in which the individual functions as part of the family, and the family as part of the individual.

We must ask ourselves how we can trace the correlation of the evolving image of the self with the image of the corresponding network of family relationships. The image of self and the image of this significant network of family relationships are reciprocal and interpenetrating phenomena. This correlation shifts through time. The way in which the image of self is linked to and differentiated from the identity of parents and family, changes, in a special way through time, and changes with the maturation of the individual family member, in whom we happen to be interested clinically. In any case, there is this organic intimacy between the image of self and the image of family which very much affects the patterns of adaptation to the required roles within the family and also outside. These relations have a profound effect upon processes of illness and health. They influence the causation of illness, its onset, the possibility of cure, and the risk of relapse. They very much affect attitudes of hopefulness, or discouragement and despair; they profoundly mold receptivity or resistance to psychotherapeutic intervention. Unless we understand these relations, it becomes virtually impossible in any reliable way to predict change in behavior.

Now, the significance of family in this context can be examined at three main levels: heredity, the role of family in the traumatization of the emotional life of the child, thus inducing in the emerging personality a specific vulnerability to illness, and finally, the role of family in the traumatization of the emotional life of the adult, impairing his adaptive competence and also acting as a precipitant of mental illness.

This is not the place to talk about the hereditary factor, except, in passing, to say one or two things. First, that as evidence accumulates, heredity is certainly no more significant in the sphere of mental illness than in the sphere of physical illness. There are certain organic illnesses that are specifically hereditary; but they are rare. In the sphere of mental illness, it used to be believed that the hereditary factor was very large. Today we are less convinced of this. The statistics upon which we relied for evidence have been shown to be unreliable. The hereditary factor must be viewed in relative terms, and as a disposition rather than as a cause. Even in the case of schizophrenia, Kallman's (1946) striking figures on the incidence of this illness in twins are in some question. These statistics cannot be taken literally because the study has not been controlled for the social factor. As we move forward in the field of behavior theory, it becomes increasingly clear that we must use a broader conceptual framework for the operations of personality, a bio-psycho-social scheme for the development of personality and for its operations in adult life. When we take this larger conceptual model, we judge the hereditary factor in another way. In any case, we can safely say that the hereditary influence is certainly no greater for certain kinds of mental illness than it is for certain kinds of physical illness. From these considerations, we derive another important value, namely, that mental illness is curable, provided we have exact knowledge of its nature.

We move on now to consider the other two levels, the role of family in the emotional life of the child, and the role of the family in the emotional life of the adult person. Surely, investigations in the psychoanalytic field have richly illuminated the first, that is, the influence of family on the emotional life of the young child. Beyond that, the ongoing relations of individual and family through all the later emerging stages of life constitute a sphere which has received inadequate consideration. This is particularly the case in respect to the role of family experience as a stabilizer for the operations of the personality and the emotional health of the adult person, and also, as the training ground for the adaptations of personality to the more vital life roles. Then, there is, of course, the intermediate stage, the interrelations of adolescent and family, which has been a critically neglected area. Unfortunately, in psychoanalytic ideology the tendency to make the long conceptual leap from the family of childhood to the family of the adult has opened the way to some error. In all fairness, theoretical speculations concerning the relation of the family of childhood to the family of adulthood are suspect, until we can correlate more accurately the dynamic interplay of individual and family at each stage of maturation, especially adolescence.

From a clinical point of view, several considerations ought to be stressed. First, mental illness is contagious. It is passed from person to person. If we test this idea, we find some interesting things, some that ought to have been obvious. Families are rare in which only one member is psychiatrically disturbed. Where one is disturbed, one inevitably finds other members of the same group also suffering a psychiatric disorder. These illnesses may differ but it is hard to know whether the first person that comes to our attention is the most sick or the least sick. There is, too, a very important ongoing interaction between the psychiatric sickness of one member and the psychiatric sickness of another, where the two are intimately bound in their day-by-day family experience. In other words, there are complementary relations between the illnesses of respective family members who share the problems of daily living. The one individual who happens to get to us first, the so-called primary patient, ought to be viewed as one link in the chain of the contagion of illness. Surely we must respect his individual distress and his disablement; but we must also examine the ways in which his disturbance represents a symptomatic or functional expression of the emotional warp of the family as a whole. Often when one looks into these matters does one find that one part of the family maintains a tolerable emotional balance at the expense of another. That is, if one person is to keep his head above water, to maintain at least a tolerable functioning without breaking down, it can sometimes only be done when another member of the family is made sick or kept sick, as is the case with some forms of depression. In a tacit, covert way, other family members behave in a manner that induces the depressed person to stay depressed. If we intervene and relieve that depression, we upset the pre-existing emotional balance in the family relations, and someone else cracks up. Now, this is generally what one finds in family groups where there is some degree of cohesiveness, some partial complementarity among the members, so that the family functions are carried on. Despite this apparent unity, on a deeper level, the family is emotionally divided into competing factions. In some families there may be open warfare between one part of the family and another. The fate of such internal war influences the susceptibility to breakdown and the outcropping of psychiatric illness.

When one examines a series of families one finds different kinds of alignments of opposing forces. Sometimes, the family is split down the middle, two against two, maybe father and son against mother and daughter. It might clearly be a war of the sexes, and if so, woe to you, if you happen to be the only man in the family. This is sometimes dramatically the case in a family where there are 4 or 5 daughters and no sons. Sometimes, it is the other way, mother and son against father and daughter. Sometimes, the family split is horizontal or diagonal. It is fascinating to trace the varied forms of alignments in these divided families. This has very much to do with expectations, goals, strivings, and value orientations of the group members. Such conflicts are often severe and very much affect the relative health or illness of family members. The scapegoating phenomenon, in particular, needs to be examined thoroughly. This is the way in which one member of the family serves as the scapegoat, the victim, the target of the tension and warring that goes on in other parts of the family. Often it is a child, sometimes it is the more docile partner in the marital couple. Where such scapegoating occurs, the behavior of one individual is an accurate index to the psychopathology of the family as a group, a reliable diagnostic symptom of the particular pattern of warp in the family unit.

Historically viewed, child guidance institutes and mental health clinics conceptualized and dealt with these problems in different ways. In child guidance work, interest moved from child to family. The first focus was on the child viewed as an individual separate from the family. Guidance personnel concentrated on the internal disturbances of the child, the intrapsychic conflicts, the anxieties, pathogenic phantasies, resultant symptoms and deviant social behavior. This was mainly a concentration on the negative pathological aspect of behavior. The sick component of behavior was not adequately assessed in relation to the total personality of the child, nor in the context of the child's role adaptation within the family group. The sick component was, therefore, not interpreted in relation to the residual potential for healthy readaptation. The movement from child to family meant first the mother, but mother was examined only in part; attention was focussed mainly on her inappropriate child-rearing attitudes and actions. This was generally appraised in a hit-or-miss manner, more or less intuitively. The relationship of child and mother was not, however, measured against the relationship of child and father, nor against the kind of emotional balance achieved between the two parents. Certainly not in relation to the family as a whole.

America is child-centered, and future-oriented, as we all know. The preferential interest in the child was a natural outcome of this. Child guidance clinics proudly declared their child-centered orientation. In retrospect, it is safe to say that this led to some errors in practice. We took the side of the child against the parent. We tacitly assumed a conflict of interest between child and parent, as if the gain of one meant an inevitable loss or sacrifice in the other. This was reflected in the traditional tendency to assign the child patient to a psychiatrist for therapy whereas the mother was turned over to a social worker. The child was the more important person, and mother got second best. Implicitly, the child was good, the mother bad. Mothers felt demeaned, accused, guilty. Guidance workers came heroically to the rescue of hurt children. Facetiously the value distortion in this style of practice is now clear. With missionary zeal in the rescue of the child, parent and family were viewed as expendable. Child psychiatry, in effect, was the tail wagging the dog. The fact is, however, that the child is the natural extension of family, and parents merit the same respect, understanding and professional devotion as their offspring. In no other way can the child be helped lastingly.

An analogous criticism can be shown for the traditional fashion of treating adult patients in isolation from the family group. We have unequivocal evidence of the fundamental dependence of the operations of adult personality on the social environment. With a radical shift of environment, the habitual patterns of grown persons change, sometimes quite profoundly. Witness the transformations in behavior in persons who migrate from one culture to another, the effects of war experience, concentration camp, prison, and other experiences of social isolation.

I want to call your attention in another way to the need to examine this whole problem with a sharp eye to what is going on in the contemporary family. [The configuration of the family is undergoing revolutionary change. Deep changes are occurring in the larger social pattern. The patterns of family life are affected thereby. Turmoil and instability are the order of the day in individual, family, and society. The integrative patterns of our social world are disturbed. This evokes an echo in the patterns of the individual and family life. Figuratively speaking, the ego defect of society is imposed upon the individual. A critical shift is occurring in the power balance between individual and group.] Society imposes on the individual an increasing obligation; it allows less privacy, and there is a mounting pressure towards conformity, toward the "collective man." We must be especially concerned, therefore, with the effects of these forces on character development. Of particular interest is the phenomenon called "acting-out." People are experiencing considerable subjective distress in trying to hold themselves together, in synthesizing the part elements of their identity to fit the requirements of modern living. They tend to experience themselves not as intact, whole beings, but rather in separate parts. They toy with this and that part of their personal identity, trying to fit different parts of the self to a range of social situations which have conflicting requirements. This has to do with the instability of norms and standards, the profound conflict of goals and values which is the feature of contemporary society.

In any case, the human situation is such that the solving of problems, the making of decisions, the ability to take one path of action or another, is complicated by the fact that persons become whole beings only with great difficulty. The solving of life's problems, the dealings with conflict and the choice of action become more a function of a transitory link of parts of the self with parts of other persons than a function of individual personality. It is on this background that we feel worried about the pressure toward conformity. [Many people feel disoriented to their position in society. They don't know what the score is or where they stand. This condition favors recourse to such defenses against anxiety as magical thinking, projection, substitution of aggression for anxiety and "acting out." Psychoanalysts sometimes overlook the fact that "acting out" requires the complicity of a partner; it is a social as well as an individual phenomenon. "Acting out" is defined as the living out of conflict in human relations in a

neurotic, irrational way. The fact is that all action is some vague combination of what is real and what is not real, what is appropriate and
what is not appropriate. Our obligation is to examine all units of action
and adaptation as a varying mixture of irrational and rational, rather
than to categorically distinguish action and "acting out," normal and
neurotic.]

Let me mention another matter in passing: thus far in our country,
efforts in psychotherapy have been profoundly disassociated from
efforts toward prevention of mental illness, toward promotion of positive emotional health, and education in the choice of healthy rather
than pathogenic life values. The moment one moves into the sphere of
the relations of individual and family, one is promptly confronted with
the challenge to merge and coordinate these several levels of influence.

Let me now state more explicitly the aims of family diagnosis and
therapy. I have already said that our main interests are twofold: to collect systematic observations so that we may evolve a family typology
as to mental health, and also to develop criteria by which we can more
accurately assess change in behavior over a defined period of time.
This is of special significance when one or more members of the family are in psychotherapy or when certain disturbances engulf the
entire family. The specific tasks of family diagnosis are the following:
1) criteria for the differential classification of the family types according to their psycho-social configuration and mental health functioning;
2) criteria for evaluating the emotional integration of individuals into
their family roles, also for identifying the emotional mechanisms by
which adaptation to one family role supports or conflicts with the
requirements of other familial or extra-familial roles; 3) criteria for
evaluating emotional disturbances of family pairs and threesomes;
4) criteria for the disturbances of individual members which emphasize
the dynamic interdependence of mental health in the individual and
family; also the emotional mechanisms by which the individual, in
maturing, separates his image of self from his image of the family
while maintaining a level of joined identity.

This requires a more comprehensive theoretical scheme within
which to explore the problems of diagnosis, a much broader dimension
for the analysis of behavior. It involves the individual and group; it
involves what goes on inside the one person; it involves the zone of
contact between the one person and others in the family, the role
adaptations and the structure of the family group as a unit. Therefore,
one must gather a considerable body of data at different phenomenological levels. That is self-evident. One must consider the longitudinal
aspects as well as the assessment of behavior at the horizontal level. Our
main interest is to find ways to correlate the emotional balance within

the individual with the balance in role adaptation and the balance of the family group *per se*.

I am going to give you a schematic representation of a tentative theory for the dynamics of family life, which we continue to test and amend; but for the time being, it seems useful. It is presented schematically in Fig. 1 with a six pointed star, two superimposed triangles, one

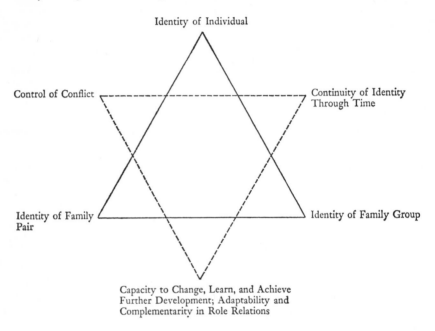

Identity of Individual

Control of Conflict

Continuity of Identity
Through Time

Identity of Family
Pair

Identity of Family Group

Capacity to Change, Learn, and Achieve
Further Development; Adaptability and
Complementarity in Role Relations

Fig. 1. Schematic representation of family dynamics

with a continuous line, the other with a broken line. The triangle with the continuous line is reserved for the interrelated identities of the family members. The upper point in this triangle represents the identity of the individual, the second point the joined identity of the family pair, the third the identity of the family unit. We are concerned, for instance, with the dynamic interrelations of the personal identity of one member and the expressions of that identity at the level of the joined and shared experience within the context of a mother-child pair, a man-wife pair, etc. In a similar sense, the identity of the individual becomes modified at the level of joinedness and identification with the family as a whole. We try to understand those interrelations with the use of three variables which are represented as the three points in the second triangle, with the broken line; the continuity of identity through time, the capacity to accommodate to new experience, to learn, to change, and through such learning to achieve further development. Continuity of identity is the conservative aspect of stability, the maintenance of a sense of sameness, wholeness, of self-integrity through time. The capacity for change is the capacity to learn from experience. So we have here the preservation of the old and receptivity of the new. The balance between the two is in turn affected by the vicissitudes of control of conflict. This is, in effect, the essence of homeostasis of behavior.

With the use of these criteria, we can better understand the ongoing relations of one person with family pairs and the family as a group. But we also make use of the concept, complementarity—minus and plus complementarity. This term refers to the potential for complementation of emotional need in the interaction of members in their respective family roles. It is not possible to consider any family role in isolation. We have to consider the balancing of the role relations in the family group.

Now, in respect to that balancing, it is important to examine these interrelated family roles to the degree to which these reciprocal role relations provide satisfaction of personal needs, offer avenues for the solution of conflict, provide support for a needed or favored self-image, and also the degree to which one person buttresses essential defenses against anxiety in the related family member. We reserve the term "negative complementarity" for those kinds of role balancing in the family group which serve mainly the function of neutralizing the pathogenic effects of conflict and anxiety—in other words, the degree to which such balanced role relations provide a kind of dynamic antidote to breakdown and illness. We reserve the term "plus complementarity" for those more advanced kinds of mutual accommodation in family role relations which not only protect against the malignant effects of anxiety, i.e., protect against psychiatric illness, but beyond that make possible a further growth of the relationship—for example, the man and wife as a pair, and also the further development of each partner as an individual. In other words, "plus complementarity" is reserved for that lovely ideal of mutuality in family relations, where the family relations spur creative growth both in the relationship and in each of the partners as individuals. This is my theory of family behavior in a thimble. *The Psychodynamics of Family Life* (Ackerman, 1958) elaborates the theory more extensively.

We have the greatest difficulty in achieving a communicable and dependable definition of what we call family identity. It is easier to spell out an accurate formulation of the identity of one person, or the identity of the mother-child pair and man-wife pair. But it is more difficult to do so in the case of the family as a group. I am convinced it can be done; it just takes a lot of work. In that connection, I should like you to bear in mind, too, that we never find family identity in any pure or fixed form. It is something that is always in the process of evolving. What one does find in family life is a set of partial identities which compete for dominance of the entire family group. Each parent, each child, has a picture of what the family stands for, its expectations, its standards, its strivings, and its value orientation. People outside in the community, neighbors, professional persons, doctors, case workers, psychiatrists, project their own picture of this family's identity. It is interesting to examine the discrepancies in the images of the family group which exist among individual family members—mother, father, child, or grandmother—and to compare these to the image resulting when they get together and talk about the kind of family they belong to. Beyond that, there is what we professional people say about that same family. Sometimes the outside picture of the family and the inside picture clash horribly; sometimes a family group has the reputation in the community of being a fine family, closely knit, secure, dependable, serious, but as one gets inside such a family one finds that it is rotten to the core.

Families behave as individuals in this respect. They put up a front; they erect a facade. They hide many things inside that the surrounding public doesn't know about. They have an inner face and an outer face just as we as individuals have an inner and outer face for our personalities. As I said, family identity is an evolving thing; it emerges out of certain partial competing representations of identity within the group. Father and mother conflict in their aims for family, but then they join and collaborate. It is this component of union and cooperation that determines family identity. You can readily understand the evolutionary nature of family identity, as beginning in the courtship of a man and woman, and changing stage by stage in the first part of marriage before children, after the advent of a child, and in fact through each and every stage of the natural life history of the family. When a new family is born, each of the partners in marriage and parenthood carry with them their respective mental pictures of the families they came from. The identity which is erected for the new family is the complex product of elements of conflict and elements of union of older representatives of family identity deriving from the families of origin.

We are interested in these aspects of family study in terms of the relatedness of emotional balance and stability in one member with the equilibrium of the family as a whole, as these pertain to states of illness and health. We like to think flexibly about families, not as either being well or sick, but as representing in their actual daily operations a certain combination of qualities of wellness and sickness. Of course, some families are healthier than others, relatively speaking; some families are so profoundly sick that one has to scrape very hard to find anything that looks at all healthy. Yet, fundamentally, there is always a certain dynamic equilibrium between forces that predispose to illness and other forces that make for the preservation of at least some kind and degree of health.

In meeting a family group for the first time, it is safe to make several initial assumptions: there is some degree of impairment of important family functions; family members experience frustration of emotional needs, conflict, confusion; there is disturbance of the interrelation of perception of self and perception of other family members; and there is also the existence of emotional barriers and distorted processes of intercommunication. Often there is a very important core of discouragement and loss of hope, a kind of giving up, because the family by itself has not been able to deal with its conflicts. Often the family is perplexed. They don't know what is wrong; they know something is amiss, but they are only vaguely aware of the actual nature of the disturbance or its cause. Often, too, there is not only anxiety but there is a tendency to blame, to mutual recrimination, a tendency to punish one another, and sometimes explosions of wrath and indiscriminate hitting out against one another. If this kind of thing persists over a period of years, family members seem tacitly to agree not to discuss important family problems, they cease to talk about certain things. It might be the lack of affection; it might be the sense of not being understood at all. It might have to do with sexual matters; it might have to do with anxiety about uncontrolled explosions of aggression, even physical aggression. Yet, most of the time when one meets a family group of this sort, though discouraged, they do not give up hope. They persist in craving satisfactions of one another, and they wait for something to fall from the heavens that will change the situation. They certainly want the help of anyone who is interested to come into it to try to bring about something better.

The unit of interview is all the people living under one roof: there may be two generations, the small nuclear family unit—the parents and children; there may be three generations with a grandmother; there may be an aunt or uncle. The basis of the interview is the living unit. The task of diagnosis and treatment go hand in hand. Naturally one can do more as one understands more, as the scope and the accuracy of the diagnostic evaluation grow. The clinician meets the family, as indicated here, in a face-to-face relation. He has opportunity to observe the personalities, their usual interaction patterns, their adaptation to the more important family roles, and also the way in which they endeavor, willy-nilly, to mobilize some of the resources of the family to deal with their problems, conflicts, and struggles. One gets a quick feeling about the manner in which the family as a group and certain individual members reach out to the clinician to intervene in the troubled situation.

It is very important at the outset to establish a meaningful emotional contact with all members of the family, to create a climate in which one really touches them and they feel they touch back. That is really what we mean by "emotional rapport"; it is a touching experience in the figurative sense, sometimes even in the physical sense. Words are less important than an increasingly open and honest expression of feeling with less and less disguise, less and less denial, less and less barricading. Since words are so often defensively implemented to conceal what a person really feels about important family matters, it is useful to cut behind the words or under the words and deal with some disguised expression of feeling, sometimes camouflaged in facial expression or expressed in mood or posture or gesture.

One gets many clues in quick succession almost from the very beginning. For example, when the family members walk into the room, one sees how they extend greeting, and also how they cope with the immediate problem of where to sit. In one instance, a young son grabbed the seat next to mother. In previous interviews, he was as far away from father as he could possibly get. So one watches the by-play that takes place. The family members push one another around; there is a scuffle; there is a transitory manifestation of indecision and balking, but the question of who sits next to whom is very important. Also, whether they look at one another or whether they avoid it is significant. Sometimes they look and do not see. One explores the reasons for that. The first step is to expand awareness at a level of honest feeling of the sense of disappointment, hurt, and crushed hope, and at the same time, to stir an awareness of the possibility of something new and better.

It is possible to activate hope much more quickly if one participates in the goings-on of each family member. This isn't too hard to do; it is not at all difficult to mobilize a relatively spontaneous interaction among the family members and also between them and oneself. When one has succeeded in doing that, one gets an impression as to how the family is emotionally divided, what the problems are, the prohibitions, the taboos, the don'ts, what the levels of tension and conflict are, and where the hostilities are apt to break loose. This is sometimes a delicate process if there is a tendency toward panic, fear of loss of control, or fear of physical violence. One endeavors to promote a better quality of emotional interchange, a more honest quality. One does this by what I call, "tickling" the defense operations of these people, both their more personalized defenses against anxiety, and the more complicated forms of defense that represent a merging of individual and group defense against anxiety. There are certain tricks the clinician can use to undercut these defenses and bring the relevant emotions, particularly the conflicted emotions, into the open. By this means, one can gradually debunk the situation of denials, rationalizations, and layers of insincerity, and more and more the real truth comes out. As one breaks down barriers, the members of the family discover that what some of them have conceived to be secrets are no secrets at all. There are very few real family secrets. All that happens is that they silently conspire to behave as if there were secrets. They just don't talk about certain things. Usually, however, when things get moving in the interview, the parents discover that what they thought the children did not know, they know very well. The kids are just kids. They obey tacit commands not to talk about certain matters. They pretend not to be aware of the existence of certain tensions that go on privately between the parents. In any case, if there is a dormant tendency to panic, to a fear of loss of control over anger, a fear of some kind of breakdown or disorganization, the clinician needs to provide the antidote—assurance that he is in control.

If there is a threat of loss of control, the therapist must do something about it, ease the anxiety or provide some assurance that as long as he is there and he is calm and unafraid, nothing is going to get out of control, that there is no real danger of catastrophe. He quickly applies certain processes of reality testing to these fears so that the dread of loss of control subsides. There are various ways of doing that, including the offering of oneself as a target for violent feelings so that they don't have to be directed against members of the family.

The therapist has many responsibilities in the family interview. It is quite complicated and there isn't time now to go into it in detail. I want to emphasize a few of his functions. He partly permits himself to be drawn right into the center of the family disturbance. When he makes himself available, various parts of the family phenomenon take hold of him or what he represents physically. They make use of him in an effort to do something with their conflicts and fears. While he allows himself to be taken into the family process as a kind of chemical reagent or a sort of hormone, he preserves for himself freedom of action. Sometimes it is necessary to be a kind of referee, controller, or balance wheel. Sometimes it is important to move around the family to provide emotional support for one member or another whose self-esteem is badly damaged. Sometimes the therapist must take a particular member down a notch. It may be that he is accused of being too harsh, or cruel. The role of the therapist is not that of an emotionally neutral person, nor at all that of a passively behaving clinician. It is an active role. He can back up one part of the family now, and later turn about and back up another part. As long as he shifts his favorites, he doesn't have to be concerned about arousing excessive resentment. If he tries to appear neutral, the members of the family won't trust or believe him.

Further Comments
on Family Psychotherapy

by Nathan W. Ackerman, M.D.

MY CONCERN with family dynamics is as a clinician primarily, secondarily as a researcher. The prime incentive for going into this area is the conviction of dissatisfaction with the more traditional ways of defining psycho-pathological disturbances in single persons viewed apart from the family entity, whether child or adult. The main interest is the question of finding a better way of conceptualizing the interrelations of illness in one person with the psycho-social processes of the family entity. This immediately involves a consideration of three interrelated phenomenological levels: what goes on inside one person; the makeup of that person as it is expressed in adaptation to specific family roles; and the structure and function of the family as a group entity. In approaching this problem, we struggle to find a tentative theoretical framework and a set of core concepts within which to tackle the relevant questions of the relations of individual and family behavior.

As clinicians, we are impressed with the variations from person to person and from one family group to the next, especially with regard to the dynamic balance between clinging to the old and receptivity to the new. We also note that where there is a great excess of anxiety inadequately controlled, the tendency is stronger to cling to the old and constrict receptivity to the new. The degree of success or failure that characterizes the effort to control conflict and anxiety influences the relative balance between retention of the old and accommodation to new experience. Anxiety verging on panic and threatening disorganization of behavior sharply reduces the capacity to learn from experience and to solve new problems in life.

In the previous lecture I defined the use of the term complementarity. The minus form of complementarity in family role relations serves the function of neutralizing disintegrating effects of conflict and anxiety. Plus complementarity, by contrast, refers to patterns of family role relations where the function is not merely to defend against anxiety in a negative way, to barricade a person against breakdown of adaptation and illness, but rather, in a positive sense it promotes the further development of the family pair and each member of that pair. It is a spur to further growth and creative development. One may illustrate this in the unfolding relations of man and wife, or mother and child. In judging complementarity, we apply several criteria: (1) the extent to which one family member provides satisfaction of emotional need in the other, (2) the extent to which reciprocal role adaptation provides avenues of solution of conflict, (3) the extent to which one member gives emotional support for a needed, preferred, or favored self-image in the other, and (4) the degree to which one member supports needed defenses against anxiety in the other member. Beyond that, of course, is the question of the degree to which the balancing of role relations fosters positive growth, where anxiety is no longer so significant a factor. This is the ideal in which creative realization of self becomes possible within the life of the family group. This is a brief recapitulation of part of the theory.

By family therapy, I refer to a level of psychotherapeutic influence that is specifically exerted upon the family as a whole, not upon individuals or even family pairs. This means all the people who live and interact under one roof. Most of the time, it is just the two generations, parents and children, the nuclear family. Occasionally it is more than that. We have had experiences of working with groups as large as 8 or 10 people reperesenting 3 generations, and including a grandparent or an aunt or uncle in the home.

Before I proceed with the more tangible questions of family psychotherapy, I want to re-emphasize the difficulty of dealing with the concept of the identity of the family unit. Conceptually, one feels a greater confidence in defining the identity of one person, or the identity of a salient family pair, but the larger the group becomes, the more complex and varied are the processes which one has to take into account. The concept of family identity, as compared with the others, becomes looser, more difficult to pin down in operational terms. As I suggested in my previous lecture, one reason why the concept of family identity is a troublesome one is that it is never a fixed or a pure entity. Although it is an abstraction, we who work with families at this level are convinced it is meaningful. Family identity refers to the components of imagery of the family group which are shared by the family members. It is composed of the levels of joinedness—the way in which family members build their common mental picture of the family. This can be represented in family aims, strivings, expectations, and value-orientation. It is a continuously changing phenomenon. It is made up of a fluid merging of partial family representations that shift with time and changing conditions of life. Family identity is thus an abstraction, representing at a given point in time a transitional union of partial family identities, mainly composed of elements of the original identities of man and wife. These original identities are modified, however, by common experience as these partners marry, have children, and share the joys and woes of life in all its vicissitudes.

I shall now turn to the problem of the psychotherapy of a family unit. The moment one initiates the task of observing and assessing a family group, one is an active influencing agent. As one watches and interprets what one sees, one modifies these very family processes. But one does so in a selective manner. As one studies the family phenomenon, one does something to it. From our point of view, we hope that this influence is a constructive one, a psychotherapeutic one. It is understandable, therefore, that the task of family diagnosis and family therapy run parallel. Naturally, the more one has an intimate understanding of the family, and the longer one has contact with it the more schooled and pointedly-aimed is one's therapeutic influence. Nonetheless, one begins that influence from the word "go," even as one is diagnosing the situation.

The family is in trouble. It has failed its responsibilities. It has disorganized some essential family functions. The impairment of family functions is selective. One may safely make other assumptions. There is frustration of personal need, there is conflict, there is confusion, there are disturbed perceptions of self and others. There are emotional barriers and there is some form of distortion of the processes of intercommunication.

Again, and I stress this, there is disappointment, there is a sense of failure, a sense of unfulfillment. There is a very important factor of discouragement or, if not loss of hope, at least a serious amount of diminution of hope for what each member needs of the family. Yet, these families have anything but a clear understanding of their distress. They are perplexed, confounded, unable to communicate meaningfully what has gone wrong, and unable to make a clear appeal for help. Sometimes it seems as though the greater the depth of the despair, the more difficult it is for the family or any part of it to tell what is the matter. They cannot be clear as to what they want of the therapist. They know they need help, they are frantic in this quest, and yet cannot say clearly what kind of help they need. They do not understand what is wrong, nor how they got that way. There is much hurt and mutual accusation. There is often deep bitterness and a good deal of indiscriminate lashing out at one another. There is the urge to punish, to place blame somewhere. The effect of this is to produce a picture of considerable irrationality in family relations.

Naturally, the longer the period of family distress, and the deeper the discouragement, the more malignant are the patterns of self-justification and defense. Insofar as the family is stuck and finds no way out, the outbreaks of bitterness and aggression serve no useful purpose. The pain of such outbreaks becomes acute, and so there is a tendency to avoid them. Often, families tacitly agree not to talk of certain matters. They become treated as dangerous and taboo. As the areas of avoidance expand, the family shares only its routines, the trivial and mechanical aspects of family life. The crucial problems of family life cease to be matters for talk, since talk leads only to bitter and fruitless fighting. These problems may have to do with extended family relations, sex, children, money, etc. The important matters are felt and yet they cease to be talked about. Peculiar things happen to the lines of communication. When such a trend has gone quite far, one has, in effect, a psychically dying family. One has only the hollow shell of a family group; in effect, a unit that lives physically under one roof, but hangs together only by sheer mechanics of day-by-day living. From the point of view of a clinician, it is most important to rekindle the hope of a change for the better.

In initiating contact with a troubled family, it has been my preference to start fresh, without any prepared history, without reading any of the background material. I have only the bare identifying information, the composition of the family, the ages and sex of the members and the presenting complaints; nothing more.

The reason for this preference rests in a long series of clinical experiences. In the case of a child patient, the line of movement is from child to mother, then father, then siblings. Ultimately one achieves understanding of the link between the child's disturbance and the family entity. Similar considerations pertain to the task of tracing the relations of psychiatric illness in an adult patient with his family experience. There are, however, some limitations in moving from the individual patient, step by step, to each of the complicated relations with family, especially if one focusses one-sidedly on the pathological aspect of such relations. I attempt, therefore, to reverse the direction. I begin, not with the isolated individual, but with the whole family. No matter what the presenting complaint, whether it referred to child or adult member, I ask to interview the person together with his entire family group.

Thus far, I am convinced I get a more accurate and deeper understanding of the psychopathology of the individual, whether child or adult, precisely by this means. The patient is part of a family unit rather than viewed and judged in isolation. In this context, I approach the question of history-taking in a somewhat different way. I believe that we get the really important pieces of history, interview by interview, as the family members spontaneously pass into the hopper those parts of background that are relevant to contemporary conflict-ridden experience. As they struggle with their current problem, they are reminded of relevant bits of the past, which are woven into the story of present distress.

The clinician meets the family members in face-to-face relations. He has instantly the opportunity to draw certain observations as to the make-up of their respective personalities, the adaptation of their personalities to family roles, and the preferred modes of action of the family as family. He has opportunity to draw some quick clues as to the given family's ability to mobilize its dormant resources for coping with the problem, whatever its nature may be. He sees the family members struggling with one another to find some avenue of solution. He also discerns the manner in which one part of the family or another projects onto the clinician a certain quality or appeal for him to inject something new and different, so as to make possible a change. This kind of experience becomes useful if the therapist undertakes immediately to enhance the quality of emotional communication among the family members and between them and himself. As I like to put it, emotional rapport is something akin to a touching experience. The clinician fosters a closeness in communication something like touching and being touched. This is the epitome of intimate emotional contact. The clinician encourages family members to put aside their hiding, their defensiveness, their alibiing—all the concealment devices which lend to family relations a quality of insincerity or hypocrisy.

The effort to establish this climate for family therapy begins instantly from the very first moment of meeting the family, whether in the office, waiting room, corridor or wherever. I have learned to pay some very special attention to the way in which the members walk in, offer greetings, and how they proceed to seat themselves for interview. The question is who sits where: where papa sits, where mama sits, where the children sit. Often, in a troubled family, this is immediately an experience around which one sees conflict and confusion—floundering, scuffling and pushing because one member wants to sit in one place and someone else disagrees. There might be a quick debate between mama and papa as to how they will solve this immediate conflict. It is also important to observe who sits next to the clinician or who elects to sit furthest away. The spontaneous behavior in taking seats reveals much in terms of family attitudes and relations. Selective forces are at work which give clues as to significant family alignments, both supportive and hostile. Then, there are further questions: Do they look at one another? Do they see and hear each other? Do they ignore one another? Or do they act as if blind and deaf?

In one family that was divided down the middle, the father and one son, Ricky, joined against the mother and another son, Jay. That kind of split arouses very considerable anxiety. Whenever anything the least bit unfavorable was said about the father, Ricky promptly came to the father's defense. The mother also came to the father's defense on occasion. At one point she described a trait in the father which was intended to prove his interest in Jay as well as in Ricky, namely, that he plays with them in a certain way. He rough-houses with them, he wrestles with them; that to her is proof of father's interest in them. Then she said spontaneously of the father, "Just like a boy. What a boy, a real baby." Then the boys picked it up; they said, "Well, if Pop's a boy, what does that make us?" So I said to Jay, "What does that make you?" He replied, "Well, that makes me more of a man than my father." I asked, "How much man are you?" He said, "Three-quarters; one-quarter baby." I said, "I would turn that upside down; it looks to me that you are mostly three-quarters baby and one-quarter man." Then Ricky chimed in and said he thought his father was about half and half, and he was exactly the same way, half boy and half man. Following that, the mother came into the picture and gave some evidence about what a baby father really is, but said she loves him. The father sat dead as a log, except at one point, when he once more got defiant toward me, saying that he likes being a boy, that he wants to stay a boy, he enjoys it. He never wants to see the day when he isn't a boy any more. Once again his voice rises quite high, evidence of anger against me.

There were all kinds of little things that one could see in this family below the level of words. In one little by-play, Jay snuggled up to his father and his father was immobile; this was followed by the mother's reproach of father. After that by-play, with no words spoken, the father once again shoved Jay's chair away. It was an eloquent but silent rejection.

It is important to observe closely all the nuances of verbal and non-verbal communication. The interview itself should be conducted with the greatest informality. One need not confront the family with the presenting complaint; one may pick up any cue that happens to come along to serve as a point of entry. One gets to the complaints fast enough. To promote spontaneous and improved communication, the clinician must aptly undercut defensive behavior. For this, I use the phrase, "tickle the defenses" as previously indicated.

Sometimes these defenses against anxiety are of a highly individual nature; often they are of a group nature, that is, the members of the family tacitly join to barricade the situation against invasion from the outside. They may close ranks against the clinician. Or, they may agree to open up to the clinician while guarding against one another. They may fortify a group defense against the outbreak of bitter arguments, with or without the risk of physical aggression.

Generally, I am very direct in dealing with family problems. Yesterday, I interviewed a family group at Billings Hospital. Following the interview, a question was put to me about my bluntness. I am so used to this directness of approach that I forget that other professionals may not be so comfortable with it as myself. They may interpret it as being over-aggressive and attacking. They respond with anxiety for the patient, as if I might inflict damage. I do not believe so. In debunking some obvious piece of hypocrisy, some transparent rationalization or projection, I believe I am promoting a better quality of contact. If a patient tells an outright lie, and I am sure of it, I tell him he is lying. There is no psychotherapy for a lie except to call it such. My conviction is that a forthright approach and great frankness works well. While perhaps threatened at first, the family learns in time to appreciate and trust this approach. In fact they imitate; they follow suit. They become more direct with me. I do not hurt them. By the time they reach me, the critical damage has already been done. They have done it to one another. They now want protection and security. They get it from the clinician's honesty. When I find myself in error, I promptly admit it. Patients are extraordinarily forgiving of small errors, but not the big ones.

In any case, in answer to the question, "Is this too direct; is it too attacking; does it do damage?," I can only say to you that so far I have found no reason to be worried.

Let me say just a word or two about the complexity of the therapeutic role here. Many things seem to be happening at once. With the limitations of the human mind, how can a clinician be attentive to the multiple events of a family interview. It is said that the mind cannot deal consciously with more than two things at one time. But here the clinician is bombarded by any number of simultaneous occurrences. I can only say that the clinician must select from all this what he chooses to deal with. He follows a certain strategy. I personally prefer to be bombarded with more than I can absorb, rather than attempt categorically to reconstruct a picture of the family through the prejudiced imagery of a single patient, seen in isolation. I would rather see for myself and run the risk of not seeing all. Whatever one misses with one's eyes and ears, one can pick up a little later.

A clinician in this position must do several things. He must permit himself to be drawn into the center of the family disturbance in order to observe in what way the dormant resources of the family, in addition to its distortion and its sickness, can be mobilized to restore a more healthy kind of equilibrium. It is important, therefore, to allow oneself to be taken into the very center of the whirlpool.

Yet, at another level, the therapist preserves his objectivity and freedom of action. In one sense, he permits himself to be used emotionally by certain parts of the family as long as this is congruous with his view as to what might possibly be useful therapeutically. But then at another level, he can exercise full prerogative for choice of action. He may intervene actively in the process. He may need to serve at certain points as a kind of referee or controller of conflict in order to offset the risk of things getting out of control. The situation sometimes gets very hot; it may reach the boiling point. At times, where there is danger of the outbreak of acute anxiety, veering toward sheer panic, the clinician must use his authority to restore control. One does not want panic, the disorganizing sequellae of panic, nor does one want an outbreak of violence. One can freely talk about the urge to physical violence, but one does not want the thing itself. This complication may emerge partly as a reaction to the clinician's active role in stripping away the hidings, the insincerities, the barricades, so that the critically pathogenic foci of conflict can come into the foreground. The clinician must also be alerted to quick shifts of these foci of disturbance from one part of the family to another. Often there are quick shifts, let us say, from one child to something of critical tension between mother and father. The therapist can be impartial perhaps, but never neutral. One cannot be an active influence in family life and be neutral. The presumed dangers of non-neutrality are somewhat counter-balanced, if one favors now one part of the family and then another. If one moves about the family, giving support now to one person and now to another, or now to one family pair and now to another; one plays favorites, but one also changes one's favorites. Emotional neutrality in family therapy does not work. It is inappropriate.

I have found, thus far, no serious drawback or danger caused by my seeming preference to support one part of the family against another, or as the case may be, to attack one part of the family and give immunity to another part, and so forth. The moments are rare when unequivocally every unit in the family joins every other unit without the slightest sense of contradiction, disagreement, or conflict in needs and values. I don't know if it has always been this way, or whether in family life today, influenced by the rapidity of social change, there is a very considerable heightening of the tendency of the members of the family each to go his own way. But, overtly seen, the forces that are conducive to alienation in the family group are more conspicuous than those other more elusive forces that maintain family union. I will seem at one time to be pointing my influence to one individual member or to a given pair, and appear to be neglecting the family as an integrated entity; but I am not really. Even though I am talking to one member of the family or talking to a given pair in terms of a common problem they have between them, I am constantly alerted to the silent but active participation of the other members. I am aware of the part they are playing even though I may be talking to others. I think it is dynamically of considerable value, even if the clinician is talking to one person or to a pair, to have the others present. These silent undercurrents of relationship are eloquent in other ways and are part of the total phenomenon.

A recent interview I had involved two parents and an adopted adolescent boy who was in bad trouble. To start with, the boy seemed severely isolated and barricaded; it seemed that I couldn't get to first base with him. I feared I might make no contact whatever with him. A variety of things happened however. I shifted attention to the mother-father pair while seeming to neglect the boy. I did that on purpose, hoping that by turning away from him, he would be motivated to pitch in. Finally he did, with a very revealing remark. Then I began talking to all three again. Therefore, the superficial aspect of my interaction with one member, or a family pair, did not mean that I was not working with the entire entity; I was. Also, the things that join a family tend to be subterranean. They are much less overtly expressed than the things that pull the family members apart—at least, in such clinical situations as these.

I also make use of such processes as transference, resistance, and employ specific interpretive techniques as well as complementarity in family relations, but I use them in a somewhat modified setting. In the case of one father whose attitude was defensive, I called attention to his having eyes only for me, concentrating on me, and not looking very much at the members of his own family. The pitch of his voice rose and he began almost to yell, momentarily. He began to show defiance and some choked-up anger. Then, the play of that small smile around his lips changed. One could see grimaces around his mouth, almost angry twitching. I would go after that; I have done it with other families. One can activate an increasingly open expression of that kind of choked-up rage. One can do that very early. It needed to be done here because the man was choked up. It was reflected indirectly by the almost total paralysis of his body from the neck down. He rarely moved any part of his physique and almost always sat with one hand over the other on his lap. When his son jumped on him and pounded his knees into his belly, he submitted. The son didn't trust the father's passive submission to assault, because there were moments when this man's immobilization suddenly cracked and he exploded. Such explosions have occurred repeatedly against his son. This is what frightened the life out of the mother, not so much what the father was doing to the son, but the expression on his face. She described it as almost maniacal, as if he had lost his head.

I also use feelings that are aroused in counter-transference. I think nothing would happen in a therapy of this kind unless one used oneself actively, used one's emotion for very explicit ends. Naturally, one tries to sift out which emotions of one's own are appropriate and useful, and how they may be optimally implemented in the interaction of the family. One chooses the right emotions, shuts out the wrong ones. I use my own emotions continually in this way, hoping that I may select with reasonable clarity those that do some good and those which don't belong in terms of the problems of the family in question. In family interview, there is constant interplay between phantasy and interpersonal reality, epitomized in contact through face-to-face relations.

I make use of reality testing from the very beginning, but in employing the phrase "reality testing," I already infer that there is something to test, namely, certain sets of inappropriate perceptions and expectations, which have a transference significance. It isn't that there is no transference; I am sure that is wrong. It may appear to be absent because one has such immediate impact with the literal reality of face-to-face contact; it may appear not to play a role, but one can observe the expression of the inappropriate images, the unreal emotional expectations that we ordinarily call transference, which derive from earlier conditioning in the child-parent experience. There isn't a doubt in the world that it is there. It is structured and expressed differently in face-to-face relations from the way it emerges on the analytic couch.

The only kinds of problems that might conceivably make family therapy impossible are those situations where an individual family member is so malignantly ill, psychiatrically speaking, as in effect to have no significant ongoing relations with the family, where the isolation is so deep and severe the connection is almost totally disrupted. Then I think one has to work in a more traditional way with that very sick person, bringing that individual up to the point where there is sufficient incentive to make possible the beginning of an emotional reunion with the family. Then one returns to therapy with the family.

Interactional Psychotherapy

by Don D. Jackson, M.D.

THERE IS an increasing interest, in the past few years, in techniques which are utilizable in brief psychotherapy and during phases of long-term psychotherapy. This interest has existed since psychoanalysis was founded, as exemplified by the work of Ferenczi, Rank, and others. There has been relatively little recent work by psychoanalysts in this area and the majority of papers suggesting specific techniques to shorten the length of treatment are largely by non-analysts or by analysts who have renounced the traditional method and are looked upon as something akin to heretics. Attempts to change the prolonged course of analysis have really not amounted to much since Reich's epoch-making work on character analysis.

As one example, you may well recall the furor caused by Franz Alexander's introduction of the corrective emotional experience and of shortening the length of therapy in relation to the patient's dependency; but what does one hear of this work currently; and who has followed it? Who has attempted to validate his impressions? One problem, to paraphrase Freud, is whether the technique of analysis is so flawless that its pure gold should not be alloyed with a baser metal. Another problem is whether the controversy that is caused whenever one suggests innovations drives would-be innovators from the field. I would suspect that this disinclination to stomach controversy does play an important part in why so little is done in attempting to change techniques, if only for experimental study. But there are a few other reasons that I think are becoming increasingly important. One is that it is becoming obvious that psychoanalytic results have not always warranted the time, money, and energy put into them. Also, the number of young psychiatrists seeking psychoanalytic training is increasing so markedly that institutes do not have room; and yet, these individuals want to practice a dynamic psychotherapy. In addition, the number of non-medical psychotherapists is increasing and these individuals may be freer to experiment with psychotherapy than are some of the more traditionally-bound medical therapists.

Another element, which is very hard to gauge, is that perhaps there have been modifications in analysis which are much more pronounced than one would suspect from, say, reading the most recent edition of Glover's book on psychoanalytic technique. That is, over the period of years, changes have crept into technique which have never been formalized and perhaps never been quite admitted, and yet they are there. I would say the most obvious such cumulative change is the importance currently paid to counter-transference and to the personality of the therapist.

One of the issues that is at heart in all attempts to change, to modify analytic technique and to apply these modifications to brief psychotherapy is the fact that interpretation is considered the real modifier of personality. That is, the changes brought about economically and topographically by a properly-timed interpretation of the transference makes advice, suggestion, and technical manipulations of questionable significance and they may even be given a negative value. But if one believes that interpretation has been given too high a value and that the analytic situation has been reductionistically under-evaluated, then the possibility of exploiting some other therapeutic innovations looms as more promising. Obviously, though analytically trained, I would not be giving this paper if I didn't adhere to this latter point of view. I think it is possible and useful in some cases to utilize technical interventions even in psychoanalytic therapy and to apply the understanding gained from these experiences to brief psychotherapy, where the therapists may never have the opportunity to analyze the effects of what they have done.

The problem is that the prolonged, intensive contact established with the patient in psychoanalysis is an excellent source of study of the effects of parameters or innovations. But on the other hand, if one is doing psychoanalysis, one isn't apt to be free to try innovations. In addition, the very training that has helped to create a skilled psychoanalyst may severely limit the kind of innovation that would occur to him. The stress placed on the almost surgical interpretation ignores all that interaction that would interest experts in communication.

My own interest in communication theory stems from work with schizophrenics and from a long association with Gregory Bateson. The rationale for the kind of interventions I shall describe strictly follows the importance I attach to double level messages, context, behavior as a message and the human's ability to simulate.

However, the use of psychotherapeutic interventions depends on a series of conditions without which their use would be meaningless or possibly harmful and I would like to name the conditions so that it is clear what I am recommending and that I am not, in a sense, suggesting that everyone go out and practice some interventions. First the therapist must have had enough experience within himself, preferably through personal therapy, so that he can recognize his own needs in therapy and distinguish between an interest in helping the patient and more power-oriented motives. He must be aware of his own value judgments in order to check whether certain suggestions or advice arise from the patient's needs or from his own wish to espouse a cause. Second, the patient must be seeking change and have a reasonable expectation to benefit from it. It is not necessary that the patient want to help in the overt sense because many patients who insist on "doing it themselves" are not especially suitable for certain techniques. The point here is that the patient's social field must be expandable so that the therapist does not whittle a square peg who has access to only round holes. Symptoms which have a family adaptive value are not treated *without due regard for reactions in other family members.*

Given these basic premises then, I would like to consider some of the theoretical notions as to why interventions should be used. Perhaps the first intervention of importance in psychoanalysis was Freud's discovery in the analysis of phobics that there came a point when the analyst had to tell the patient to take action, to face his phobia; and many of the attempts to modify psychotherapy or psychoanalysis depend on changing verbalizations into action. I think it is a simple fact that people can talk about something as a way of not dealing with it; and the therapist by merely listening to what they say may be unwittingly condoning procrastination. To give you a simple example, a young man, who had been under therapy for some time and was quite adept at expressing hostility toward his mother, which among sophisticated people is a rather common indoor sport, remarked that she had just sent him a muffler for his birthday and that he had a drawer full of mufflers which she had sent him on previous birthdays. He used this as an explanation of her lack of interest. It was suggested that he return the muffler with a note expressing his interest in having her exchange it for something that he could use and which would be more suitable for the California climate. He should also remind her that he had now several mufflers already on hand. He should not allow a simple five or ten dollar item to interfere with what little relationship he had with his mother. The patient was literally unable to do this. He rationalized the item as of small monetary value, that the mother would take this as criticism, that it wasn't worth it. After a number of hours of struggle he was impressed by his inability to do this small thing and recognized that he was more afraid of his mother than he had realized. More important, he realized that he was much less of a conforming and "good" patient than he had ever thought. In this instance, as in most instances which I will describe, the function of the advice is to point up the problem area just as an interpretation would do. But, advice also serves two other purposes, it aids the patient to translate intellectual understanding into action; and it forces the patient to focus on his relationship with the therapist regardless of whether he rejects the advice or accepts it.

Some of you may know of the interest of our research group in double bind communication, which is based on the fact that all communication is multi-level. Every message is qualified by another message, or by the context, and these qualifications may be congruent or incongruent. If I say I am angry and my tone sounds angry it is a congruent message and quite different from the incongruent message uttered when I say I am angry with a level tone and a smile on my face. It is, perhaps, easiest to think of incongruence in relation to messages in the hypnotic situation. Here the context is important. We assume that a subject is experiencing an involuntary phenomenon in hypnosis when, for example, his arm begins to levitate and yet he says in a surprised tone, "Why my arm is rising." He is doing something; and yet he is denying that *he* is doing it. In the hypnotic context, such incongruence is appropriate since the subject feels the hypnotist is really responsible for the arm raising.

On applying the idea of the double bind to psychotherapy and the general idea of multi-level communication to psychotherapy, we have noticed that there are a number of factors in therapy which automatically bind the patient to this situation and that this attachment can be utilized in maneuvers which we would call a therapeutic double bind. This term is used loosely since the therapist need not express two orders of messages, one of which denies the other, as in a typical double bind situation; but he may take advantage of the fact that the patient expresses such order of messages when he is confronted with a situation that taps his own ambivalence. How often in therapy we use the expression "the other side of the coin." If the therapist wishes to get the patient to see this other side, and this cannot be accomplished by verbal explorations because of conscious or unconscious resistance, it may be possible to bring out this "other side" by a *reductio ad absurdum* approach to what the patient is revealing. The therapist uses, even over-uses, what the patient offers rather than hunting by attitude and questions what the patient is hiding. The reasoning is: if A is a function of B, but not all of B, then extending A to its ultimate may reveal the B that it does not include. This situation may occur inadvertently with the inexperienced therapist whose patient maintains a uniformly lovely positive transference whose presence is discussed routinely by patient and therapist while the patient creates all sorts of hell on the outside. A simple example of the deliberate use of this technique would be one in which the patient uses denial to cover up his critical feelings. He is presented with the idea that one cannot really like someone else unless he can be critical of that individual. If he is asked to think of something critical, he is bound to experience some annoyance at the therapist and in the process of being critical he may actually feel the criticisms. In addition, the criticisms he makes against others are almost certain to have been experienced against the therapist as well.

A typical psychotherapeutic situation occurs when a patient tries to please the therapist by talking about what he thinks the therapist wants to hear; and the therapist accuses him of using pleasantness as a resistance. The patient can only feel hurt and insist that he is trying to do what the therapist wants. However, if the therapist focusses on teaching the patient to *be really* more pleasing, then he may be able to demonstrate to the patient the areas in which he is not really pleasing and the patient can be prevented from utilizing his standard technique of being pleasing in the therapy situation. An actual clinical example would be a young woman who had been married for some years and sought psychiatric help because of urging by her physician, after years of pills and shots for unexplained fatigue and listlessness. She turned out to be a rather martyred soul who honestly felt that she was doing her best to please her husband; but despite her efforts, he was not satisfied. She was aware of not feeling loved but not aware of anything resembling rage. When the area was approached in terms of as mild a word as "dissatisfaction" she was literally unable to agree that such an affect could be present. In the face of such resistance the therapist recommended that, since her marriage was so important to her and since her husband's mood produced a marked response in her, then it was important that she learn to become really pleasing. A good deal of discussion went into her husband's likes and dislikes and how she might go about satisfying them with renewed vigor. The first dent in her martyrdom came when she was greeted by the news that she really wasn't pleasing after all. By implicitly accepting the therapist's suggestion that she learn to be really pleasing she admitted to a certain lack in her pleasantness. She also was caught up enough in her old patterns that she had at least to attempt to carry out what the therapist described. She was spurred on to some really superb efforts when she felt her husband liked what she was doing for him in her new efforts; but it also made him uncomfortable, and he was driven to protect himself by attempting to do something for her. In the process, both people found a few pleasant surprises. The manner in which they finally achieved closest collaboration was in a coalition against the therapist. They were able to delight each other with tales of what a stupid procedure he had instituted, how it didn't get at the real cause of their troubles, which lay much deeper. They then agreed to come in jointly for continuing psychotherapy. Thus, if the patient is taught to be more pleasing when she feels that she is already "too pleasing," and not fully appreciated for her efforts, then several events occur dynamically. In order to please the therapist she must do what he says but she does this with a tacit admission that she isn't pleasing enough; and, in addition, she is being pleasing only because the therapist orders it and not because she really is. If she is resentful at the implication that she isn't as pleasant as she thought, this shows up in the therapy situation. We now have a look at the other side of the coin.

If she reveals annoyance then she is really pleasing the therapist, who is searching for genuine affect. The therapist's intervention usually produces one of two reactions, either of which can be useful in the spouse or other significant individuals. A coalition can be established against the therapist if the patient is annoyed with him, and the spouse can seize on this opportunity to get out from his own load of guilt. Or, the spouse may switch complaints, and if the patient is able to carry out the pleasing campaign and thus demonstrates that the problem in their relationship is not solvable by the techniques of being pleasing, she may discover for the first time that her husband's complaints are not the basic issues between them.

This idea of developing messages which carry a multi-level significance and impinge on the patient's dynamics was first systematically carried out by our group with patients who had severe plantar warts. We have found that patients with severe plantar warts that have not responded to years of dermatological treatment could not have the warts removed by simple suggestion even though they went into a good trance. As you know, these are warts which are continually irritated by walking, since the bottom of the foot has to bear the body weight, and they are much more difficult to treat than the so-called juvenile variety.

In the course of talking with one such patient, a petite, attractive, feminine-looking woman, who nevertheless had strong masculine strivings, it occurred to us that the wart had brought her a good deal of attention and annoyance from her husband, whom she seemed unable to handle. It also accounted for her poor moods when it was hurting, and thus she tended to ignore other factors in her situation that might be producing unpleasantness. The wart was so continuously inflamed that she could not go dancing and this disappointed both her husband and herself, since she was vain, pretty, and a good dancer. As with the other female patients in this series, the wart mysteriously was connected with pregnancy and children and received the same ambivalence felt by the woman toward her children, especially males.

This particular patient was instructed to smoke a pipe each evening for nine evenings in the presence of her husband. The therapist provided her with the pipe and tobacco. Detailed instructions, which I'll not attempt to cover here, were given her, including reaming out the bowl and how to tap out the residue which had various possible bearings on her psychodynamics. When the patient awoke from the trance she was in no hurry to leave. She wondered how long it would take her to smoke a full pipe and stated that she would have to "pin her husband down" for that amount of time. She gave a slightly uncomfortable laugh at this and then said that she hoped that it wouldn't make her sick. She looked at the can and remarked "mild tobacco." Three days later, she called the therapist on the phone and her first statement was "I might as well return your equipment"; she went on to say that the thought of smoking the pipe nauseated her and that she was more nauseated since she had been in the office than she had ever been in her life. She remarked that "I'll never be comfortable holding that thing. The trouble probably is that I really don't believe in it, and I think one has to believe in something in order for it to work; you might as well tell me to plant a piece of me in the backyard and it will grow into a cow. It's obvious that I don't believe in that kind of thing." She got increasingly angry as the conversation continued and she said that she had a small operation coming up in two months and that the pipe smoking was too much on top of this. "This on top of it is too much. Why do I have to have something difficult?" As she got increasingly angry, she stated that the practice of smoking the pipe would upset her whole household, especially her husband, and that since she was not allowed to tell him what it was for, it would cause more trouble. "Wouldn't it bother your wife if you wore a bra and panties around the house? Besides, it would take at least six weeks to get him pinned down for nine nights; it's just too long; must I be humiliated in order for this thing to work?" She was assured that the suggestions were tailored to her personality and not to humiliate her and that she could make up her own mind about carrying them out. Several months later, she called to say that she was asking another woman to drop my "equipment" off. She had had the pipe and tobacco on her bureau for six weeks or so and had not been able to go through with the experiment; there was now no need to go through with it because the wart had healed up. It is important to note that the equipment, and this is her term, was on the bureau where she saw it every day and there were undoubtedly other members of the household who could see it too.

The principle of developing dynamic insight through action suggestions is, of course, utilized in non-hypnotic cases as well. The theory on which such apparently ridiculous suggestions are based can be described again in a slightly different framework. This is the notion that people are constantly attempting to determine the nature of their relationships (Jackson, 1958; Haley, to be published). This is done most directly by taking action and by uttering congruent messages, and most indirectly by uttering covert messages.

Every symptom may be considered as a covert message—that is, an attempt to bring something about in a relationship. I say "may be considered" since it is unimportant whether the symptom was unconsciously developed for this purpose or not. For example, if a headache develops on the basis of prolonged tension in the occipital muscles, it nevertheless becomes a message, since it is a report on how the individual feels and a command to be responded to. The intent is not important because the receiver of the message is influenced if he has a relationship with the headache bearer. He may be annoyed, sympathetic, deny that it has anything to do with the relationship, or whatever; but he does make an overt or covert response to the headache as a message.

If a symptom is seen as a covert message, then theoretically if the patient is persuaded to make the message overt, he will not need the symptom. Thus, if a woman with an easily tiring larynx is instructed to tell her family that her therapist won't allow her to speak to them, she may find that when she spontaneously has to make a protest against some injustice her voice rings out loud and clear. The therapist's instructions have made her message overt. The effect of changing the level of the message has been known for a long time, but not thought of in these terms. Thus, Ferenczi (1955 b) suggested that if a patient is blocked in his attempts to free associate, the therapist get him to fantasy. He made this suggestion in order that unconscious material continue to be made available to the therapist. But there is a further aspect to this suggestion. If a patient can't free associate, he is merely an innocent victim of some unconscious force. If he also can't carry out any attempt to change the level of his method of communication, then it begins to dawn on him and the therapist that he is just plain stubborn. That is, we allow the patient one symptom or a group of symptoms, but if he extends these during therapy, it becomes apparent that this is a comment on his relationship to the therapist.

I am not sure how clearly I have been able to communicate the theory that these suggestions are based on, so let me make one further attempt. If a patient comes to a psychotherapist for headaches, he learns to label them as suppressed anger. Once he has accepted this labeling, the headaches no longer have the same meaning to him that they did. If he were to have a headache, he would now know that he was angry, and thus, his anger would not be covert and the symptom loses some of its meaning.

In the course of learning to label, the patient experiences resistance to change which comes about not only because he has learned about a new system of labeling but mainly because the old problem is also experienced in the relationship to the therapist. As he attempts to influence the nature of his relationship to the therapist, the same need for covert communication that he had on the outside will rise again. However, if the therapist does not deal overtly with the symptom as such, nor make its meaning overtly clear to the patient, but instead intervenes in a way that will help the patient change his level of messages, he may avoid the need for the symptom being used against him in the therapy situation. This idea is again most easily demonstrated in hypnosis. A patient with a tic involving the tongue that is creating annoyance in her husband because of the clicking sounds that she makes, is asked where she would like to have this symptom transferred to. It is subtly suggested that a wiggling toe is not a bad thing to have since one is free to wiggle it and no one else knows about it, and she accepts the suggestion. Once the symptom is transferred it wears off in a period of days or weeks because a wiggling toe is not annoying to one's husband and the toe is not connected with speech as the tongue is.

In describing how such a suggestion works, I would emphasize that the patient is given permission to have a symptom, whereas her previous symptom was reinforced because it was something she was not supposed to have and because it annoyed other people. Secondly, the therapist has tacitly labeled the symptom as a covert attempt to annoy others and he has changed the level of message by saying in effect, "you will be responsible for wiggling your toe." This taking of responsibility for a symptom (like toe wiggling) is quite different from a tic, which is merely mysterious to the patient and which, of course, she can't help. This was a pleasing person who had to accept the therapist's suggestion. Once she agreed to the notion that the symptom could be moved, she tacitly accepted responsibility for it, i.e., she changed the level of the message. At the same time, the implication that she was willfully causing her symptom was avoided by allowing her another.

In some brief therapy cases where a followup has been possible, it appears that the original symptom has not returned nor been replaced by another, as one might expect. This is not true of the majority of cases where only symptom transference by simple suggestion is used. If a change in the level of message is achieved and if overt behavior is brought about that will make overt the covert meaning of the symptom, then more lasting results can be expected. For example, the lady with the tongue tic could be instructed to bring her husband to a session, and, acting under orders from the therapist, she would have to be critical of him. Since both of them would be told that someone he really cares about is someone he is able to be critical of, and someone he knows well enough to have spotted his faults, then it is not as difficult to get the patient to be critical as it might seem. Once having been critical, even though it is under the therapist's aegis, the patient cannot retract it completely, nor will the spouse ever forget it. In this manner, a symptom is made a part of overt behavior and the behavior is made interactional by bringing in family members or by making the behavior appropriate *vis à vis* the therapist.

I would like to illustrate these ideas in a more complete manner in several case histories showing the type of thing that one may do, both in brief therapy and in utilizing them as a part of intensive analytic therapy.

A 64-year-old woman was brought to the office by her daughter-in-law, who was very solicitous about her depressed mental state. The patient had been having anxiety attacks for a year and a severe depression since her husband's death two months previous. She came from a distant town to stay with her son and daughter-in-law and their two children in a fairly small house. She was a conscience-ridden woman who was always aware of having done her best and she had a certain air of helplessness which was both an appeal to the therapist and an insurance that her son and daughter-in-law wouldn't kick her out. Although her constant self-recriminations annoyed other people, she felt justified in them because she felt that she may have contributed to her husband's death. She felt vaguely that there was something more that she could have done that might have prevented his heart attack. Under questioning she revealed that her husband had had twelve years of alcoholism and that this had been a terrible period for her, but that during the last ten years of their marriage, he had not touched alcohol at all. Also, his alcoholism was strictly confined from Friday night to Sunday morning, and she, without too much therapeutic leading, was able to see that he seemed more comfortable at work than at home. She had also taken care of her invalid mother for thirteen years, and under the pressure of her husband had finally sent her to another sister, who had never since masked her feelings of anger toward the patient. The mother's illness covered a good bit of the period of the husband's alcoholism and the patient spoke of feeling torn between her husband and her mother. Although the husband was consistently good to her mother, he resented having her in the home.

It occurred to her that her feeling that she had contributed to her husband's death from the coronary attack was related to her own anxiety attacks which had started a year previous to his death. When she was the one who was down and unable to take as good care of him, then he was obvious in his displeasure. There were hints that he was intolerant of her having difficulty, but there was little he could do about it since the family physician assured him that she had had heart spasms. Subsequently, several specialists diagnosed her condition as hyperventilation and stated that there was no medical evidence that she had had coronary disease. However, they would not go so far as to say that she could not possibly have had a heart attack. So this left her for a number of months, prior to her husband's demise, with a mixed feeling about whether she had been really sick or whether she had just been nervous and had taken advantage of him. She punctuated all of her history with statements like "I'm trying my best, doctor, I'm ashamed of myself; I am trying my best."

After the initial interview, the therapist decided that she was not an ideal candidate for insight therapy; she was deeply religious, conscience-stricken, and not especially sophisticated. She was not used to being introspective and she would probably be running into increased resentment if she remained indefinitely in her son's crowded home. Although the situation was currently being covered up by benevolence, it was possible to pick up hints from the daughter-in-law, and later from the son on the telephone, that they were not too happy about it. Her natural obedience and her conviction that she "could lick this thing" could be exploited by giving her explicit instructions. Also, since her son complained that she was appearing in rather undressed states in front of him, the therapist decided she would respond to a certain amount of flirtatious bantering.

She was told that she must get out of bed every morning, rather than have her breakfast brought by her daughter-in-law, that she must do part of the housework, and that she must engage in a graduated series of trips away from home. The first trip involved a junket to the local store about a block away and the final trip involved taking the train to another city several hours distant, eating lunch, and returning. She was assured that she need not spend any time in the city beyond meeting these requiremnts.

In actuality, her defiance of and attachment to the therapist allowed her to prolong this last trip for an hour and a half while she did some shopping. The son and the daughter-in-law were instructed not to be so benevolent, because their mother would pay for their benevolence by feeling increasingly guilty and depressed, and she couldn't stand much more of this. The one pleasure period emphatically allowed her was when her son came home in the evening. She was instructed that they must have a cocktail together. The son normally did this and the mother *never touched alcohol*. She was told that alcohol was a specific drug for depressions, equal in some respects to modern-day tranquilizers, and that she must have at least two ounces of bourbon before dinner. This was done in order to facilitate her acceptance of her husband and his drinking problem, as well as to allow her a structured context in which to enjoy her son's company. She complained initially that she couldn't stand the taste of bourbon, but that she was getting it down. Several weeks after this procedure was inaugurated, the son and daughter reported that she had honestly sparkled during her cocktail hour, and subsequently, she reported to the therapist with smiling annoyance, "You know, I think you had me drink deliberately in order to remind me of my husband." Little reassurance was used, but a somewhat teasing, provocative manner which both intrigued and irritated her was employed. She was heard by the secretary to mutter in the waiting room that she did everything that damn doctor told her, and he never gave her any praise.

Within two weeks after this regime had been inaugurated, she was noticeably better; she was able to deal with everyone but her son and daughter-in-law. With strangers and neighbors she could be gay and interesting, and not grunt, moan, or engage in self-recriminations. A period of several tiffs between her and the daughter-in-law, especially over matters of household cleaning (which I had anticipated when telling her to do some of the housework), increased her feeling that she was on borrowed time. She was then able to admit her terror of going back to her home town and living alone, and the therapist was able to help her arrange with a friend of hers to spend the first week with her in the empty house. After six weeks, she was asked how soon she thought she could make it home, whereupon she thought two weeks, and the therapist insisted that she take three. When she left, the therapist advised her to take six meprobamate tablets daily, although she had been on the drug for several months without noticeable effect. She had been engaged in a struggle with her previous psychiatrist who was fearful of the possibility of addiction. Again, her Presbyterian conscience came through, and two weeks after she had returned home she called to say that she had cut down the meprobamate tablets to four a day, but asked my forgiveness for still taking them.

In summary, a 64-year-old woman exhibiting characteristic signs of an agitated depression was handled by being seen five times over a period of two months. No claim of cure is made, but it did seem that she responded to a regime developed according to guesses about underlying psychodynamic factors. Evidence for conscious and unconscious insight existed in the fact that she made a connection between drinking bourbon and her husband's alcoholic period, long talks with her son in which they both decided that the husband had been a somewhat difficult character, and a statement that, despite her sending her mother to her sister after thirteen years of caring for this bedridden patient, the sister had perhaps had it coming to her, and the mother's death could not have been prevented whether she was in California or elsewhere. It is difficult in this kind of case, because of the lack of follow-up, to know what procedures the patient carries out on her own. All I know about this particular patient after about six months, is that she is still living in her home in another part of California from her son, and, according to her, is doing all right. She still is not happy about it, but she is not depressed.

An example of conscious insight occurred with a young man who had been in analysis for several years and whose progress was slowed by recurring quiet recriminations, mainly against his parents. Although they lived in a distant city he often felt misused by them in the present, as well as in the past, and duplicated this situation in many of his relations with other people. The analyst had had little success in analyzing this situation in a way that led to anything more than intellectual understanding. It gradually dawned on him that the patient was afraid of his parents and that there were not only deep religious overtones to this, but also the parents unconsciously, and to some extent, consciously, were perceived as all that he had in the world. Naturally, this kind of dependent hostile involvement kept him away from other people and kept his parents in their exalted position.

During one session, when the patient was complaining in his typical hopeless and non-productive manner, the therapist cut in to ask him, "What would you be willing to give up in relation to your parents?" He was rather taken aback by this, but stated after some thought that he would be willing to give up his right to his inheritance. He expressed definite annoyance at the idea of giving up anything in relation to the people he felt deprived him; it seemed inexplicable. He explained, however, that giving up his inheritance might not mean too much to him because his parents were relatively young. The money would go to his mother and then to him and other siblings, and by this time, he would probably have an adequate income of his own. He also felt that since his siblings had children they would be more in need of extra money than himself. The point of the therapist's question stemmed from the fact that the patient's father had kept an exact account of every penny spent on his higher education and the patient was engaged in paying this back on a monthly basis. The patient didn't believe this was fair of the father, but he continued to send the monthly allotment; and this, of course, kept him and his parent involved with each other. After the patient stated that he would be willing to give up his place in the will, the therapist pointed out that, since he had given up something, he was now in a position to ask for something. Therefore, he should write his parents a letter stating that he was renouncing his place in his father's will because he could no longer continue the payments on his education, since it interfered in his relationship to the parents, and it was not worth sacrificing this relationship for money. It took the patient nearly two weeks under pressure by the therapist to get the letter written. He and the therapist went over the document carefully, sharing a joint project. Following the writing of the letter, the patient experienced a good deal of anxiety and showed a noticeable increase in his self-confidence, and had a dream in which he became a father himself for the first time in therapy. Evidently, in giving up his place in the will, he gave up being a son and was able to conceive of having a son of his own. The therapist had little doubt that the father would respond favorably to the letter because of his and the mother's need for the son, and this turned out to be correct. The father stated that he hadn't realized the patient felt so strongly about the debt and that he was willing to cancel it. However, he didn't want the patient to give up his inheritance and suggested that he simply subtract the education debt from the amount coming to him in the inheritance. He assured the patient that he was as much his son as the other children.

Of course, the patient was delighted with this response and it immediately led to several more profitable and aggressive adventures in other areas, including his job and his girl friend. The anxiety toward the therapist for influencing him to such a degree was minimal. Although he immediately had some reaction after getting the letter written, out of fear that he had substituted one father who had pushed him around for another one, this was analyzed and, in addition, other successes on the outside made the patient feel that he was improving on his own.

As an example of how this anxiety manifested itself—following writing the letter and prior to having heard from his father, he industriously started relandscaping his house. He was concerned over how extensive a job he had started and he had a dream in which he was a patient in a mental hospital; he wandered away in a confused state and was brought back by the attendant. When the therapist mentioned that it was too late to take back the change instigated by the letter, he broke into spontaneous laughter. Any improvement in such a patient does result in some increased anxiety, which the therapist expects and accepts.

Most analysts certainly would be critical of the kind of intervention I have described, on the basis that the use of techniques like these irrevocably distorts the transference situation. They interfere with the use of abstinence as a motivating force, since the therapist is gratifying the patient by his activity, and they do an injustice to the patient's trust. I have certainly been told outspokenly that "with the kind of parents these patients have had, you know very well that what they need is absolute honesty and not manipulation." Let me try to answer these points individually. In regard to distortion of the transference, until there is better data as to the effect of the therapist's personality and of countertransference on the course of therapy, I would suspend judgment on how disastrous it is to deep insight when the transference situation is deliberately disturbed. If the therapist is covertly dissatisfied with the patient's progress, I am afraid the transference would be distorted despite his most avid attempts to remain a fly speck. Also the enduring nature of the transference phenomena and the vigor of repetition compulsion has led most patients, as far as I can tell, to place interventions in the framework of their own past life. They do not see them as a continuing interruption in the therapeutic process.

Interventions may also be criticized on the grounds that they involve manipulation or trickiness. I think this is a value judgment which ignores the fact that all psychotherapy or psychoanalysis attempts to influence the patient. In psychoanalysis the use of the couch, of silence, and of non-gratification are technical devices employed to influence the patient. Recently Fairbairn (1958) stated that he has renounced the use of the couch because he feels that it is too humiliating to the patient. I think most psychotherapists operate implicitly by putting the patient in the "one-down" position. If he is able to extricate himself, he is cured, and if he can't extricate himself, he usually quits. The happy outcome is something like growing up and leaving home, it is achieving an equal status, and I think that if one follows a few rules, it will lessen the possibility that the patient may feel that he has been used or tricked.

Manipulations or interventions must not be employed if the therapist has any negative feelings toward the patient and if they are especially counter-indicated as a way out of some sort of therapeutic impasse. That is, when the therapist feels that he does not know what is going on, things bog down and then a bright idea occurs to him. *This is exactly the time when an intervention should not be used.* The therapist must frankly answer any questions that the patient asks in an attempt to understand the meaning of his recommendations. The therapist must be prepared to be wrong if his intervention fails or if the patient becomes angry, as mentioned in the description of the married couple who formed a coalition against the therapist. He should accept his position, non-defensively and be free to lose a patient.

I hope these remarks will not be interpreted as a "cookbook course," designed to get around the need for intensive training in order to do psychotherapy; the opposite is the case, for only an experienced therapist can tailor an appropriate intervention to each individual patient.

This is one of the paradoxes, and one of the stumbling blocks in psychotherapy: the experienced therapist is best able to conceive and execute innovations; yet his experience is apt to render him chairbound and a devotee of his own style.

Family Therapy in the Family
of the Schizophrenic

by Don D. Jackson, M.D.

I BECAME INTERESTED in family therapy about seven and a half years ago, when I went from Chestnut Lodge to Palo Alto. At Chestnut Lodge, we had treated schizophrenics with psychotherapy, so I of course did so in Palo Alto. But, at the Lodge, we had never had anything to do with their families. This, I understand, has changed somewhat now. But in my day, it was really a disgrace for the therapist to encounter the parents. This was something he avoided and always left to the administrator. In Palo Alto, which is a small university town, I couldn't avoid the relatives; and this led to a lot of surprising and sometimes not very pleasant results. I became interested in the question of family homeostasis, which seemed most marked in the families where a schizophrenic patient was able to live at home. If he then went through psychotherapy and benefited from it, any move on his part would usually produce all sorts of disruptions at home. Surprisingly, there is very little written on this topic. It is something that people who do psychotherapy can confirm, and to which they can add horror stories of their own of what occurred when they undertook psychotherapy with schizophrenics and ignored the patients' relatives.

Since schizophrenics have been treated largely in hospitals away from relatives, the idea has only recently received sufficient attention that schizophrenia could be, in part, an adaptive disorder which links itself to family pathology—a situation in which change in the patient's symptoms produces feedback into the family situation.

At any rate, then, for practical reasons, I started seeing the patients' parents, and then eventually, largely for research purposes, started seeing the parents and patient together. About this time, I joined forces with Gregory Bateson and his staff and we decided to work on data obtained from conjoint interviews with the family. These interviews usually take place for an hour or an hour and a half once a week; the longest follow-up we have had concerned a family which was in treatment for about two years. We have had perhaps fifteen families in therapy and have now been able to add several delinquent families for purposes of contrast, but we have almost no normative data. At least, if there is such a thing as a normal family, we haven't encountered it because we haven't focussed on that aspect, but we would like to enlarge our data and see how these families compare with families with other sorts of difficulties.

The lack of normogenic data limits our ability to generalize. However, comparisons between the families of so-called "process" schizophrenics with "reactive" schizophrenics reveal such marked differences, that we assume *mutatis mutandis* there will be observable differences along the continuum to healthy families.

Initially, the patient was seen in individual psychotherapy as well as in sessions with the family, because traditionally the schizophrenic is the patient. We now tend to see the family together right from the beginning in order to avoid the bias of patient-oriented sessions. We may start with the patient in the hospital and have him brought to the session. But however it is done, we usually see the family right from the beginning as a group, and tell them that we will only meet when we can meet as a group. If the father is a traveling man or something of that kind, we will meet without him; but if we do, we cannot talk about him. In other words, a session is deliberately structured to make the focus a family one, and to avoid focussing solely on the schizophrenic patient. Despite the rules, the parents constantly try to break them because they are used to thinking in terms of having a sick member of the family, rather than of being a sick family. Thus, the first several sessions almost characteristically begin with statements to the effect that "We would be just fine if it wasn't for poor John being in such terrible shape." But this doesn't continue for long.

The other thing we do initially is to make a movie of the family and, again, it is in a structured situation. The game might consist of everyone offering a thought, much as you would play a card, and then the next person can trump that thought or can play another suit; that is, have a completely unrelated thought, and so on. We do this because it is easier for us to get non-sick families whose data are used for comparative purposes to come for a short movie-making period than it would be to ask them to come for a number of conjoint sessions. These movies are another source of data about how these families operate. Insofar as therapy itself goes, without any reference to its research aspects, at this juncture, after about three and a half years of experience, it looks promising. We have been surprised by the amount of change that has taken place in some patients. We have been surprised at how ill some patients can be and still remain out of the hospital, if the family and its own difficulties are being attended to in some fashion. But it is too early to say whether conjoint family sessions will ever be a contribution to psychotherapy.

Our goals at the moment are limited. Our main goal is to get the family to live apart. Now, this doesn't mean that we want to ship, say, one to Chicago and another to New York. We simply want them to be able to live in some sort of autonomy so that they then can live together. This is very difficult to achieve. We will listen for months to the story of how the patient is upsetting the whole family, but as soon as the patient improves and, let us say, wants to get a room by himself, it usually is another matter of months or longer before we can get the parents to permit that. This is one of the really striking things about these families. They just don't seem to be able to do without each other when the patient is living at home. We have seen other families where the patient has been hospitalized for a significant period of time. The parents, in effect, form a coalition against him so that he cannot return home. Hospitalization is one acceptable way for these families to be apart. It is obvious that the patient is labeled as sick—and usually as organically rather than psychologically ill. Hence the hospital. We try mainly to get the family to see how much they intertwine with each other. We are not attempting to bring about profound personality change, but in the course of trying to get them separated, a fair amount of change can occur. Following is an example of change that occurred in one of the families.

In the first case, this family consists of a mother, father, a 32-year-old daughter, who looks really about 18 or 20, and her 18-month-old child. The daughter has been having catatonic attacks since she was 19, and has had a total of five years of hospitalization off and on. Many of the times when she has been out of the hospital, she hasn't been able to function but has been cared for at home. She got married a couple of years ago during one of her periods of being out of the hospital, and had a child, and then promptly went back into the hospital. So, she has never cared for this child and has actually seen very little of her. When she got out of the hospital, she made arrangements with her husband to divorce him, and went to stay with her parents. The child, meanwhile, was in a foster home in the town where she had lived with her husband. I started with them, the family, about the middle of October, 1958, and after five or six sessions the patient, who is usually fairly mute and rigid, began to respond, in that she looked more alive at the sessions, more interested, and would comment occasionally. The mother told me that she had cared for the patient for so many years that she had sacrificed a good bit of her chance to be an artist; that not only was the patient a problem, but that her very successful father was subject to spells in which he folded up and couldn't go to work. During these spells, she would take him off to a cabin in the woods, or somewhere, and stay with him a couple of weeks until he got back on his feet. She also said that the brother, just before he went to Korea, had a similar episode and that she nursed him out of that. I asked the mother if she ever had had the privilege of breaking down, or if she always had to be the one who was strong. She looked as if she had been kicked in the stomach. She gasped and got red. She couldn't talk for a little while. When she finally could say something, she simply muttered, "Well, it is over with now, it was just a silly business anyhow," and literally would not permit me to return to that topic. At the end of this session, the patient, sensing the session was drawing to a close, said, "Would it be all right with you if I went to get my baby?", and I said, "Of course, if you want to." She looked surprisingly in control of herself. The mother protested vigorously because the plan had been that she would go get the baby after things were squared away with the patient. The grandmother would, in effect, take care of the baby. It wasn't assumed that the patient would be in good enough shape to take this responsibility. Late that afternoon, the patient came to my office with her mother in tow to get a letter to the foster home saying that she was in shape to bring the baby back from the foster home on the plane. The mother said, in a pitiful way, "I haven't been able to cash a check; I don't have enough money for your ticket," appealing to me somehow, not for money, but for something. The patient calmly told her that she had already checked with the travel bureau, that they would take a check, and that there was no problem. They left, with the mother again sort of following along behind the patient in a little pitty-patty kind of way. And the patient went for her child.

Let me present the initial session with the family I described. It is similar to all initial sessions we have had with the very sick, or what I call stable, unsatisfactory families. It is characteristic in that the parents focus completely on the patient's illness and indicate no problems of their own. The patients usually cooperate with such an endeavor and the net result is an impression of a family being victimized by the patient's illness. In fact, after many months, it invariably turns out that the parents not only have problems of their own, but that the patient's illness has become an explanation for their way of life.

M *(mother)* (to father)—You talk.

F *(father)*—It's your show.

T *(therapist)*—No, it's all of yours.

M—It was very pleasant. We had a very nice weekend. Barbara wanted to see the Van Gogh exposition so I drove her into town Sunday morning and we had a very pleasant weekend, didn't we, Papa?

F—Yes, yes.

T (to father)—Did you go along?

F—No, I stayed home and worked Sunday morning, as usual.

T—Do you like to work around the place or on your scientific work?

F—Yes.

T (to mother)—What seemed to be pleasant about it?

M—Barbara was her old self.

F—It was Barbara's proposal to go in and see the show.

M—Her proposal—

F—We were happy about that.

T—Well, does she have the responsibility of determining how things in the family go—happy or unhappy? Is she sort of your weather vane?

M (laughing)—Well, anyway, we're just fine when she is happy, then everything is all right.

T—I was thinking of what a tough spot that is for her to be in. You know, the feeling: "When I'm down the rest of the family is down; and if I get up again, they'll come up again with me. It's like walking around with a huge weight. Do you see that it might be difficult?

F—Well, it can't very well be any different. The girl has had a shock and naturally—

M—I was just so glad that she wanted to go in and I was so tickled to death we saw the pictures and came back. It isn't always that way. We had quite a full life and so on. You see, she hasn't been at home for six years.

T—Well, what else? You went in to the museum on Sunday morning.

M—Came back, had a late dinner and Barbara looked at the TV and then we all looked at it.

T—You watched.

M (interrupting)—And while we slept, Barbara wrote a letter to her best girl friend while we took a nap because we had been out Saturday night and Barbara very nicely wanted us to go and we were out from 8:30 to 10:30.

T—Well, what did you do, where did you go?

F—Oh, just visited this friend's house and the friend's apartment.

M—That was the first time we really left her and went out. She wanted us to and it went very nicely.

T—Well, that's fine. (To patient) What did you do while they were gone? Watch TV or read or what?

P *(Patient)*—I think I read (very quiet voice).

T (approvingly)—At least it wasn't so bad that you weren't able to concentrate while they were gone? (To parents) How long has it been since the two of you were out together, would you say?

M—All three of us?

T—No, I mean just the two of you.

M—Well, since she's been home, I guess, isn't it?

F—Yes, one other time.

M—Oh, yes, we did. Saturday afternoon, a cocktail party. We had my cleaning woman in. She is a very nice woman that just loves young people and children. She offered to come anytime she could and the first time she came she stayed for two hours. But this is the first time in a long time that Barbara stayed alone.

T—Well, that might encourage you to do it more often, do you think? Is that all right with you, Barbara?

F—Yes, she's been very good about letting us go out.

M—Oh, yes.

F—She's very cooperative.

T (to father)—I imagine in some ways you might feel a little roped into this. I am aware that your wife can be pretty persuasive.

M—(laughs).

T—As I told her it was more or less up to me over a period of time to see if we could sell you on the notion that there was something here for you. Otherwise, if you come along, it's just another body in the room and doesn't amount to much. In order to help me get some picture, is there anything currently about your own situation you would like to change? In terms of your responses to other people?

F—The problem is simply to help Barbara get adjusted to the way of life and I think we're making reasonable progress. I think it's going to work itself out all right so I'm not going around under the burden of a terrific problem. Of course, we are facing it and getting along all right.

T—Apart from Barbara's difficulties, everything would be just fine?

F—Yes, I think so. Just the usual problems and it doesn't pay to worry about those.

M—Yes, that's our major problem. It's just a period of readjustment.

T (turning to mother)—What would you say about that?

M—I agree with him one hundred per cent, because they are both the same kind of people, (looking at her daughter) enjoying the same kind of things and if she could just get well and ask for records occasionally to be played and to play the piano together occasionally, well, I agree one hundred per cent.

T—Now I'm not sure that you are agreeing with him. Let me see, you lost me. Your husband was saying there was nothing about himself or his way of life—that everything would be fine if Barbara's problem would be solved.

M—Her being sick. There would be no problem at all if she were well.

F—Sure, we are in agreement on that.

T—Do you feel that if Barbara were well and living somewhere else?

M—No, not necessarily, if she wants to, okay, but right there with us is perfectly okay. We like the same kind of things, the same kind of people. There isn't any problem.

F—Let's not make problems where none exist.

T—Believe me, I don't want to do that either. On the other hand, I don't want to overlook any that do exist. Otherwise I wouldn't be of much use to you. You see, it's a little puzzling to me how Barbara would get sick in the first place if there wasn't something wrong, except for her being sick. I don't quite understand it.

M—Oh, well, perhaps you won't understand the gravity of what she's been through and that she has been sick before this and so on. I feel sure, at least, I hope, that when things get settled down. Now yesterday she had a bad day because she tried to write to her girl friend. She thought the one she had written Sunday, while we were sleep—she had said too much, has asked too many favors. So she struggled all morning trying to do this letter and I went out and left her alone. She got rapidly worse until I sort of persuaded her to stop and rest and then it got too late, about five o'clock, for the mail and so I said it didn't have to be written anyway. I didn't say that in the beginning because she really wanted to write. I let her go along but when I let her write, a whole sort of crisis developed about it. I . . .

T—I don't want to go off on a tangent, but I wonder if this happens very often; that is, I would say there seems to be something in the family situation that contributes to this difficulty.

M—Okay, that's why a doctor has to help me. Maybe I did wrong to let her write the letter, when probably the day would have been different. After all, I want a doctor to help me. I try my best but I just play by ear, sometimes it works and sometimes it doesn't, that's why I want you to help me not to play by ear. But, tell me what I should have done and point out what I should do. Should I have let her gone ahead and write the letter—what would you have done? Everything I've done ever since she was born, I've tried to do my best. I'm willing to do everything for her—if she likes to sleep, I let her—what would you have done? We had a bad day yesterday, not nearly as bad as two other days we had but it was sort of bad. We got the letter yesterday about the settlement. She told you she was willing to sign it. Now it would be a very nice thing if she could sign that today and we could get it in the mail. Because it has nothing to do with the divorce. It is to get it signed so we can get the child. Dr. X said it was important for the child to get settled. Her paternal mother-in-law was taking care of her and it's not very good if the father doesn't come and see her as when I was there in July. She says he has to go and have polio shots for the child and buy her a pair of shoes and the child gets hysterical so we should get the child as soon as possible, provided she will sign. I haven't told Barbara the letter just came last night at 6 o'clock and that was no time to tell her on a bad. . . . Now provided she signs this and we send it right back, then the foster mother has nicely offered to come here and bring the child. She doesn't want the child to have to go through another siege with her father.

You will notice several things about this excerpt. One is the mother's tremendous devotion to her daughter. Notice that as soon as I mentioned that the patient might get well and live some place else, the mother, in a somewhat anxious tone, stated that it was all right if she lived with them. The father's reply to this is very obscure. He states, "Let's not make problems where none exist." What does this mean? Since it is said to me, I assume he means, "Don't try to cause trouble by intervening between my wife and daughter. I have learned not to do this myself." Note also that the parents are able to agree on the topic of their daughter's illness being their major problem. This is the only thing they are able to agree on. Even on this topic, they don't agree completely since there are implications about who is more at fault and about how sick she is and the nature of her illness. The father espouses a more strictly organic cause, whereas the mother feels that the fact that they were away from her so much when she was a child may have played a part.

Notice also that at the end of the excerpt, the mother produces a letter which she wants Barbara to sign. This is typical behavior and one reason why the patient has learned not to trust her parents. My position in this was that I did not know the family well enough to suggest whether Barbara sign or not and that I did not want to take sides. Naturally, the mother denied that there were any sides. I suggested to Barbara that she take the letter home, read it, think about it, then decide whether she wanted to sign it.

Let us consider an excerpt from another family session for comparison. This is a family being seen by John Weakland, in which the patient is a 24-year-old male schizophrenic. The family is interviewed in their home, in a structured situation. In this situation, as with all of our families, we ask them to plan something together and the therapist leaves them alone while they discuss a plan. Next, the therapist asks the question, in the context of a game, "Who is boss in the family?" The game is that each person is allowed to ask a question, much as he would play a card, and then the next individual can comment on the question, as one would play a card of the same suit, or he may trump it or play a different suit. The therapist's question, "Who is the boss in the family?" usually causes all sorts of hell. In the excerpt I am going to play, the therapist says to the mother, father, sister, and patient that they might discuss in detail something they would like to do together. He then leaves the room.

D (*daughter*)—I have a wonderful idea.
M (*mother*)—Bridge.
D—Oh, no, fishing in Guaymas.
M—Oh, would you like to do that?
F (*father*)—What?
D—Go fishing in Guaymas. I think that would be fun. Paul (the patient) likes to fish.
F—He likes to fish.
M—Don't you think it might be a slightly expensive thing to do? Maybe we could fish in the Bay.
D (turning to Paul)—Oh, Paul, you'd get a kick out of this. The M's went fishing down there and caught 45 pounds of sailfish, each of them

nine feet long. It was exciting. They jump out of the water like marlin or something.

(Overlapping) Oh, it is thrilling.

It is, it really is. And they only run in certain seasons. He said that they go down there and . . .

M—Can you eat them?

D—No, I don't think so. You just hang them up and have your picture taken and give them to peasants, probably, or something like that. But it's sort of exciting.

M—How long did it take to land them?

D—What?

M—How long did it take to land them?

D—Oh, forty or fifty minutes, I guess it was.

M (to patient, Paul)—Did you ever fish for sailfish?

P—No, I guess not.

D—I figured that you and I would get a kick out of something like that. Of course, that's my idea (laughs).

P—I'd love it too (laughs).

M—(short laugh).

F—Well, Paul, as Mother said, it's kind of expensive, we were down there once. It's better fishing.

M—It was. . . .

D—You have to go down there at the right time. You didn't go when the fish weren't running, I mean. If you go when the fish are running or something, then you are bound to get something because everybody . . . all the boats are out and what not and they have marlin and sailfish, a few marlin. I don't know if they have something else or not, I don't know, but it would be exciting. I am just suggesting that it might be kind of fun or something like that (laughs). You know my ideas.

F (laughing)—Catalina would be closer and cheaper.

M—Yeah.

D—Or a river or something. I just happened to suggest that because the M's were talking about it so much.

M—What kind of. . . . This is the only time of year I would think. . . . It's not too hot.

D—Oh, yeah. Well, I guess it is as a matter of fact. But if you can go to a place where you're—you know you can catch a fish then you always have a good time.

M—What would you like to do, Paul?

P—What?

M—If you had a choice, what would you like to do?

P—Oh, I don't care.

M—We could plan something together. I was sure Mary was going to say, "bridge."

D—No, I think Paul likes to fish. I know he does, as a matter of fact.

Here you have an interaction that is again typical in that the patient occupies the central position. This is not obvious because he doesn't say much but it is obvious when you break down the communications. It is exactly like the first interview I played for you, in that the only thing on which the family agrees is the patient's illness.

This is shown by the fact that the daughter suggests fishing because that is what her brother likes, it is alleged, and although both mother and father disqualify her remarks as well as each other's, they do return the topic to the patient. One small indication of this is shown by both the mother and father. The mother states to the patient, "*If you had a choice,* what would you like to do?" The point of the game, you see, is to plan something that one might do and the position of the patient is shown by the fact that he has no choice. He then appropriately replies, "Oh, I don't care."

The same sort of thing occurs when Father asks him, "Did you ever fish for sailfish?" Since the patient has always lived at home, except when he was in the hospital, it's difficult to account for the father's not knowing whether or not his son had done anything so spectacular as fishing for sailfish. Notice too, how much the daughter is disqualified with her remarks by the parents and also disqualifies herself. If she states something positively, even if it's only in the framework of a game, she must take it back or else the parents pull the rug out from under her. For example, she is talking about how exciting a time the M's had and the mother asks her if sailfish are good to eat. When she attempts to answer that question, Mother says, "How long did it take to land them?"

I would like to say something more about the sibling question, since I mentioned that the daughter in this family disqualifies herself. But first, let me describe the physical setup we use so that you can appreciate the surroundings and a family's expectations. They are seated around a table with a microphone suspended vertically above it. There is a one-way viewing glass and they are shown the control booth and recording setup. They will be observed from time to time but only at irregular intervals. They are aware that this is research, and they cooperate because they usually have tried everything else and nothing has worked. The patient may be in the hospital or may be living at home. Usually the patient has an administrator, that is, someone to take care of medication, job questions, etc., in order to leave the therapist free to deal with the entire family at once. The various members of our research group, Gregory Bateson, Jay Haley, John Weakland, Bill Fry, Virginia Satir, Jules Rifkin, and several of the psychiatric residents, all have somewhat different ground rules. In my own case, for example, I will see the other members of the family if one member has a good reason for not showing up. However, the absent member cannot be talked about.

Now, to return to the siblings. As you know, there have been several papers written about the siblings of the schizophrenic and the general conclusion has been that they are fine, which proves that schizophrenia is a recessive disorder, since it only hits one in four or so of the siblings. Our own experience has not been that. We find that the patient has had a special relationship to the parents but that the siblings have not escaped completely. It has been difficult to keep them involved in therapy but to the extent that they have come, we find that they are not as unlike the patient as they would like to think. Take the first family I discussed. The patient's brother was described as a paragon of virtue by the parents. He was working for a company in India and we were fortunate enough to get him for three visits. Although initially I had the same impression of him as the parents did, namely, that he could not possibly be more different than the patient, this facade quickly broke down in the family setting. He told me specifically that he worked in India in order to stay away from the family. He had married a girl who had his mother's artistic temperament and who ran him from hell to breakfast. Here is a short excerpt from one of his initial visits. Previously, he had denied having any recollection of his sister whatsoever. However, under direct questioning, he responded to the statement, "We used to fight a lot."

B (brother)—We used to fight a lot. Until, let's see what age, maybe as late as twelve.

T (therapist)—When you were twelve you mean?

B—Yes, maybe not quite that late. Around there, up to there.

T—What kind of thing would you fight about?

B—Probably I was just teasing her. As I recall, I wasn't mature enough to fight about anything specifically. Well, for something to do. Bored.

T (to father)—Do you remember the fighting? What is your impression of what it was about. Did you feel it was a teasing sort of a thing?

B (cutting in)—On my part I don't think there was any animosity. It was a pretty superficial thing, as far as I remember.

F (remains silent).

T (turning to mother)—Do you remember the fighting?

M—Well, all I remember is that on the back seat they used to kick each other's shin sometimes. We didn't have a car until the war because we were always living in New York and didn't need one. And then suddenly, '40, I guess it was '39, we got the car so that made you how old when we had it?

B—About nine. '39, so that makes nine.

M—That was something. I don't ever remember fighting on the boat. You were a bit older then. Couple of years older.

B—You got rid of it in '41. It was around then.

M—He (father) didn't have any interest in boats. He wouldn't have anything to do with it or work on it or do anything with it. I don't think either of them were very interested in the boat. We couldn't go to Europe and I happened just that time to get some extra money. We bought a boat and as I was raised on the water, and used the boats and. . . .

T—Was it some kind of a sailboat?

F—A thirty-two-foot cruiser.

M—And as I talked him into it then he went all overboard for boats much more than I did. I was so tired of it. It was so much work to keep up and neither of us had time to do it and I told him and he still likes boats and I can't bear the sight of them but neither of the children took much to the boat. . . .

T—Quite a bit of boat.

B—Yup, thirty-two foot.

T—Where did you cruise?

B—On Lake Michigan right across the canal, and on the Mississippi River, and St. Paul one summer when we were staying on a farm there.

M—We took them from the Mississippi down.

T (to Barbara)—Well, was this the summer that you were in that camp you've spoken of?

M—(cutting in) Yes, Minnesota. And Barbara came home feeling pretty low. . . .

B—(cutting in) It was during the war and. . . .

M—Minnesota it was. They were staying in Minnesota. So this summer we went up and brought them back in the sailboat.

T—Well, you had the cruiser too?

B—Yeah.

T—You had the sailboat at the time, though?

M—No.

B—Also the cruiser.

M—Of course. We didn't go out all the time but we had fun.

T—You had the cruiser before. . . .

F—Sold the cruiser.

M—That's right, the sailboat.

B—Didn't get the cruiser either until we came back from Europe in '39 or '40.

M—'40. But we couldn't take it through the locks so it had to be the cruiser.

B—Well, now (tentatively) every summer we were in a sort of camp-farm or farm-camp something like that.

M—It's always been *that he's wanted to* (firmly looking at her son).

B—Well, yeah, as she got older (looking at sister).

T—Whatever that means (puzzled at switch in topic).

M—Well, then she didn't go. Well, then she didn't go because he continued to go and she didn't. Well, kid's stuff. I hate to talk about this.

B—Well, as I remember, all through this I don't think Barbara played a very big part in my life, well not a conscious part, because I really had difficulty in recalling her, how she acted and how she felt and so on to the age of twelve or so.

T—You might have been a little less close than some brothers and sisters are?

B—Perhaps.

M—Age difference was about three years and three months.

B—Well, as I recall, I don't think she was particularly happy in this period. When we were always together up until eleven or twelve. These summer camp sessions and other times.

T—And she would not be apt to let you know that she was pretty unhappy. So I wonder what cues you picked up to tell how she felt?

B—Well, we were usually at different camps . . . it's hard to remember.

You notice how confused the discussion is. Yet, at several points, the mother speaks up rather loud and clear. This occurs especially in two places, one, when the brother states that every summer, he and his sister were in some sort of a camp and the mother replies that he wanted to. When he switches to his sister from himself, his mother again firmly states that this is a forbidden topic. The brother complies by saying that he doesn't recall much about his sister. I might mention that during the brother's third visit with us, he got into quite a tangle with his mother over the exact circumstances of his marriage. He indicated at this time that he wished he could stay longer because there were problems he would like to get clarified. The parents, however, kept emphasizing that he was short on time.

One of the most rewarding occurrences in family therapy is the concordance between a symptom in the patient and a piece of family interaction that explains the symptom. In this sense, I am stating that schizophrenia or schizophrenic symptoms are adaptive behavior. For example, Barbara's parents complained more about her indecisiveness than about anything else. Evidently, it is a problem when she gets up in the morning as to what she will wear and everything else in the day becomes a similar crisis. When one listens to the sessions, it is striking that when Barbara makes a decision, the parents refute it in some fashion and then she backs out. Yet, they in no way see themselves as having anything to do with her indecision. One striking example was an incident in which a friend of her ex-husband was going to visit them. The mother implied that this was a friend of Barbara's although it had been the mother, in fact, who had invited this girl to stay with them. Barbara exhibited some paranoid symptoms, speaking about spies, and the mother wrung her hands and said, "She's getting worse." In that session, I asked Barbara, "Are you talking about Genevieve acting as a spy for your husband? That she is going to tell him what is going on in the house and whether she approves of the way you treat your child, etc.?" To this, Barbara was able to reply quietly, "Yes." The parents keep insisting that this was a friend of hers, that it was a silly idea, but I suggested that since the divorce was not final, and since the husband might ask for the custody of the child, perhaps it was not silly to look on Genevieve with suspicion. I suggested that they have her stay in a nearby motel, rather than in an already crowded house. They also had no idea of how long she would stay because they failed to clarify this.

The parents felt that to have her stay in a motel would be inhospitable, and I asked Barbara what she thought. She said, "It would be simpler." She then looked at her parents and stated, "I suppose some people would see it as inhospitable." So the father immediately stated, "You see, she agrees with me. She thinks it would be inhospitable." I then stated: "Well, I thought she said: 'It would be simpler,' but let's play it back." One of the advantages of having a tape setup is that we can play back into the room through an external speaker and check what was said. We don't do this very often because it makes all of us too tape recorder conscious. However, I thought it was worthwhile on this occasion. I had to run that piece back three times before the mother and father could hear Barbara say, "It would be simpler." The father couldn't hear it at first because he kept saying, "She agrees with me." The mother couldn't hear it because she kept saying, "I sound like a man, I sound like a man." This was the first occasion on which she had heard her own voice.

Another example of this kind of thing is a patient of John Weakland who spoke very little, saying mostly, "I don't know," or "Mental illness is all a matter of physics and chemistry." The parents constantly undercut anything that he said so that he had reason for feeling, "I didn't know." And the mother on one occasion literally stated that mental illness is a matter of physics and chemistry. One amusing incident occurred some months after family therapy had been started, when the patient was much improved. We felt this was because the parents were talking about their own relationships and the patient was learning some family matters for the first time. The heat was off him, so to speak. Then mother accidentally discovered that the administrator had put the patient on chlorpromazine about the time that his apparent improvement began. Immediately she claimed that it was the drug and not the family sessions that caused the change. The dosage was small and we thought it could not account for his change, but there was no way of proving it. However, one day, a nurse in going through his bedside table found a huge mound of tablets that he had been collecting over months. He had not taken any. I don't know whether the patient was clever enough to play it this way, but it had quite a surprising effect on his parents.

Perhaps one of the most impressive things about family therapy is the rigidity of the family structure and the difficulty that is encountered when the patient makes a change for the better. An improvement in the patient's symptoms may be very detrimental to the parents, for the patient himself may have to renege on his getting better. With the young man I was just talking about, there was a striking episode in which it became clear that he was responding violently to the tendency of his ward doctor to forget about promises that he had made. The therapist then brought this up in the context of knowledge he had about the parents having reneged on promises. Immediately the patient got very upset and angry, swore at the therapist, and told him that he was crazy, that he was dangerous, and didn't know what he was doing. This tape was played at the next session to show the patient and his parents how afraid of them the patient was. When the patient responded that "mental illness is all a matter of physics," the mother commented, "I agree with him that it's all a matter of physics." Attempts to clarify what she meant became exceedingly vague. She made general statements like, "Well, you know, what you read in newspapers." She thus stopped any attempt on her son's part to stand up to them, and this was followed by an increasing emphasis on both parents' parts on the importance of not being rude. This topic was stressed so much that the therapist finally had to say on one occasion, "Look, you have a choice. You can either choose between rudeness and letting your son stay sick." The mother replied, "I don't think there is any choice. If he is rude, there is no sense in being well." This sort of thing is very difficult to break through. I mentioned earlier that we use a structured situation during our filming sessions which includes the question, "Who's in charge of the family?" or "Who's boss of the family?" The difference in response to this question between the stable, unsatisfactory families and more average families is very striking. For example, here is the response to this question in Barbara's family:

T (therapist)—Anyway the idea I want to throw out to you now is the question, "Who is in charge of the family?"

F (father)—(Slight laugh) Well, you could only answer this question, uh, if you ask who is in charge of what aspects of the family. It's a very simple question. Why, my wife is rather obviously in charge of what goes on in the household from day to day but, uh, I'm in charge of the check book.

M (mother)—(slight laugh).

F—In the many questions connected with the more practical aspects. . . .

M—I guess that's very . . . (slight laugh). Naturally, I do the marketing and see that we eat well because I like to eat well. (Ends with slight laugh.)

F—(slight laugh).

M—And then I take his shirts to the cleaners and his laundry to the cleaners and see that he has clean shirts and pants.

F—Yes.

M— . . . cleaners. And his laundry to the cleaners and sees that he has clean shirts and pants are pressed and whatnot and there are a good many parties and things I arrange, not however, without consulting my husband first.

F—Hmmm.

M—Because he likes to be consulted on such things. Any serious amount

I spend, of course, I wouldn't think of going out and doing it even without consulting him.

   T (to patient)—Do you have any comments on who is in charge of the family?

   P—(in rather low voice) My mother keeps things going.

You will notice how tentative and cautious the parents are in defining each other's roles. They usually manage to keep things so literal that they are difficult for interpretation. You will notice also that Barbara's remark is obscurely clever. "My mother keeps things going." That is a difficult remark to argue with and yet it could be a loaded remark. We find that these patients are capable of clever bombshells which have little to do with brain deterioration.

   I would like to conclude by saying that our work is far from complete. Although we have studied a number of schizophrenic families and a good bit of data on them, we need many more control studies. We need normal families, delinquents, etc., and then we will be in a better position to describe the uniqueness of the schizophrenic family. I am sure that someone will ask, "Couldn't the parents' response be because of the patient's illness?" This cannot be answered with finality until we have longitudinal studies. My present opinion is that mother, father, and child are caught in a reverberating circuit. None escapes wholly, not even the siblings, and there are a number of reasons why the child who becomes schizophrenic is the chosen one.

The Context of Psychotherapy

by Rollo May, Ph.D.

I SHOULD LIKE to make clear at the outset the relation of my remarks here to what is called existential psychology and psychiatry. I am trained in psychoanalysis in the neo-Freudian school, but I have been all my life one who believes that the nature of man itself must be understood as a basis for our science and art of psychotherapy. Therefore, I valued greatly the existential emphases long before I heard about the modern movement in Europe. I am not an existentialist in the European sense. I think we in America have to develop approaches that are indigenous to our own experience, that we must contribute to what we need in our own situations—an attitude in itself which is the only "existential" one, in my judgment.

There are several emphases in the movement known as existentialism that I think are of great value, and which will be of increasing value in the future development of psychiatry and psychology. The phenomenological and existential emphasis in the fields of psychiatry and psychology has, as you know, been prominent in Europe for several decades. Whether one likes the terms or not, the issues leading to that development need to be faced more and more directly. Let me begin with three emphases in the existential psychoanalytic approach.

The first emphasis that this approach makes is a new way of seeing the reality of the patient, called phenomenology. The phenomenological method has been prominent on the continent of Europe since the work of Edmund Husserl.* It is essentially and in simplest terms the

*Gordon Allport (1955) makes the distinction between the Leibnitzian tradi-

endeavor to take the phenomenon as given. It stands against the tendency in western culture, particularly in the Anglo-Saxon countries, to explain things by referring exclusively to their causes. When, in teaching my classes of psychologists and psychiatrists in New York, I cite an example of neurotic or psychotic behavior and ask what it means, the answers almost always have to do not with what it means but *why* the patient does it. "He does this *because—*" and "The genesis of this is . . ." are the usual phrases. One tends then to assume that if we have a causal explanation, or if we describe how things develop, then we have described the thing itself. This is an error. For example, if I ask, "What is shame?," nine out of ten answers will probably deal with why shame develops. They may not tell anything about what shame is. The phenomenologists hold that we must cut through this tendency in the West to think we understand things if we know their causes, and to find out and describe instead what the thing is as a phenomenon —the experience, as it is given to us, in its "givenness"; this is not to rule out causation and genetic development, but rather to say the question of why one is what one is does not have meaning until we know what one is.

The second emphasis in the existential psychoanalytic approach is the emphasis that *all* ways of understanding men, all methods of psychotherapy are based on some presuppositions, and each approach needs to examine continually these presuppositions. The point comes out clearly in an exchange of correspondence that is now quite famous; I propose to read parts of it to you from the little book called *Sigmund Freud—Reminiscences of a Friendship* (Binswanger, 1957). This is the correspondence between Ludwig Binswanger, a leading existential psychiatrist, and his close and dear friend, Freud. Binswanger, incidentally, was the only man who remained in close friendship with Freud and with whom Freud differed radically. Binswanger was invited by the Vienna Society of Medical Psychology to give an address at the eightieth birthday celebration of Freud. He delivered a classical paper, unfortunately not yet translated into English, in which he held that Freud had advanced the understanding of man as a part of nature more than anyone since Aristotle, but that Freud dealt with *homo natura*, that is, natural man, man in what the Germans call the *umwelt*, the environment, the natural world of drives and instincts. But Freud, Binswanger continued, did not deal with man in the *mitwelt*, that is, man as fellow man, in interpersonal relationships; nor did Freud deal

---

tion and the Lockean. In the countries in which the former is dominant, phenomenology has been the dominant method; in the countries where the latter has been dominant, such as England and the United States, the methods tend to be more behavioristic and operational.

with man in relation to himself, namely the *eigenwelt*. Hence, art, religion, love (in its normal sense), creativity, and other activities of man in which he transcends the simple natural world environment, are not adequately dealt with in Freud's psychoanalysis. Freud, because of age and infirmity, did not attend the meeting; but on reading the address, he wrote a letter to Binswanger in which he stated his appreciation, but said, "Naturally, for all that you have failed to convince me." And then Freud added, "Probably our differences will be ironed out only after centuries." Binswanger then wrote in his book, "As can be seen from the last sentence of Freud, Freud looked upon our differences as something to be surmounted by empirical investigation, not as something bearing upon the transcendental conceptions that underlie all empirical research." The word *transcendental* is a red flag in America. I propose to substitute the word *ontological*. Binswanger meant that the real differences between him and Freud are not differences that are to be settled by continuous empirical research, but rather differences having to do with the *assumptions and presuppositions that underlie all empirical research*. Binswanger pointed out that Freud finds it impossible to conceive of the fact that all research is based upon presuppositions.

The critical battles between approaches to psychology and psychoanalysis in our culture in the next decades, as always, will be on the battle ground of the image of man. That is to say, the conception of man which underlies the empirical research. The error Binswanger attacked is no more clearly illustrated than in the assumption so prominent in America that somehow scientific research is the one thing that has no presuppositions. It is as though one could stand outside one's own skin and perch on some Archimedes point, and have a way of surveying experience that does not itself depend upon the assumptions that one makes about the nature of man, or the nature of whatever one is studying.

Freud was a child of the modern Western age in this respect, and in this error. Every approach in psychotherapy or empirical research unavoidably has its assumptions and presuppositions. Every scientific approach is historically conditioned, just as are religious or artistic approaches of whatever kind; and we can approach objectivity only to the extent that we analyze the presuppositions on which we stand.

The physicists, such as Heisenberg, point out that the physicist must define himself as the point from which he studies phenomena. He must define himself as part of his experiment. If this is true in theoretical physics, how much more must it be true in psychology that our presuppositions are already part of our research and part of our psychotherapy. The error that comes from not realizing this seems to me to be shown most vividly in the present contradictory, and to my mind, deteriorating form of many psychoanalytic concepts. Take, for example, the concept of ego. In traditional psychoanalysis, this is the organizing principle in personality, the principle by which some union of the different aspects of personality is achieved in consciousness. "The ego," says Freud, "controls the avenues of motor center." And he goes on to describe it as that point where there would be in the individual some potential conscious unity.

Of late years, psychoanalysts in the Freudian tradition have been pointing out that there are many different egos in the same person.

They hold, for example, that there is the "observing portion of the ego," and there is the "repressing portion"; the "reality ego," the "pleasure ego," and so forth. Some of my highly intelligent colleagues in New York now speak of "multiple egos" within the same person. And they refer to normal, not neurotic people. What is odd is the adding of layer on layer to this poor ego that Freud, to begin with, said occupies a most difficult position, buffeted by unconsciousness on one side, and the demands of the world on the other. This decking it in new clothes does not change the nature of the original concept. I think this idea of multiple egos is a contradiction in terms. The very meaning of ego, namely, the unifying principle, has vanished. The error is not in the clinical observations, but rather in the concept itself. The very principle of unity is destroyed. All of this demonstrates that we must ask the question on a deeper level, namely, "At what point is the person himself conscious of the fact that he is these different egos?" At what point can one be aware that one is the being who has these various tendencies—moods, pleasures, realities, or what not? Now, at the point where one can ask the question, "How may I be conscious of the fact that I am the being of whom these different egos are an expression?", one is asking the question on the ontological level. I do not think we can have any consistency in our psychoanalytic development or research until we can ask the question on this level, the question that underlies the specific components. The problem always, when dealing with components of behavior, is what assumption does one make by which one selects these components, and in what form does one unite them? One must unite them in some way or other. One must assume some form of relationship between them, and this is a point that requires an investigation of the underlying conceptions which are assumed.

The third emphasis of the existential psychoanalytic approach stems directly from the first two. You will pardon me if I reintroduce the technical term, *ontology*. Ontology means the study of being, the science of being. All I have said so far with respect to phenomenology and the question of the presuppositions on which our research and understanding of psychotherapy are based, pushes us toward the problem of ontology. The existential approach assumes that we must ask the question of the nature of the man as man.

Permit me to begin after this introduction as I would begin in my own thinking, namely, with the scientific unit of study in psychotherapy. It is a very curious situation when one comes to think about it, that somebody comes to a therapist's office and sits there in a chair within this strange world of four walls, with some expectation that he may be helped. How would one describe the unit of study in that situation? Does one describe it as a patient with a problem—a problem of flunking out of college, inability to love or marry, or what not? I don't think one would say that, for that would be the oldtime way of defining a patient as a problem—speaking of the "gall bladder on the seventh floor," as some of my medical patients say is still done in some hospitals. This depreciates the situation radically. Shall we say, secondly, that here is a patient who is hysterical or compulsive, psychotic or neurotic, with such and such symptoms? This is more often the form of description in our day, but is this not also partial and therefore inadequate? It implies that we do not see him as a person but that we are thinking in terms of these diagnostic categories about him which are the spectacles through which our perceptions are sieved.

Thirdly, should we say, here is this person who has a problem and comes to the therapist because he wants to get well? This gets closer to the real situation. But it is also precisely what we don't know; we cannot know that this person wants to get well. What we can be sure of is that this is precisely what he is ambivalent about; he comes needing to remain ill until other aspects in his existence are changed. All we can say is that he comes in conflict and that his motives are very much confused.

What we must say concerning our unit of study is only this: we have two persons in a given space, in a given world. (By world here is meant the classical sense of the structure of meaningful relationships.) These two people, patient and therapist, have different motives for being here. We do not know the motives of the patient; he got here, however, and therefore, there is some meaningful act involved. We can only say that he, like all forms of life, seeks to preserve some center, and we assume he is here in the process of doing that.

I want here to draw one ontological proposition from what I have said thus far. I propose this as a characteristic of all human beings with whom one deals. They are potentially *centered in themselves*, no matter how much that centeredness is distorted in conflict. They also have the character of self-affirmation, that is, the need to preserve their *center.* This I propose as an ontological characteristic of man as man. Here, Paul Tillich's (1952) concept of the *courage to be* is of fundamental importance. Tillich as you know, holds that if we do not have courage, we lose being. Man is the particular creature in nature whose being depends upon his courage; and if he does not affirm his being, he gradually loses it.

The second thing to be noticed about the patient who has come to the therapist, is that here immediately is a relationship. Nothing goes on between the patient and the therapist outside of this relationship, even in anticipation when the therapist or patient thinks of the meeting. In the second place, therefore, we can deduce the proposition that the patient, like all other beings, is always in process of relationship. Concretely, that is, he *has the need and possibility of going out from centeredness* to participate in other beings. He is now struggling with the possibility of participating with the therapist. Now, this going out always involves risk; if the organism goes out too far, it loses its centeredness, its identity; but if the organism does not go out at all, growth is blocked, development is impossible, and shrinking of the organism (ultimately to death) is the result.

We note immediately that the neurotic problems which Freud described are pictures of people who were so afraid of losing their own conflicted center that they refused or were unable to go out. They held back rigidly, and lived in narrowed reactions and shrunken psychological world space. This is the typical picture of neurotic inhibitions.

Thus far we see that sickness and health, and specifically the neurosis, have a quite different meaning from what is generally given them in our society. From the ontological approach that I have suggested, we see that sickness is precisely the method that the individual uses to preserve his being. The symptoms are methods of shrinking the range of his world in order that the centeredness of his life may be protected from threat. Sickness is a way of blocking off aspects of the environment so that the patient may then be adequate to the remainder of his world. We cannot assume in the usual over-simplified way that the patient automatically wants to get well; we must assume, rather, that he cannot permit himself to give up his neurosis, to get well, until other conditions in his existence and his relation to his world are changed. This indicates immediately the inadequacy of the concept that neurosis is a failure of adjustment. Neurosis is precisely the opposite; it is a method of adjustment, and the trouble is that it is all too successful; it is a method of adjustment to a curtailed world. Neurosis is a creative activity which has within it the creative potential of the individual that must in one way or another be shifted to the constructive side of life in a process of his overcoming his problems. Neurosis is a creative way of adjusting to a world, and it has within it the constructive potentialities which we hope to call forth in psychotherapy.

The next thing we observe about this patient who now sits in front of the therapist, is that he is participating with the therapist on a level of *awareness*, and, as I shall indicate in a moment, a level of self-consciousness. I want to talk first about awareness as the fourth onto-logical characteristic. I use awareness now as a characteristic that is shared by forms of life other than human. My dog will leap away if you raise a stick; he is certainly aware of the physical threat to his centeredness. The biologist von Eüxkull has described how different organisms have different blue-prints; he calls them action plans and perception plans with respect to their worlds. The trees and plants are relatively tied to their particular worlds; animals possess a greater degree of freedom with respect to the world; and human beings have the greatest degree of freedom of all. (Freedom here is described as world-openness.) This range increases with the range of awareness, that is, the range of possibilities in relating to the world.

The distinctive form of awareness in human beings is *self-consciousness*. I want to suggest here that the tendency to substitute the term "awareness" for "consciousness" is to my mind ill-advised. Awareness more easily fits the conventional scientific framework; it is more amenable to being broken into components, to be studied and experimented with in discreet situations and in models of mechanisms in animals and man. Whereas consciousness is characterized by the fact that if one breaks it into components, one loses what one is studying. The word, "awareness," comes from the root Anglo-Saxon term, *gewaer*, which in turn comes from *waer*, which refers in this whole family of terms to knowledge of external threats—that is, knowledge of danger, of enemies, knowledge requiring defensive strategies. The siblings of this term, "aware," are the terms "wary" and "beware." Awareness is the right category which Howard Liddell uses in his studies of so-called animal neurosis. He calls it their vigilance; he described the seal, for example, in its natural habitat, lifting its head every ten seconds to survey the horizon to make sure that no Eskimo with bow and arrow is sneaking up on it. Liddell identifies this vigilance as the primitive, simple counter-part in animals of what in human beings is anxiety.

Consciousness comes from the Latin term, *conscire*, and refers to knowledge which is felt *inwardly*, that is, to *knowing with*, not only with others (which is a secondary form of it), but primarily with oneself in the sense of consciousness of the fact that one is the being who has the world. I can be aware of this podium from which I speak.

This is awareness and must be studied as such. Consciousness refers rather to the fact that *I can be aware that I am the being who has this podium.* Consciousness is related to my conception of myself as the being who deals with these ideas which he endeavors to make clear to you. It is a term that in my judgment must not be lost. It is a term that deals with the central ontological characteristic that constitutes the self in its existence as a self, namely, the experience that one can be aware that one is the being who has the world. I am using consciousness in the sense Kurt Goldstein (1939) used it to describe the "capacity to transcend the immediate situation," to use abstractions and universals, to have language and symbols, and, on the basis of these capacities, the capacity to survey in one form or another the greater range of possibilities (greater compared to the rest of nature) in one's relating to oneself, his fellows, and his world. In this sense, human freedom has its ontological basis and must be assumed in all psychotherapy.

Let us at this point define the term "unconsciousness." Certainly one of Freud's great contributions was the emphasis upon the vast reservoir of hidden depths in human potentiality, fears, anxieties, early experiences, hopes, instinctual drives, etc. In this, Freud broke with the Victorian compartmentalization of the human being which saw only rational man, who supposedly controlled by repression all other aspects of the self. Now, the great gain of Freud's in describing the unconscious must not be lost. But I think the description itself is inadequate. I think that unconscious experience can be understood only on the basis of our concept of consciousness. We must posit that the patient comes as a unity, no matter how clearly we can see that various neurotic symptoms have been blocked off and thereby have a compulsive effect upon him. The "unconscious" is the experiences that the person cannot permit himself to actualize. The questions in understanding unconscious phenomena are, "How does the individual reject or accept his possibilities for being conscious of himself and his world?" "How is it possible that he should shut out something which on another level he knows, and even also on this level *knows that he knows?*" The thing that continually surprises patients in psychoanalysis, and even sometimes surprises the analyst, is that when a buried memory or experience which has been subjected to radical repression into unconsciousness erupts into consciousness, the patient will maintain that he has the strange experience of having known it all the time. On the level of awareness, this makes no sense at all. He has not been able to be aware of it, but he has on another level known it all the time. The chief problem that we should set ourselves, then, is not the mechanical one of what particular trauma blocked off the experience;

rather, it is the question what is going on in this person that he cannot let himself fully experience. "I am I; I am this being with all the potentialities and possibilities that constitute this being, this I."

I want now to demonstrate the problem of the emergence and meaning of consciousness by referring to the Oedipus myth and complex. The Oedipus situation was taken as basic in Freud's work, in the classical analytic tradition. It is present in practically all other schools in some form or other. In Freud's formulation, it refers to the sexual love attraction between a child and the parent of the opposite sex. The child thereby experiences guilt, and fear of the parent of whom he is the rival, and particularly in the case of boys, fear of castration. Fromm refers to the Oedipus conflict of the growing child with the authority of his parents. Adler makes it a power struggle. All the various schools have their own particular definition of the Oedipal situation.

Now Freud assumed in his Oedipal description a tragic picture of human experience. The infant was cannibalistic, driven by primitive instinctual demands. Freud's view of the infant was identical with that of St. Augustine, who said, "The innocence of the child consists of weakness of limb." Freud's tragic view that in the Oedipal situation there really is a conflict between beings who on some level are engaged in destroying each other, is to my mind closer to the truth of the Oedipal situation than the general view in America. Our view is that of Rousseau's—that the infant is not a cannibal but either an angel, if he is our own, or potentially an angel if he is the child of somebody we are counseling. He is potentially an angel if only these mothers and other cultural representatives would feed him with more care to his real needs and train him correctly. In the Oedipus conflict, as taken over in our thought in this country, the tragic aspect, by and large, is omitted. But the tragic quality is precisely the reason that Freud hit upon the Oedipal myth to begin with. I think it is a considerable loss that the tragic emphases that are present in Freud are the things generally thrown overboard first of all when psychoanalysis crosses the Atlantic Ocean.

I want to propose that there is another approach. This is the approach of understanding the Oedipal situation as the tragic conflict within the person and in his relations to his world and other human beings involved in the emergence and development of consciousness of oneself. If one looks back at the drama itself, in Sophocles or in other forms given to us in its long cultural history, one will discover that the drama has nothing whatever to do with sexual conflicts or conflicts about killing the father. These are all long done and past. In Sophocles' drama, for example, Oedipus has married his mother; he is very happy and comfortable in Thebes. The only question is, shall Oedipus recognize what he has done? The tragic issue is the issue of seeing the reality and the truth about oneself.

The drama, one will recall, opens with the curse on Thebes. In order to have that curse lifted, Oedipus, the present king of Thebes, must find out who killed Laius, the previous king. Oedipus, a very good king, calls Teresius, the blind seer. (In the drama, Teresius is often associated with the role of a psychoanalyst, not because he is blind, but rather because not seeing externally is symbolically related to the capacity for a greater degree of sensitivity within. This is the meaning of "the blind prophet." Blind men, not distracted by the things they see, are, in this symbolic form, supposed to develop a greater sensitivity to truth in a psychological and spiritual sense. I hope this will carry over to psychoanalysts and psychologists and psychiatrists without our having necessarily to be physically blind.) Now Oedipus asked Teresius who was guilty. Teresius said, "How terrible it is to know. I will not bring remorse upon myself and upon you." Oedipus insisted, regardless of consequences, that he must know who killed Laius. Then, step by step through the drama, we see an absolutely marvelous portrayal of the struggle, ultimately tragic, of a man, Oedipus, who first finds out the truth about his objective situation, the death of his father, and then discovers the truth turned inward, becoming truth about himself. He senses very soon that there is a mystery that surrounds his own birth, and that Jocasta, his mother, whom he has married without knowing the relationship, is somehow associated with the mystery of his birth. (It will be recalled that he had been taken out by Laius and abandoned on the hillside because of the oracle's prediction that he, Oedipus, would kill his father.)

In the course of the drama, Jocasta suddenly becomes aware that Oedipus is her son; then she grasps the terrible knowledge that confronts him and tries to dissuade him. She cries, "But why should men be fearful, o'er whom fortune is mistress and foreknowledge of nothing sure? Best take life easily as a man may. For that maternal wedding have no fear, for many men ere now have dreamed as much, but he who by such dream sets nothing has the easiest life of it." Let me interject here that all too often our psychoanalytic and our psychiatric and our psychological relationships with patients are of the nature of the Jocasta's speech. What she really is saying is, "Be adjusted. Do not take dreams as reality. Many people ere now have dreamed as much, but by such dreams set nothing."

Oedipus, however, would not stop at this point; his dreams are his being. He says in effect, "I must have the courage to face the truth whatever it is." And then Jocasta cries out, "Don't seek it, I am sick and that is enough. Wretch, what thou art, oh mightest thou never know!" Oedipus answers, "I will not harken not to know the whole, break out what will, I shall not hesitate." Then he concludes, "I must know who I am and where I am from." Toward the end of the play, he finds the old shepherd who had found him as a baby up on the hillside and kept him alive. The shepherd, being called in answer to Oedipus' question, moans, "Oh, I am now at the horror, now to speak." And Oedipus answers, "And I to hear, but I must hear, no less."

Then he does learn the tragic truth, that he is the one who killed his father and married his mother. Thereupon, he plucks out his eyes, the organ of seeing and recognition. Finally, he exiles himself. I think this theme of exile is also very important: he was exiled as a baby; this is where the tragedy started. Now, he exiles himself. I think the tragedy of exile, or ostracism in our day, the tragedy of a man alienated from his fellow men, is very close to the real psychological problems of contemporary men in the middle of the twentieth century.

The drama is of the tragedy of seeing the reality about oneself, confronting what one is and what one's origin is; the tragedy of man knowing and facing in conscious self-knowledge his own destiny. Let me illustrate this by citing a dream of a patient of mine.

The dream is one of a long series, and therefore it is in truncated form. I hope, nevertheless, it will be clear. It is a dream of an intelligent, sensitive woman of thirty, who was greatly blocked in her professional activity and in her sexual role (she had been married and divorced and had a good deal of sexual experience, but never had experienced orgasm). Her parents were well-to-do intellectuals who had left the girl most of the time and gone to Europe from her birth until she was three. She had very strong feelings of isolation, anxiety, and hostility. Early in life she had learned to play roles in order to be accepted. She had a very obvious and pronounced Oedipal relation to her father, who, now dead, had been a gifted and weak man; and the patient also had a very strong rivalry with her mother.

In the dream she met her former husband, who had come back from Europe married, in a dentist's office. Two of his front teeth were missing. He introduced her to his new wife and two children. She realized that she could not have been that kind of wife to him, and she accepted and affirmed the fact that he was happily married now. The second scene of the dream had her standing *vis à vis* some feminine person, and she was feeling and playing a masculine role; then she was *vis à vis* some masculine person and she was feminine. She thought to herself in the dream, "I have always tried to be these different things." In the third scene in the dream, as she put it, "I was with another person, a man with whom I could really be myself; there were no roles anymore. I could be my feminine self. It was a tremendous experience. Then I found myself looking down into a stream, and I experienced a great anxiety; I had the feeling I would have to jump into the river and commit suicide."

Her associations to the dream were fairly obvious. The first part showed that she now could accept her husband's marriage; the two missing front teeth referred she said, to the fact that she had castrated him, which she had. (Fortunately, the two missing teeth could be fixed; I think the dentist's office—incidentally, something that comes up not infrequently with patients—is the office of the psychoanalyst to whom her husband goes.) In the second part of the dream she was simply trying on these roles for size as though she were saying to me, "This is what I have been doing all my life." The third scene relates the tremendously important experience of being herself, throwing off the roles with great relief involved. All of this she saw in the dream. But what she could not understand was the terrible anxiety, the feeling that she would have to jump into a river and commit suicide. This was an exceedingly constructive dream, a radical landmark in her psychotherapy. It actually foreshadowed a breakthrough in several ways, for example, in her capacity to have orgasm.

Now, why all the anxiety? Well, one could say she was giving up her defenses, giving up the roles by which she had been able to survive since her early childhood, roles that were absolutely essential to her. One could also say she was cutting through rationalizations and illusions about herself, for example, in the admission that she castrated her husband. But, on a more basic level, something else was taking place in this dream. It was a tragic recognition of fate itself—I borrow the word fate from Freud, and I use it now in the sense of the Oedipus drama. When one is able to be aware in his self-consciousness that he is the person who is the conscious responsible being, there comes pronounced anxiety, a potentially tragic anxiety. It is on this last point that many will not agree with me. I think it is fair to say that a good many, if not most, therapists would tend at this point to reassure the patient. The patient's anxiety is obviously over being herself, and the tendency would be to say, "Yes, you have had to cut out all of these roles and these methods that you have used to gain security; but now you can be yourself and you do not need to be anxious about it."

I propose, on the contrary, that she does need to be anxious about it; and that this is precisely the constructive aspect of the mature, tragic anxiety that is shown in the drama of Oedipus. The symbol of suicide, the capacity to confront death, is placed in a central position in the existential approach in psychology and psychiatry. These things are not negations, though they are a tragic aspect of life. The capacity to confront death is a prerequisite to growth, a prerequisite to self-discovery and self-consciousness. I would take the orgasm as a psycho-physical symbol. It is the experience of the capacity to abandon oneself, to give up present security in favor of wider experience. It is not by accident that this experience often appears symbolically as a partial death and rebirth; and it should not surprise us that this capacity to "give oneself up," to "risk oneself," should have had as one of its manifestations her being able after the dream to experience sexual orgasm.

If one looks further into the typical dream, one will see a fas-cinating myth involved. Though it is fairly obvious that the man in the third scene of the dream, the man with whom she could be herself, is myself (the Hudson River flows outside my office window in New York), there is something much more profound occurring than what can be described in the context of a relationship. The second myth involved is the myth of going underwater, being drowned and born again, a myth that comes down in different religions and different cultures, namely baptism. To be drowned in order to be born again—the myth of the positive side of experiencing truth. Sophocles fortu-nately wrote a succeeding play about Oedipus, Oedipus at Colonus, in which the old Oedipus meditates about all of the tragic events that have happened. In doing this, Oedipus experiences the positive side, that is, the reconciliation with himself, the new unity that occurs after the tragic experience of consciousness.

Many will not be happy with that phrase. I prefer to use strong words even though they have many connotations that are misleading. If we want to inquire psychologically what this tragic aspect of con-sciousness means, it is not difficult to describe it fairly convincingly. First, it means certainly to admit what we have done: "If I am Oedi-pus, I have killed my father." We need to admit our destructive atti-tudes and behavior toward people we may genuinely love. Secondly, it means to admit our present motive of hatred and destructiveness. Thirdly, it means cutting through our rationalizations above our own nobility. At this point, we arrive at an existential level, for to cut through these rationalizations implies not only taking responsibility for "what I did yesterday," but responsibility for, "what I shall do and feel and think tomorrow." This attitude implies another corollary, namely, aloneness. At the point where I am aware that I am this being, this one who is acting, I am at a point where nobody else can stand. No matter what the extenuating circumstances, this is *my* hatred and *my* destructiveness; and at this point a man relates to himself in a state of aloneness. I am the only one who can take that responsibility.

This tragic consciousness also implies (and this is the most difficult point of all) that a person recognizes the fact that he never can love

completely the people to whom he is devoted, and there will always
remain some elements of destructiveness. (The emphases that Freud
made here are of great importance.) By the same token, we can never
know absolutely whether a decision we now make is really the right
decision, but, nevertheless, we must make the decision anyway. This
risk inheres in self-consciousness. I think it involves the giving up of
childhood omnipotence; we are no longer God, to put it symbolically.
But we must act as though we were; we must act as though our decisions were right. This is the reaching out into the future that makes
all of life a risk and makes all experience precarious.

Down this line, I think we shall find the most profound meaning of
consciousness. I point it out only briefly, though we could discuss it
endlessly. This is why there is such a close relationship between development of consciousness and psychosis. And when people, in therapy,
go through these emergent levels of consciousness, they often have the
fear of becoming psychotic. I propose these deeper reaches of the
problem of consciousness for further study.

I should like to close with some practical comments about the
goals of therapy. What I have said implies that anxiety and guilt are
never wholly negative phenomena. It implies that some of our general
assumptions about mental health—for example, that mental health consists of freedom from anxiety—are inaccurate. Rather, should not the
approach be, that our goal with respect to anxiety and guilt is not to
wipe them out but to help people, our patients and ourselves, to confront anxiety and guilt constructively? It is sometimes said that in
psychoanalysis at certain points one has to inject anxiety into the
patient; otherwise he basks forever in the warmth of the relationship.
But I propose that we only have to inject anxiety if we have watered
it down to begin with. I think a great deal of our error lies in a tendency to reassure anxiety, to dilute it, and to do the same with guilt
feeling. I believe, rather, that the function of therapy is to give people
a context in which they are able to confront and experience anxiety
and guilt constructively—a context which is a human world, as well as
a real world, of a person's own existence in relation to the therapist.

It may clarify matters if I differentiate between neurotic and
normal anxiety. Neurotic anxiety is anxiety which is inappropriate
to the threat of a situation. Secondly, it involves repression into
unconsciousness. Thirdly, it is expressed in symptom formation.
Fourthly, it has destructive rather than constructive effects upon the
organism. I think the same criteria could be given for guilt feelings,
though the area of guilt feeling is much more controversial.
"Normal" anxiety would now be accepted much as I have described it
to you. But between normal and neurotic guilt feeling, there is

still a battle line. In general, my colleagues do not like my insistance on normal guilt feeling. Normal guilt, in contrast to neurotic, is guilt that is appropriate to the situation. The woman whose dream I cited did castrate her husband, and did hurt him greatly. In the dream she has accepted normal guilt. Secondly, there was no repression into unconsciousness. Her guilt toward her husband for a long time had been simply repressed under the idea that, "Well, he deserves it, look what he does to me." Thirdly, conscious or normal guilt does not involve symptom formation. (It does not involve symptoms of self-righteousness. Repressed guilt shows itself very often in insistence that one is right, in lack of humility, lack of capacity to open to the other person, etc.) Now, normal guilt is associated with admitting that one can know only partially, and involves admitting that what one says always does partial violence to the truth. We can only partially understand each other; this is normal guilt. It helps us to do the best we can in presenting our thoughts to each other, and it also gives us a humility as we communicate that makes us more open to each other and more sensitive. Therefore, fourthly, normal guilt has a constructive effect.

In New York these days, there are discussions about whether we shouldn't say "shame" rather than "guilt." I think that waters it down, and I do not agree that the best word is shame; I think it is guilt. Shame has with respect to guilt somewhat the same relation as fear does to anxiety. Now, if fear is the specific objectified form of reaction to a threat, it can be dealt with as a unit in itself and can be experimented upon; it can be described on the level of awareness, it can be objectified. Fear is removed when the specific external cause is removed. But anxiety is the general, the underlying common denominator of the person's capacity to experience threat, to experience his vicarious situation. I would say, therefore, that anxiety must be the generic term and fear can be only understood as an objectified form of anxiety. I think shame can be understood in relation to a specific incident, say, if I were compulsive and mispronounced a word, I might blush. But we cannot understand that blush of mine unless we are able to relate it to some underlying stratum in me, which then will be the problem of guilt that shows itself in neurotic guilt, probably, in that illustration.

I think that normal guilt must be dealt with existentially, which means that all aspects of experience must be considered. Not only is it reparation in respect to fellow man (the term reparation is too much associated with Buber's mystical Jewish tradition), but I would say rather, an openness. That is, normal guilt can be expressed conceptually by one's being a fellow man, by being open, humble, by loving—if one may use the term in that sense. Normal guilt must be involved in all aspects of experience, and it can only be lived out. One can always be specific about the neurotic aspects of these things, because they are, by nature and by definition, a truncating of experience; but one cannot be as specific about the positive aspects. All one can say is that a person must be open or free to do whatever is involved, and the guilt, must be lived out existentially.

To be able to sit in a real relationship with another human being who is going through profound anxiety, or guilt, or the experience of imminent tragedy taxes the best of the humanity in all of us. This is why we emphasize the importance of the "encounter" rather than "relationship." I think the term relationship psychologizes it. Encounter is what really happens; it is something much more than a relationship. In this encounter I have to be able, to some extent, to experience what the patient is experiencing. My job as a therapist is to be open to his world. He brings his world with him and therein we live for 50 minutes. Learning to do so may be highly taxing; to experience somebody else's anxiety may be extremely painful. It is painful enough to experience one's own, when one has no choice but to experience one's own world. Practically speaking, this is why therapy for oneself is so important; my own psychoanalysis certainly helped me in being able to accept this in patients, not to try to push aside the pain that I must share or the anxiety, or guilt, or tragic possibilities. In addition, it requires that we ourselves be human beings in the broadest sense of the word. This brings us to a point where we can no longer talk about it merely psychologically. It helps us to realize that we also have gone through similar experiences, and though not involved in them now, we know what they mean. This is part of the grandeur and the misery of man, and this is why reading Sophocles and other ancient tragedians, I think, is a very great help for us as psychotherapists.

Our chief concern in therapy is with the potentiality of the organism. The goal of therapy is to help the patient actualize his potentialities. The joy of the process of actualizing becomes more important than the pleasure of discharged energy—though that itself, in its own context, obviously has pleasurable aspects too. The goal is not the absence of anxiety, but rather the changing of neurotic anxiety into normal anxiety, and the development of the capacity to tolerate normal anxiety. The patient after therapy may well bear more anxiety than he had before, but it will be conscious anxiety and he will be able to use it constructively. Nor is the goal the absence of guilt feeling, but rather the transformation of neurotic guilt into normal guilt, together with the development of the capacity to use this normal guilt creatively.

I have proposed here a number of ideas which I realize are left hanging in the air. I have no guilt, however, about the fact that I have left them hanging there. This is what I meant to do. I hope that these ideas will not present concise answers, but rather that they will act, as a leavening in the loaf, to open up existential psychological experiences for others.

Adaptational Psychodynamics

by Aaron Karush, M.D.

THE PSYCHODYNAMIC theory of healthy and disordered behavior which I shall briefly discuss is based upon an adaptational frame of reference. It is a theory that defines the inter-relationships among psychological processes apart from the classical assumptions of instinct and energy.

Let us first consider the different meanings of the concepts of "psychological function" and "psychological structure" which figure so prominently in psychoanalytic theories of ego psychology. "Ego function" describes mental activity that is directly inferred from specific and characteristic forms of behavior, such as perception, memory, etc. These may be called primary ego functions, or, as Heinz Hartmann (1958) has labelled them, "autonomous ego functions." The ego functions associated with pleasure seeking or libidinal drives, with defenses and with aggression, are really combinations of primary functions organized about specific need tensions or drives. Kardiner (1945) has called these organizations of ego functions, action systems. "Ego structure," on the other hand, represents an assumption about the way in which functions are combined and integrated. Structure is, therefore, purely hypothetical; it is a convenient fiction which helps us to visualize, first, how functions are combined and directed toward the achievement of goals; second, the degree of effectiveness the functions display in attaining their purpose; and third, the extent of and reasons for disordered integration of ego functions. A conception of structure reduces itself therefore to a model for describing complex behavioral activity. In that sense, more than one model can conceivably be advanced to depict the same psychological functions. Freud, in fact, did use more than one. His earlier structural hypothesis of conscious and unconscious was replaced by his final structural theory of id, ego, and superego. Rado has suggested a somewhat different structural schema that involves several levels of integration. Regardless of the visualizing model one may prefer, the subject matter of psychodynamics remains the functions of the ego and their integration toward recognizable goals.

When, as therapists, we observe the operation of the ego's functions, we are concerned with a variety of functional organizations or action-systems and follow their development under the impact of changing environmental conditions. The specific ways in which these functions combine to form complex patterns of behavior are determined by experience unique to each person. Some of these experiences can begin with the perception of internal physiological needs, gratification of which brings the individual into critical contact with the significant persons about him. A second group of formative experiences begins with the perception of others and their expectations. Once these external objects are recognized by the young child to be necessary for his security and pleasure, the expectations of others tend to crystallize within the child as learned needs. Such needs do not spring from physiological systems but from the cultural environment. In either case, physiological or cultural needs become focal points for action-systems which, once formed, prove to be repetitive and identifiable. By keeping track of the conditions of life and their impact upon perception, emotion, thought and action, we discover how and why a particular action-system came into being.

In the course of my discussion a special integrative factor has been introduced. Functions and structural models relate to mechanisms. Their meaning for behavior becomes clear, however, only when they are connected with the reasons they are brought into play—i.e., the motivations and their sources. Motivation always presupposes a coexistent need tension or drive that has been created by internal physiological requirements or by external cultural demands.

No behavior can be fully understood unless the motivating needs and the psychological mechanisms by which one reacts to these needs are both taken into account. The question of motivation by needs reminds us that we must combine teleological and causal thinking in psychodynamic theory. There is actually no contradiction in the use of both approaches. Teleological thinking in psychology is essential because the human organism is oriented toward the future.

To grasp the unique meaning of man's behavior, we have no choice but to chart his purposes. Teleological thinking helps us find the problem to be investigated; it is a poor device for explanation, but is useful for reconnaissance. Only causal thinking can explain how problems are created in behavior and how they are resolved.

For a long time, Freudian theory was concerned primarily with explaining the sources and courses of development of motivational forces. The mental mechanisms which Freud (1953) described in *The Interpretation of Dreams*, and which are part of his most important discoveries, did not become the focal point of psychoanalysis until the final revisions of the instinct theory and the renewed interest in the ego. Adaptational theory, as developed particularly by Rado (1956), Kardiner (1945), and Levy (1956), is essentially an ego psychology concerned with mental mechanisms.

Adaptational psychodynamics are based upon the following assumptions:

When need tensions arise, a set of mental operations is induced which leads to an action, real or phantasied, that is designed to produce a temporary state of equilibrium. An endless cycle of homeostatic shifts takes place throughout life. Each operational system of actions brings with it, however, an altered set of conditions: first, perception of the sources of stimulation changes according to the degree of gratification and comfort which has been achieved; second, new memory traces with an emotional charge are laid down; third, an expanded or diminished self-image is created in terms of successful mastery. This self-image consists of thoughts and feelings, pleasurable or painful, about one's resources and abilities to satisfy his needs. How the future will be anticipated depends upon the nature of these three effects of activity that was originally intended to satisfy a need.

From this viewpoint, adaptation becomes the relationship of means to ends. Adaptation and function are, therefore, complementary views of the same thing. The problem of adaptation is the problem of functional efficiency as measured by survival and health. However, this definition of adaptation needs refinement.

Not all activity of living organisms, psychological or otherwise, is to be considered adaptive. Certain properties, such as assimilation, reproduction, and reactivity, distinguish living from non-living matter. They define life itself. It would be tautological to speak of life as an adaptation since adaptation refers to the devices used to carry on life processes under prevailing environmental conditions. The intrinsic properties of living protoplasm can take on a variety of expressions—i.e., they can become specialized and improved in their functioning during evolutionary development to meet the changing demands of the environment. For example, gastric juice is secreted when nose or eyes are stimulated by the smell or sight of food. This is an adaptation concerned with assimilation. Reproduction is a property of living protoplasm, but the emergence of internal fertilization is an adaptation.

The same criteria hold for psychological adaptations of the ego. Psychodynamics of ego functions cannot explain the nature and essence of mental activity that arises out of the essential biochemical and biophysical organization of the central nervous system. Such neurological activity determines the basic capacities for learning, recall, attention, anticipation, motility control, etc. The nature of the processes cannot be explained in an adaptational "psychodynamic theory of the ego." However, *what* is learned, *what* is remembered, *what* is perceived and reacted to, and how these are combined in executive patterns of behavior all reflect the psychological adaptations of the ego.

An exhaustive review of adaptational psychodynamic theory is beyond the scope of this paper. There are, however, certain concepts which relate closely to our understanding of the psychotherapeutic process. Rado has devised a structural model derived from the newer biological theories of emergent development. He postulates a series of levels of psychological integration, each in turn related to a different level of central nervous system organization. The most primitive is the pain-pleasure or hedonic level. Phylogenetically, the hedonic regulation of behavior precedes the appearance of the distance receptors. There is, as yet, no visual, olfactory, or auditory sensory apparatus for sampling the environment. Anticipation and foresight are impossible at this level of integration, since reactions come only after direct contact with a stimulus. The subjective phenomena which in man are associated with pleasure and pain may variously be described as arising from physiological tension states, biogenic tension, or in more classical terminology, from instinctual tensions. In this sense, the hedonic level of integration reflects the psychological aspect of the instincts or drives elaborated in the libido theory.

• The second broad level of integration is the emotional level. Adaptational theory places greater emphasis upon the role of emotional integration than did the classical libido theory. Freud started from his discovery of the basic pain-pleasure organization of behavior and chose the sexual drive as the expression of the pleasure principle that was most accessible to psychological study. He believed that the energy of this drive determined the choice, duration, and distractability, i.e., intensity, of all behavior. The sexual drive, therefore, held supremacy over all the other adaptive integrations which could not resist the influence of sexual pleasure-seeking. Today, we have partially reversed this formulation: the prevailing level of integration determines how sexual gratification will be obtained. Freud stated that affect represents a part of instinct. By contrast, in the adaptational view, emotion rather than instinct is the critical integrative force in behavior.

The emotional level of integration makes its biological appearance with the phylogenetic emergence of the metazoans. Psychologically, in man, it includes four basic affects—love, grief, fear, and rage. The pain-pleasure organization continues, but with greater refinement and efficiency. Emotion becomes possible with the development of distance receptors which permit preventive behavior and allow the organism to alter the environment to gain pleasure or avoid damage. The new element introduced is foresight or the anticipation of future events.

Once the cerebral cortex becomes a dominant feature in the central nervous system, we find that emotions tend to be replaced by corresponding types of thought—fear by apprehensive foresight, rage by angry anticipation, etc. The difference between thoughts and the corresponding primary emotion is that the organism is now able to contemplate future events without being thrown into a heavy state of preparedness for immediate action. This makes possible long-range foresight, as well as that of the immediate future, and increases the range and flexibility of preparatory behavior.

Thought and emotion may be contrasted in another way. The affect level of integration in man continues the self-centered evaluation of events which characterizes the pain-pleasure level. On the thought-level, as affective involvement diminishes, objectivity becomes possible; man can contemplate the world beyond the self-centered post of observation of the emotional level. He no longer evaluates events in terms of himself alone. Most important, his perception of reality changes.

The primacy of reason in man is, of course, far from established. Emotion and thought are intermingled. As a result, there is a constant swing between thought, and its rational view of reality, and emotion, which is rooted in the cruder pain-pleasure evaluation of reality.

Emotional thought is one of the essential ingredients in all psychopathology. It reveals itself in different ways. It is aroused by the perception of danger and expresses therefore the defense or emergency function of the ego. Rado was one of the first to emphasize the emergency function as one of the primary functions of the ego. It operates on three integrative levels—pain-pleasure (hedonic), emotional, and thought.

Pain is the most primitive perceptual signal. Since it occurs after damage to the organism has been sustained, emergency behavior on the pain-pleasure level of integration is in a sense hindsight. Characteristically, the reaction to pain is an attempt at riddance of the source of pain.

The arousal of the hedonic response also sets in motion the other higher integrative levels. Pain not only excites riddance behavior, but it also leads to fear about future development—that is, fear of more pain and damage.

This has far-reaching consequences. The coexcitation of emotional thought integration is responsible for the anticipation of future injury and the subsequent attempts to forestall the feared danger.

Unfortunately, the arousal of emergency behavior in childhood, calls upon instruments for rational inspection of the future which are poorly developed and seldom reliable. Causality tends to be interpreted in terms of concrete connections, that is, by *post hoc, propter hoc* thinking. As a result, the child develops associations to the source of threat and pain which give the pain a much broader and even threatening significance than it should have.

For example, a child is punished for wrongdoing. The actual pain inflicted may be relatively light, but the punishment also signifies disapproval and anger of the parent. The anticipated danger of future repeated punishment now becomes greatly overestimated. It is not simply fear of physical hurt, but is fear of alienation from the parent whose love and care are so essential.

Such an expanded notion of danger leads the child beyond simple avoidance of punishment by flight; instead his goal becomes one of regaining and holding on to the love of mother or father. The child finds it necessary to learn techniques by which to bind his parents more closely to himself. Only in this way can he end his anxiety about alienation from his parents.

What happens if painful apprehension persists? The most primitive emergency response, riddance, may be directed against the sufferer himself. In some instances self-destruction to end intolerable tension may be carried out. More often, additional defenses are called upon to control the riddance impulse. Among them are denial, repression, distortion of the nature of the impulse to injure one's self by projection, and faulty explanation of the reasons for the impulse by hypochondriacal delusions. Repression, which is usually combined with other defensive devices, seeks to alter or erase awareness of the self-destructive impulse. Unfortunately the state of tension may continue even though the true source is unconscious. Not uncommonly, it contributes to the development of intense masochistic behavior. The excitation of emotional thinking in the face of danger has other disorganizing consequences. Anxious thoughts bring with them a sense of helplessness, weakness, and vulnerability. Even if the threatening situation passes, apprehensive thoughts about the return of the danger and the painful experience of helplessness may continue. The new apprehension is concerned with the reappearance of anxiety. Repression of the apprehensive thoughts about the future is a favored emergency defensive mechanism just as with the riddance impulses described earlier. Unfortunately, repression is often imperfect in its action. Daily living tends to expose one repeatedly to the very stimuli which threaten the return of feared dangers. A painful tension may persist and invites a second line of defensive reactions. Without awareness of the true reasons, steps are taken to avoid situations or activities that can arouse anxiety. As a result, opportunities for healthy functioning are given up, in whole or in part. Such inhibition and avoidance are basic ingredients in all psychoneurotic behavior. The effort to achieve security impairs the fruitful use of other ego functions. Ego constriction is always the price of neurotic defenses against anxiety.

When apprehensive or angry thoughts have been repressed, we may speak loosely of "unconscious emotions." We mean that one has become unaware of the nature of his feelings. It is true that the ideas which identify emotion can be repressed and rendered unconscious, but the physiological aspects of emotion cannot be repressed. The tension which accompanies emotion may involve the whole autonomic range of preparation for action and, despite one's lack of awareness, continues to exercise an impetus toward characteristic behavior. The purpose is to rid one's self of the painful tension. Unconscious fear, for example, tends to invite flight or avoidance behavior. As a rule, the true reasons for his behavior remain unconscious to the person who invents rationalizations acceptable to the self.

The same holds true for repressed rage as for fear. Explanations for angry behavior will be advanced that bear little resemblance to the underlying ideas of the emotion. At times, a person becomes aware that he is running away or behaving destructively and will confess helplessly that he does not know why he acts so.

It seems clear that one of the weaknesses in man's psychological organization is his difficulty in controlling emergency emotions by reason. Although deferment of response is one of the great adaptive gains provided by thought level integration, to live continuously with apprehensive thoughts is often more painful and threatening than the original feared danger. It is this defect which invites repression. Although repression is a self-protective emergency device directed at painful thoughts by the emergency function of the ego, it provides security at a high price—the constriction of other ego functions which gratify needs.

One of Freud's lasting contributions was the clinical demonstration of the universal existence of unconscious mental activity. At every conscious level of operation, activity goes on in lower levels as unconscious thought, feeling, and perception. The unconscious levels contain the residua of each person's developmental experiences. They represent storehouses of previous childhood patterns of perception, emotion and thought. Thoughts or ideas thus retained are strongly emotional in quality and typically self-centered. In the main, they are the products of past repressions.

Repression is perhaps the most important dynamic principle of psychoanalytic theory. It is a concept that describes an adaptive operation which excludes from awareness and easy recall, ideas or impulses to action, whose acknowledgement would in some sense endanger or cause pain to the person. Repression is the result of regulation on the pain-pleasure level. Painful thoughts and impulses, when removed from consciousness, tend to lose their effective influence upon motivation. The exclusion process is directed not only at dangerous thoughts and feelings as they first appear, but at the return of memories as well. Repression serves to keep the person from divulging distressing ideas either to himself or others.

Two consequences of repression are to be noted in particular. Repression alters the perception of stimuli both from the outer world and from the person's internal organization, and it alters the goals of a forbidden impulse to action. Once perception of that part of external reality which might arouse anxiety has been changed by excluding some part of it from awareness, the person's motivated behavior changes in accordance with the newly altered view of "reality" that he has created.

Freud recognized that the removal of offending ideas by repression is never complete and absolute. Additional barriers must often be erected by substituting more acceptable gratifications for an abandoned impulse and by displacement of interest to neutral objectives. But the repressed is in a sense always subject to recall. Freud held that the return of the repressed accounted for the formation of symptoms.

The mechanisms of defense which constitute the dynamic core of ego psychology are adaptive maneuvers which are designed to maintain repression more effectively. Some of the mechanisms of defense try to hold on to an altered perception of reality (projection and isolation, e.g.), some are primarily directed toward maintaining the substituted motivation (reaction-formation, regression), and others seek to stabilize the newly-organized system of action that results from the first two changes (rationalization and intellectualization). The point is that any such adaptive defense can become the starting point for a whole new integrated series of action-systems. This is the basis for character formation.

This is not the place for an exhaustive examination of the various integrative systems such as defense, superego, identification, ego-ideal, and especially the system of self-integration. Each polarizes and organizes the primary ego functions in characteristic ways. Each also affects how the other integrative ego functions operate. And each is attached to the key integrative element, the motivating needs.

The conception of self is especially helpful in our understanding of the therapeutic process. The concepts "self" and "ego" are not identical in meaning. A simple way of understanding the difference between the two terms is to consider the "self" the subjective reflection of the larger organization of adaptive functions collectively called the "ego." The self reflects the way one "feels" about himself and the world; the ego is the collection of functions and psychological processes as they might appear to an all-seeing observer. The self is one of these and has an integrative function. Much of the ego does not figure directly in the personal experience of self, as for example, the processes of memory, perception and learning. The results of these processes do, however, become incorporated in the self.

The self may thus be defined as the representation the individual has of his own adaptive capacities in action. How does such a representation come about? The essence of the self would appear to be activity. The self is a functional composite of the thoughts, feelings, and perceptions which comprise action.

The philospher's "self" is not the self of psychoanalytic theory. William James' (1901) use of the term comes closest to our view. In trying to give a physiological basis for the origin of the self, he wrote: "The self is found to consist mainly of the collection of . . . motions in the head and between the head and throat."

Rephrasing James' intuitive statement, we define the core of the experience of self as proprioceptive sensations of motion which are emotionally charged. The self is constituted by movement or willed activity with an emotional charge or feeling; that is, by actions consequent to physiological or cultural need tensions.

James' intuition takes on special significance when we recall that the earliest emotionally charged proprioceptive sensation of movement is the sucking activity of the mouth in infancy. Sucking therefore may be assumed to provide one of the earliest organizations of a variety of ego functions as well as the first subjective representation of the self.

Infantile activity that centers about the mouth and the upper end of the digestive tract is a composite of at least three ego functions:

1) *Sense perception,* including painful sensations stimulated by hunger; tactile, olfactory and taste sensations stimulated by the food itself; visual, auditory and tactile sensations stimulated by the source of food, the mother.

2) *Motor activity* in the form of sucking, chewing, swallowing, and grasping.

3) *Emotional reactions* accompanying each type of sensory experience and each type of motor activity; the feeling tone is determined by the painful and pleasurable quality of each sensation and the degree of gratification created by the motor responses.

These emotional charges, associated as they are with sense perception and motor activity, enter significantly into the earliest image of the self. The regular recurrence of prompt gratification and relief of painful tension seems to create a subjective sense of magical power and might. At the very least, we recognize that all infants display an automatic expectation of immediate satisfaction of their needs with no concern for the realities. Such a totally unrealistic reaction is cultivated and encouraged in the sanctuary provided by the mother. It is the starting point of the development of the infantile sense of omnipotence. Let me hasten to point out that the notion of a stage of infantile omnipotence is an assumption that makes it possible to explain much of infantile behavior. Conversely, failure to gratify oral needs and the need for contact with the mother perpetuates painful tensions that are unrelieved by sucking, chewing, and swallowing. It leads in time to a massive anxiety-like reaction that merges with a depressive apathy. The resulting anticipation of pain and damage alters the perceptions of objects as sources of security and gratification. Whereas pleasurable infantile experiences encourage a delusional sense of magical power that in time changes into affection and love for the objects providing gratification, chronic frustration blunts the capacity for love, often irreparably.

As the infant acquires awareness of his body parts, they become associated in varying degree with his experiences of pleasure or unpleasure and affect the quality of self by expanding or contracting the sense of magical omnipotence.

Having assumed a state of infantile omnipotence, we may make still another assumption that the self is the site of self-love or narcissism. That is to say, the infant for a long time associates his gratification with his own sensations and behavior as if his needs magically produce satisfaction. Love is therefore attached to himself, not to external objects which, as far as he is concerned, have no objective existence. The adaptational conception of narcissism is not that of a built-in reservoir of libidinal energy that is constitutionally self-directed. It is rather a self-image that reflects the limited resources of the infant for understanding its true dependence upon objects in the outer world. His inability to distinguish external reality from his own needs and his own reactions is better defined as a problem of maturation than of built-in constitutional energic distribution.

When at last the parents move into the orbit of the child's awareness as the real source of his gratification, they come to share in his self-love. One of the earliest evidences of emotional thinking in the young child is his extension of his illusory sense of power and control to the persons that provide his gratification and security.

Before describing the successive stages of self-development, it is necessary to emphasize the qualities that are characteristic of the self at the earliest level of infantile omnipotence. The infantile omnipotent self is egocentric, bound to concrete but illogical thought processes, and rooted in wishful anticipation. Gratification is expected by means of the magical power of emotionally charged imagery that is stimulated by need tensions. Freud's "primary process" describes the qualities of thinking that are typical of this earliest omnipotent stage of self-development.

The belief in omnipotence is doomed to fall in the face of realities. The child learns that nothing occurs solely because of his desires and gestures, and that it is the parents who actually perform the "miracles." When this insight is reached, there is a shift of emphasis in the sense of omnipotence. The parent now becomes the mediator of omnipotence rather than the child himself. His majesty, the child, so to speak, confers power upon his prime minister, the parent. This new state of affairs constitutes the second stage in self-development—the stage of delegated omnipotence.

The change is an impressive one although in actual fact the child has not renounced omnipotence. Mother and Father are treated as if they existed only to exercise their delegated omnipotence for the egocentric satisfaction of the child. The delegation of power continues the young child's omnipotence by proxy.

Like the infantile stage, that of delegated omnipotence remains indestructible. They are each revivable depending upon circumstances. No matter how mature the adult may become, he carries with him the potentiality for magical omnipotence, either delegated or self-directed. If a realistic interpretation of his resources fails to work, each adult seems ready to fall back upon a primitively-integrated, emotionally-charged orientation. In general, however, with maturity, the experience of self is more and more filled with realistic awareness of one's place in the world of human relationships. Renunciation and the capacities to pursue rational alternatives become attributes of maturity.

A third stage of self development emerges as critical thinking reduces the distortion of infantile illusory thinking. The coincidental reduction in the sense of personal omnipotence requires self-observation and self-criticism. This third stage may be designated, therefore, the stage of self-critical reduction.

The dramatic change in the self comes about because the growing child is observed and criticized by his parents and other adult figures upon whom he is still realistically dependent. Parental displeasure and criticism threaten alienation, and in anticipation of the forthcoming critical observation by his parents, the child attempts to control his behavior before his parents are displeased. Self-observation and self-criticism thus begun are socially-determined experiences that bring about mature development of the self. It is a slow process that gradually reduces the megalomanic infantile self-image.

We may ask what happens to the narcissism or self-love characteristic of the early omnipotence of the self. The original idea of self is indestructible and although its infantile purpose must be abandoned, it never completely loses its effect. Thus, part is retained unconsciously as the goal of future attainment. In time, it becomes the core of the ego-ideal. It is as if one were to say, "I am not omnipotent now, but I will do all I can to become omnipotent." As a rule, the means chosen for achievement of one's ideal is identification with an admired authority. Narcissism polarizes the identification toward the fulfillment of an omnipotent sense of power and mastery which is acceptable, however, to one's chosen models.

The ego-ideal is a fundamental mechanism in the shaping and regulation of social behavior. Its emergence as a psychological structure signifies the development of a fourth social stage of self-integration.

In general, the stronger the original desire for omnipotence, the more powerful will be the ego-ideal and the greater will be the incentive to strive for omnipotent accomplishment in later life. If one fails to achieve his ideal, he suffers a painful loss of pride and self-esteem. Fulfillment of an ideal is felt as a triumph and produces elation and expanded self-esteem.

The social level of the self usually makes its initial appearance during pre-adolescence. At first, the self represents an internalization, by means of the ego-ideal and identification, of the attitudes other significant persons display toward the person and toward each other. Later on, the social level of self is constituted not only by the organization of particular individual attitudes, but also by internalization of the attitudes, expectation and ideals favored by society as a whole. Once the latter have been incorporated, the individual becomes an integral part of the group. He reflects in his personal behavior the preferred pattern of the group to which he belongs with a minimum of conscious effort and without the arousal of the emergency emotions.

To understand the integrative action of the self, it is necessary to see clearly how it relates to consciousness. All that is conscious or preconscious, that is, capable of easy access to consciousness, is part of the self. It is linked to the levels of emotion or reason which are operating at any given time. The prevailing level of integration—reason, emotional thought, or brute emotion—determines what part of past experience, present perception, and future anticipation will be "identified" with the self. Although the self activates behavior in consciousness, unconscious processes in fact exercise a crucial pressure upon it. Unconscious, emotionally-charged needs lead to emotionally-falsified or distorted perceptions in the here and now. These altered perceptions of one's own needs and the attitudes of others become part of consciousness and therefore part of the self. In this way, the self's perceptions will not reflect reality, but rather the unconscious motivating forces and the defensive maneuvers that have been called in to play by the ego's adaptive emergency functions. A paranoid projection is a case in point. Once reality is perceived as threatening because of unconscious conflicts, defense is necessary. The projective distortion becomes conscious and part of the self. A victim of its own perceptions, the self is concerned only with security as it conceives it. The paranoid delusion seems subjectively to be the true picture of the world. It is unquestioned because it is part of the self and its conscious perceptions. When, in the course of psychotherapy, interpretation brings unconscious motivating ideas and emotions into awareness, it also brings them into the realm of the self. Only then can the self make genuine choices in integrating behavior. Only then does correction of perceptual distortion and the associated defenses become possible.

In the final analysis, the level of psychological integration (hedonic, emotional, or thought) which prevails determines the level at which the self will act. To the extent that unconscious processes are set in motion at a given level of integration, the self is affected more by emotional thinking and less by reason.

Summing up, we note that the self is a part of the full organization of adaptive mechanisms that we call the ego. Repression is a function of the ego, not of the self. That which is repressed cannot, by our definition, become part of the conscious aspect of the self. Instead, the self is organized about the altered perceptions, emotions and thoughts that were unconsciously set in motion to maintain repression and repair the damage to adaptive function caused by the resultant inhibition. These emotions, thoughts, and actions will not be recognized by the self as repressive adjuncts. They will be experienced as natural ways of creating security and pleasure. If they are generally successful in limiting anxiety and frustration, they are acceptable as right and appropriate ways of handling problems and in that way become fixed adaptations. If, on the other hand, the defensive and reparative maneuvers prove inadequate, they form new focal points of anxiety and induce new symptomatic changes in the prevailing level of integration. When that happens, the self changes too, and a less mature and more infantile organization takes place. Regression becomes the order of the day and infantile omnipotent phantasies take over as exaggerated dependency demands or as undisguised narcissism. Neurotic psychopathology involves, therefore, a succession of stages of adaptive breakdown. Conflicting motivation induces repression, other defensive processes that may be followed by secondary lines of symptomatic defense and repair. At each step, the level of psychological integration changes as more primitive emotional levels take control, the self-image changes regressively and tends to fix the person's object relationships in a more infantile mold. The self not only reflects the consequences of adaptive failure but also perpetuates them.

Reparative Psychotherapy and Adaptational Theory

by Aaron Karush, M.D.

PSYCHOTHERAPY may be divided into two broad categories—reparative and reconstructive. Although a sharp line cannot always be drawn between them, reconstructive or psychoanalytic therapy aims at more extensive structural changes in the personality of selected patients than is possible through the use of reparative methods. Furthermore, the techniques of each type of psychotherapy differ in fundamental ways. As its title indicates, this paper is concerned with reparative psychotherapy in an adaptational frame of reference.

Briefly stated, the goals we set for our patients and the means we adopt to achieve them are limited by the level and quality of self-integration which prevails when we begin treatment.

The total therapeutic approach may be divided into the *therapeutic situation* and the *therapeutic process*. An accurate appraisal of the therapeutic situation goes far toward helping us to make the proper choice of treatment technique. It helps us to determine the dynamic quality of the therapeutic process that we are likely to encounter and how much change we can expect to accomplish in our patients.

The examination of the therapeutic situation when the patient begins his treatment requires that we identify and evaluate four emotional attitudes. I will omit a review of the practical issues that affect treatability, such as age, money, physical status of the patient, etc.

319

The first item is the *patient's insight into his illness*. It reflects his intelligence, his psychological aptitude and to some extent, the severity of his pathology. Such insight is revealed by the patient's ability to view himself with some objectivity, that is, to be sufficiently aloof from his suffering so that he can see himself as an object who interacts with others. He must be capable of accepting responsibility for his own emotional conflicts. Delusional projection, for example, or the refusal to accept the possibility of an inner causation of difficulties makes for a very dubious prognosis.

Secondly, we try to weigh the *patient's desire for recovery*, a factor that is closely related to insight into his illness. If he projects blame upon others for his troubles, then it is they who should change, not he. Of course, we recognize that every symptom provides some measure of secondary gain. Even the most realistic patient will often exhibit some confusion as to how he can be expected to change himself in order to recover. His emphasis tends to be less upon his own capacity, and more upon the therapist, the magician, who will guarantee the outcome and will bring it effortlessly about. As a rule, magical expectations come up as a resistance to psychological change during almost every treatment. We interpret it to the patient according to our view of his ability to deal successfully with his problem by means of his own resources. Undisguised demands that the therapist do everything for the patient usually indicate that he is unsuitable for a treatment which aims at substantial improvement in adaptive effectiveness.

Not uncommonly we discover that the patient's life situation rewards his illness to such an extent that makes it impossible and even inadvisable to attempt anything but the most superficial therapeutic intervention. An instance is chronic traumatic neurosis in which pension or disability awards put a high premium upon the maintenance of illness.

Thirdly, we must take into account the *patient's confidence in the therapist*. Not too many years ago, this meant that the patient had to be impressed by the high position, titles, and authority of the therapist. He tended to be intimidated and overawed, and was invited to overestimate the magical powers of the physician. All a sick person needs to know is that his therapist is honest, has integrity, will not exploit his patient for personal gain, and is competently trained. All ritualistic techniques that are designed to impress are out of order and really increase the difficulties of therapy.

Finally, we try to appraise the *quality of the cooperation that the patient is prepared to give*. In part, it is revealed in his attitude toward the therapist. The ideal emotional attitude to treatment is one of hope, but unfortunately patients seldom maintain so constructive an attitude. They are, on the contrary, always strongly tempted to recreate the conditions which gave rise to their emotional difficulties, and to become involved with the therapist on a level of infantile attachment. The hope, which should spring from the desire to master more effective and mature techniques of coping with other people and the tasks of living, tends to change into a yearning for magic. When this happens, the therapist is confronted with displays of infantile omnipotent expectation in which the patient tries to delegate power to him as a surrogate parent.

Fear of the therapist, rage at him, and erotic love for him all express the patient's childlike wish for magical solutions. It is as if he were to tell his therapist, "If you do everything for me, I shall love you; if you disappoint me, I shall be desolate and do anything to get back into your good graces."

Our task in therapy ideally is to help the patient to renounce his magical expectations and to operate on a more rational level. This is particularly true in psychoanalytic therapy, but in reparative psychotherapy with more limited goals we are usually less ambitious. We may have to settle for aiding the patient to function more comfortably, at least for a while, within his prevailing limitation without disturbing his wish for magical dependence upon his therapist.

A word about the reaction of disappointment with the therapist. If rage predominates, the patient looks for ways of reproaching and even hurting his therapist. Not uncommonly, he will try to "ruin" the doctor's reputation by clinging to his symptoms so all the world can see the therapist's incompetence. Ultimately, if the problem is unresolved, he will leave the treatment and perhaps will try his luck elsewhere.

If fear predominates, then submission, ingratiation and expiation become the order of the day. The patient repeatedly avows his love or veneration, and if he is also guilt-ridden, with a need to atone, he may become so enthralled as to try to remain in treatment indefinitely as a kind of appendage to his therapist.

The appraisal of the therapeutic situation and a patient's treatability by more or less intensive psychotherapy, as I have already mentioned, also requires consideration of his age, the nature and extent of the disordered functions, the duration of the illness, the patient's residual flexibility, and the extent to which his life situation can be modified. One must always keep in mind the realistic difficulties which prevent a patient from pulling himself out of the hole in which he finds himself.

Psychotherapists must not be health fanatics, since the neurosis may in fact be the best solution possible in a given life situation. This was a criterion for treatability emphasized by Freud. For example, a woman in her menopause who develops an increased sexual appetite, who has an impotent husband, and is herself prudish and rigidly inhibited, may suffer a paranoid-depressive reaction. In such cases, Freud suggested that the psychotherapist should "tactfully withdraw." Drug therapy may be more suitable.

Thus far, I have discussed some of the important factors that influence the therapist's judgment about treatability and the choice of treatment method and goal. What about the therapeutic process itself and the interventions which the therapist can call upon to achieve a desired outcome?

Reconstructive psychoanalysis works with the patient's problems as an unconscious product of his developmental history. Its aim in therapy is to alter previously-fixed perceptions, emotions, and thoughts in such a way as to allow the patient to make choices in his behavior that were not possible for him in the past. To accomplish this, the analyst relies heavily upon interpretation of his patient's patterns of behavior. In particular, interpretation is directed at the ways in which the patient unconsciously repeats his neurotic conflicts in the relationship with the analyst, and tries to convert the analytic situation into a repetition of infantile expectations and experience.

It is not always possible, as I have noted before, to establish an arbitrary dividing line between analytic and non-analytic techniques. For one thing, transference interpretation seldom plays as prominent a part in the reparative treatment although on occasion it may be necessary and useful. Such was true in one of the cases to be described. As a rule, therapeutic influences other than interpretation of the unconscious and of the transference play a larger part in reparative therapy. In brief, these may be described as follows:

1.) *Support*. This technique usually implies some degree of manipulation of the patient's environment. The therapist helps the patient to alter his life condition sufficiently so that he may better cope with his problems using his own resources, limited though they may be. Support presupposes one thing more. The patient is given an opportunity to communicate his distress and emotional reactions to another human being in a setting where no harm or humiliation will follow the self-exposure. The human contact of treatment often proves to be a boon especially to people who have been lonely and emotionally isolated. The therapeutic relationship serves, however, only as an ersatz social experience. It cannot and should not be permitted to replace more realistic life experience. Nevertheless, for a time, as will be seen in the first case to be described, it may offer a reparative sanctuary that temporarily conteracts the frustration of other painful relationships. Symptomatic relief is given when supportive therapy kindles the magical yearning that the physician will exercise his wisdom and strength in the patient's behalf. If one were to dispel this illusion too quickly by telling the patient, "I cannot give you any advice or direction about changing your life, but please go right ahead and pour out your troubles," the patient would, I am afraid, get little benefit.

It is not merely the opportunity for a person to pour out his troubles that gives supportive therapy its value, but rather that he expresses himself with wishful anticipation. That is, he expects something magical to take place simply because he has found a sympathetic ear. There is little question that the pouring out of complaints, when combined with magical dependence upon the therapist, does give the patient temporary relief. And not infrequently, while this favorable effect lasts, the patient may even return to reasonably effective functioning and for a time will seem to have recovered.

2.) *Release of impounded affect.* As a second form of therapeutic influence, the release of affect goes beyond the simple verbalization of complaints. When we permit the expression of hemmed-in and suppressed emotions, the patient gains an illusion of strength, as if he had succeeded in really acting out a self-assertive impulse. The affective decompression temporarily increases self-esteem, but sooner or later, the pressure rises again and the process has to be repeated. The release of hemmed-in affect was the cornerstone of Freud's earliest cathartic approach to psychotherapy. It continues to play an important role in most forms of treatment, although of itself, it seldom produces lasting effects. One of its most useful functions is the easing of guilty self-reproaches so that self-punitive defenses become less rigid and can be more effectively discussed with the patient. Affective release is an important part of most psychotherapeutic approaches.

3.) *Persuasion* or *suggestion.* Applied directly or indirectly by the therapist, this technique of intervention seeks to incline the patient either to act or to refrain from doing something. Suggestion may be used to overcome an inhibition or to help the patient find new satisfying alternatives. If he is successful, the patient will feel stronger for it and at the same time will emerge with a re-enforced conviction of the therapist's omnipotence. Suggestion may help a patient over an immediate hurdle, and if by doing so it establishes him in a more stable and rewarding life situation, the improvement may be real and lasting. In other words, the illusion that the therapist is magically omnipotent may be the means of positive change. It goes without saying that suggestion, if it is to have a reasonable chance of success, must never invite the patient to undertake more than is permitted by his intelligence and skills, by the realities of life, and by his capacity to tolerate anxiety.

4.) *Direct intervention.* This technique, wherein the therapist actually makes decisions, does things for his patient, and literally takes over the function of a parent with a helpless child, is the least satisfactory and least effective tactic in the therapeutic armamentarium. Unfortunately, it is occasionally necessary with severely disturbed patients, but rarely serves other than an emergency purpose. Inexperienced therapists not uncommonly fall into the error of yielding to the demands of dependent patients that they decide all important matters. To do so merely convinces the patient of his helplessness, and worse, rewards his neurosis.

5.) The creation of insight is the goal of interpretation, one of the most important therapeutic maneuvers. Insight is a loosely used concept and is often given a variety of definitions. Understanding of one's motivations and even of one's characterological defenses is usually equated with insight. I would suggest, however, that understanding should be distinguished from true insight. Whereas understanding is essentially an intellectual grasp of the meaning of past experience, insight requires an added inner sense of emotional conviction that comes from action based upon new understanding. Insight, therefore, results from applied understanding. In this sense, it represents the emotional impact of effective learning and often has a lasting effect upon the adaptive efficiency of the patient.

Defined in this way, understanding is an intellectual grasp of the meaning of past actions; insight is primarily an emotional experience that accompanies understanding of ongoing behavior in the present. All too often we meet psychoanalytically-treated patients who have a meticulous grasp of their past conflicts—but who have not changed. Their understanding has never been converted into new activity and they have never gained the true insight that in turn leads to an altered anticipation of the future. One cannot "understand" how he will behave successfully in the future. It is only possible to look forward to future accomplishments that are not simple repetitions of past actions, with hopeful anticipation of success. Insight gained during adaptive activity helps to create hopeful anticipation. Insight supplies a sense of emotional conviction about the reliability of our perceptions and our executive capacities. It helps one to meet new life situations with a minimum of anxiety.

It would follow therefore that if insight is created by the effective application of understanding, it cannot be achieved solely on the couch. I believe that the only true insights gained in the consultation room refer to the relationship of the patient with his therapist. Insight into relationships with others comes about through the practical application of understanding in real life. Interpretation of the transference and of other motivational conflicts that impede healthy adaptive behavior provides that understanding. But unless the patient uses the new knowledge, his perceptions of his way of interacting with others will not change.

The depth of insight gained in reconstructive psychoanalytic therapy is usually much greater than that obtained by reparative techniques. The analytic process makes it possible to improve the adaptive efficiency by helping the patient to realize that he must do more for himself and give up his excessive dependence upon others. He is expected to surrender his infantile illusions, to alter his perceptions of himself and his environment, and to create new action systems. Ego organization must undergo a fundamental change. Reparative psychotherapy, on the other hand, seeks more modest goals by giving the patient an illusion of strength and security which comes primarily from his unconscious belief that the therapist's omnipotence is being used in his behalf. He operates with the security of the child dependent upon a powerful parent. The insight given in reparative therapy is generally on a more superficial level. As a rule it relates to the patient's faulty behavior in a particular life situation or in a particular object relationship, but does not alter significantly the level at which the self operates.

Admittedly, this distinction between reconstructive and reparative processes is an idealized one. For in practice, we often use both approaches in different proportions regardless of the ultimate goals. Still, the more a therapy aids the patient in gaining realistic techniques of adaptation and in renouncing his illusion of omnipotence, the closer it comes to the ideal reconstructive process. Reparative techniques are less likely to produce long-lasting effects. Temporary illusory strength will usually falter in the face of continued demands by reality. When this happens, these stresses signify to the patient, not a call to action, but collapse of his magical powers. When he cannot wishfully have his way, he loses his sense of security, his anxieties grow, frustration mounts, and a relapse to helplessness follows. I hasten to point out that this is by no means an invariable outcome of reparative forms of treatment. Many people are able to maintain their gains. But why some do so and others do not remains a largely unsolved problem for all psychotherapeutic procedures, analytic or reparative.

I should now like to describe two cases to you with somewhat similar presenting complaints. Each, however, had different underlying psychodynamics and presented very different therapeutic problems. Both patients established an emotional relationship with me that became the starting point for more or less far-reaching changes in the perception of reality, emotional reactions, and general behavior.

Mrs. B., a woman of forty-four who looked somewhat younger, despite her graying blonde hair and careless way of dress, came to me with a desperate plea for help. She had been depressed for several months and had become increasingly agitated by her doubt and indecision in her household chores, such as shopping, cooking, and entertaining. The immediate reason for her seeking treatment at this time was the paralyzing quandary in which she found herself. She could not decide whether to accept a professional opportunity to spend the summer abroad without her husband and their three children, ages 16, 12, and 10. On the one hand she feared the prolonged contact with her eldest daughter whose defiance enraged her; on the other, she felt guilt for deserting the family. Despite Mrs. B.'s conviction that her anger at the daughter was justified, it was invariably followed by intense self-condemnation. The daughter was obviously well aware of this and did not fail to take advantage of her mother's conflict by arranging frequent provocations.

Our patient was a professional worker who had achieved considerable recognition and status in her own right because of her skills. On occasion, the organization that employed her sent her out to offices in other cities to train personnel. Her husband was a prominent and respected businessman. Mrs. B. had just come to the end of a leave of absence from her regular job, in which she had been assigned to an important and specialized kind of work. She admitted that despite her emotional turmoil, the assignment had gone off very well. In other words, the symptoms of which she had complained had not invaded her activity outside the family relationships. As quickly as she could, she turned away from her successes to tell me in tearful agitation that her indecision about spending the summer with her family arose from fear of "spoiling their fun" if she stayed with them. She anticipated quarreling with her daughter, her son, and with her husband, who would surely side with the children. She was sure it would all end in her becoming helplessly depressed and she begged me in her first interview to tell her what was best to do.

Mrs. B. was clearly a woman of superior intelligence and lively emotionality. Her mood swings during our early interviews, however, were striking. She ranged in rapid succession from sobbing depression to coy flirtatiousness. Nevertheless, from the first, she displayed a great anxiety about her growing loss of self-control and about what was happening to her relations with her family. Despite this suffering, she frequently withheld information or evasively announced, "I'm too ashamed to tell you now." This pseudo-blocking usually had a seductive quality about it as if daring me to force her to reveal her secrets.

During the first interviews, I had some concern about the diagnosis, but from the beginning I responded to her with genuine liking and sympathy and an impulse to be supportive and even directive. At no time did I feel out of touch with her emotional responses. But I was struck by the ease with which Mrs. B. evoked the *protective response* in me. Although she suffered intensely, Mrs. B. had remained a sharp, able and creative person whose function in an important segment of her life had never been impaired by her symptoms. In her professional activities, throughout the deepest depression and most intense anxiety, she remained incisive, made immediate and responsible decisions, and worked easily and effortlessly with her large staff. The paradox in my reaction to her consisted in this: I was sympathetic not only to her pain but to her as a person—as if in spite of all the contrary evidence, Mrs. B. had been denied access to gratification and self-realization, a victim of cruel circumstances over which she had no control.

The point I wish to emphasize is that although I could not in the initial interview know why she had to present herself as a helpless waif, I accepted it as essentially true, I trusted my reaction and from it began to plan a tentative approach to the treatment.

It is worth underlining how important it is for the therapist not to rely entirely upon his empathy, or upon his warmth and desire to reach out a helping hand to unfortunate sufferers, as a substitute for psycho-dynamic knowledge. Intuition must be given a scientific base.

I therefore avoided any implication that she was, in her words, a "spoiled baby" who should count her blessings and stop complaining. It seemed necessary to convince her that I believed that she was indeed deprived and that at this time her frustration was more significant than her realistic accomplishment, great as that was. I did not try to remind her at this point of her very real assets and accepted her self-presentation without trying to convince her of her genuine worth. Before that would serve a useful purpose, she would have to understand what her motivation was for the self-depreciation. It was a defense that was necessary to maintain; it seemed to make it possible for her to expose thoughts and impulses that aroused guilt and a need for self-punishment. I relate this aspect of my handling of the initial relationship with Mrs. B. in some detail because it set the tone of my future work with her.

At first, she talked only of her current problems; her husband and daughter were the center of her concern. She needed little encouragement once she got started. Most of the initial interviews were unstructured except for an occasional encouraging sound or word, or a questioning repetition of her last word when I wished her to pay particular attention to a thought she had just voiced. My interest was focussed clearly upon her feelings regardless of what she chose to discuss. In that sense, my interviews were by no means unstructured. Any hint given to the patient about the therapist's interest almost always becomes a therapeutic directive. Indeed, one may question whether there can really be a totally unstructured interview. What, as a rule, is best avoided is a strong expression of approval or disapproval, or the verbalization of a value judgment.

The first interview has a therapeutic importance, regardless of the type of psychotherapy being practiced, that cannot be over-estimated. It reveals not only the nature and quality of the conflicting emotions that have helped create the presenting symptoms, but also the nature and quality of the patient's self-image. It tells us what he wishes to receive from the therapist and equally important what he really expects will happen to him in the treatment relationship. The role the patient has in mind for the therapist is already structured before the treatment begins.

Of course, all this insight may not always be obtained in the first session or two, but it never ceases to astonish me how often it can be, and worse, how seldom the therapist is prepared to receive it. Unless one can grasp the nature of the conflicting emotions in the symptom picture, the nature of the patient's level of self-integration, and the nature of his desires and expectations of the therapist, one will neither understand the patient nor be able to plan the therapy and one's role in it.

Every therapist has a primary obligation to relieve his patient's disturbing symptoms as soon as possible, and to try to prevent their recurrence. Psychoanalysis may approach this goal in a more leisurely fashion and may accomplish it more slowly, although not necessarily so. Reparative psychotherapy, however, cannot afford to be so leisurely, and an early therapeutic commitment is imperative. The analyst, by the very nature of his therapeutic method, has more leeway as a rule, but even he must formulate an early working hypothesis.

Let us now return to our patient. It soon became apparent that the conflict that induced the paralyzing doubt and depression in Mrs. B. grew out of her relationship with her husband. He was a strong, aggressively domineering man who bullied everyone—in his family and outside—by the force of his intelligence and biting humor. He demanded adulation and praise and blustered about in social situations with an almost total lack of sensitivity and tact. Mrs. B. feared his criticism but was slavish in her admiration for his great ability. She unquestionably enjoyed the prominence he had attained. It gave her entree with important people, and status and recognition that overshadowed the significance of her own accomplishments. From the beginning of their marriage Mrs. B. had made no important decisions without first consulting her husband, but her dependence upon his judgment usually ended with secret doubts about his wisdom. Mrs. B's decisions about family matters were impulsive and came not from reason and careful consideration of the issues involved, but from a need not to be troubled further. These areas of impulsive decision-making which Mrs. B. invited, were precisely the areas in which she was afflicted with doubt. The patient would acquiesce to her husband and subsequently be eaten up with doubt and remorse at *her* terrible mistake. Her husband would get no peace and her doubt and self-punitive wailing became a remarkably effective weapon against him.

The quarrels between them were especially intense when their eldest daughter was involved. Mrs. B. seemed to be killing two birds with one stone. She was caught in an endlessly recurring conflict between her rage at the daughter and husband and her counter-balancing guilt. Although she was aware of her anger at the girl, she could not admit anything but love for her husband.

I noted earlier that she had given me the impression of being a helpless child overwhelmed by external pressures she could not understand. It was the same face she presented to her husband, who had in general encouraged and rewarded it throughout their marriage.

What about her desires and expectations of the treatment? She insisted that all she wished for was relief of her suffering. But throughout the first sessions her depressions would momentarily lift and an incongruous coyness would emerge whenever she talked of sex. Her sexual relationship with Mr. B. was "ideal." She did offer one embarrassed complaint—Mr. B. was too rough in his caresses. Periodically as she talked of sex—and I did not press her for information—she would blush and cover her face so that she could peep out at me through her fingers. I guessed she was covering up much more than her face and that she enjoyed describing her sexual experiences in spite of her protestations. It seemed highly likely that she would plunge rapidly into an erotic transference and in this I was unfortunately correct.

What did she anticipate my response would be to her sexual interest in me? The blocking and frequent expressions of shame and her inability to tell me this or that dramatized her conviction that I would hold her in contempt for her transgressions in fact or phantasy—whatever they might prove to be.

During the first three or four weeks of therapy, she managed to tell me enough of her history to give substance to most of my early impressions. She had been the youngest of four children, the others having been boys. When she was four, her next older brother had died. Her mother had been a singer, was driving and ambitious, and clearly showed contempt for her weak and passive husband. She had seized upon the patient to fulfill her frustrated musical ambitions. Mrs. B. recalled that she had been completely obedient and compliant as a child, had shunned her father because the mother seemed to prefer it so, and studied diligently to please her tyrannical mother. She proved to have considerable talent and by early adolescence was being prepared for an operatic career. The hours of study and practice were passively accepted without protest at the exclusion of the usual childhood pleasures available to her friends. At seventeen, however, the first break in her submissiveness appeared. She was suddenly disabled by recurrent hoarseness and although no organic cause was discovered, abruptly renounced her singing career.

Shortly afterward she fell in love with a much older man but kept the relationship carefully hidden from her mother. After she had revealed this much to me, she had great difficulty in talking freely for several subsequent sessions. Finally, she confessed details of her life that had until then been a painfully buried secret. A year or two later she became involved in an affair with a man of whom she said only that "he was inferior and stupid, but he was very exciting to be with." During this period she was alternately filled with shame and defiance of her mother who predicted that dire consequences would befall her unless she broke up her relationship with this man. At 25, there was another complete turn about and she renounced her sexual freedom. Shortly afterward, she met her present husband and married him, grateful that she had escaped her mother's prophecy of doom. She was guilt-ridden however, because she had "deceived" her husband by hiding her "lurid" past.

It is hard to convey the agony of shame and guilt that she relived in telling her story. She was certain that I was repelled and must hold her in contempt. She was especially guilty because she had pretended to her husband to be innocent and naive—so much so in fact that she had converted sex into a comparatively pleasureless experience. Because she felt so unworthy of him, she had driven herself in her career to succeed and make him proud of her. The way in which she repeated her early compliance to her mother indicated how she had replaced the tyrannical mother with an equally demanding and critical husband. Her striving for success and recognition took on the aspect of expiation for the injury she believed she had done to her mother and to her husband.

The enormous guilt and unyielding need for self-punishment and expiation, as might be expected, became a focal point in the therapy. It was never completely given up, but in time she gained sufficient insight into her masochistic impulses to become less submissive to her overbearing husband as well as to other exploiting friends and authoritarian figures. Two tactics were used to gain this end: one sought to free her impounded aggression and to support her in reasonable displays of self-assertion and anger; the other used her transference attachment to me to correct her perception of me as a wrathful and punitive Mosaic figure.

It is not possible to give a detailed description of the movement of the patient's therapy during the two years that I treated her. She proved to be a vividly imaginative woman, gifted in her capacity for emotional expressiveness. She fought desperately to coerce me into playing the principal role in her re-enactment of the family romance. Her mood swings were frequent but never psychotic. The oral level of demand and expectation often seemed insatiable. And there were times when I frankly felt discouraged. Invariably she would sense this and confronting me with my lapse, we would together examine how and why she had sought to get me to give her up as hopeless. Progress was slow and painful, but she grasped the meaning of her provocation. Whenever she was enraged at her husband or had failed to cope with a family problem for which I offered no specific help or show of siding with her, she acted out her rage by trying to prove that I was a failure as a therapist. As she later said, "I've tried to cut off my nose to make your face bleed." The castrating implication of her humor is obvious enough. Nevertheless, time and time again she pulled herself back to the real work of reappraising her perceptual distortions and her coercive dependency attitudes. As important as any other quality of strength was her capacity for humor about herself. She had that wonderful ability to stand back and view herself, and to laugh at her childishness, that is always a heartening sign to any therapist.

After each session she would write out the free association and self-analysis that she continued between interviews. Knowing that I would read her diary, she managed to extract from me what she wished—more of my time and interest. As a matter of fact, she was able to reveal herself in this way more freely than in our vis-à-vis interviews. The following are some excerpts from early notes and may be compared with those written a year or so later:

Embarrassment at talking to you about you. Fantasy: you floating above a cringing me, with a big, enveloping pair of arms and a divinely forgiving expression.

Fantasy: me groveling at your knees and you placing a soothing hand on my fevered brow.

Fantasy: my lying on the couch (which you deny me) and extending my hand and clutching your hand for moral support, and feeling repose and tranquility coming through the touch as I talked.

The proof of whether I can eye myself clinically and overcome my embarrassment will be if I really show this to you. If I do, it will be because:

(1) I know that I am not responsible for my fantasies in the way I am for conscious acts.

(2) I know you expect people to have outlandish and fantastic thoughts and I think you encourage them to express them.

(3) If I don't, I'll sit fish-like and be unable to talk when I see you.

I wrestle with myself to break down my self-built walls and I consider that if I can communicate this foolishness, it is a sort of personal triumph. Some time some person must have said equally silly things to you. I don't really think that this is the most shocking thing you ever heard. And for me maybe it will be a good learning experience. Still I am moved to say "excuse me."

This was one of her first notes written about three months after treatment had started. A short time later, she showed me the following:

When I left Monday I felt exhilarated. I made these findings—I find suits easier to buy than dresses; I reject the feminine role as I am afraid I cannot compete successfully; instead I get the masculine type of satisfaction —driving a car, taking cabs, spending money where it doesn't show. Is this why I feared to give up my job and keep house? There I am accepted easily.

I gave myself these instructions: buy some stunning clothes; go to the beauty parlor; get ready to compete in feminine roles.

Interpersonal relations: your voice as well as your words were in a way cold and cruel—and I ate them up and pressed the steel blade to my heart. I reminded me how I could not stand the cold courtesy in people's voices and would goad them into saying nasty things just so it was directed at me and I would internally shiver but felt I was recognized as me.

You were critical (coldly and accurately)—gave me some insights— demolished me; I am not going to concern myself with process and say I think maybe you did it so I'd rise and respond; I should not be concerned with techniques but with responses. I know I went right home elated; perhaps now the relationship was one I could accept or define without fear and hesitancy. Your critical expression, combined with the fact that I like you, gives me a pattern to fall into and to make me more comfortable—though in a sense, dependent. If I try to keep thin, get better clothes and hairdos because I cheerfully accept your severe criticism the result will be good anyway.

After each such outpouring, which for many months to come were variations upon the same theme, she would return to her next session ashamed, embarrassed, and watching me carefully to see if she angered me. This was in part her goal and she kept at it unrelentingly. I would interpret her motives, she would listen impassively, leave, and write another passage of reproach and expressing determination to suffer to earn my regard.

After several months, there were signs that she was ready to give up the provocation and to alter her dependency demands. First came a new tone of cold anger at my having withheld the responses she had aimed at eliciting. It followed a few days of minor illness because of which she had missed two of her appointments. I had been unable to offer her alternative times to make up the lost hours. She wrote:

This is not a daydream, not a fantasy, but a direct communication from me to you without love. To me it is understandable that you take so calmly and impersonally and remotely my telephone call to you last Saturday which was really an SOS and again today. If you recognized that I was seething and just are waiting for me to cool off and calm down I fail to see the point of the treatment. I really think you don't even know too well who I am—just one more hour to fill up your time. It's nice and easy and pleasant to sit and split a hair in four and dissect remembered or past feelings—but here I am with a fury, a rage, an impotence and the help I get from you is to wait and see if I feel uncomfortable on Wednesday. I have been working on the 'as if' theory as I have told you several times—placing full confidence in your power and particular willingness to help me. I must tell you that today was a sad disappointment to me.

This was soon followed by a serious look at the years in which she had avoided playing a maternal role with her children and a wife's role with her husband. Instead she recognized that she had tried to be a child and had renounced her responsibilities. At first she thought bitterly of permanently giving up any efforts to change her position in the family.

She did not, however, give up, but began to assert herself at home and to gain, for the first time, a new respect for her place in the family from both her husband and her children. A few months before we agreed to terminate her therapy, she made some remarks that I shall quote verbatim. She had, as I said, begun to establish her maternal role more clearly. Her husband at first protested any move toward an independent assumption of authority with the children, but usually she managed to stand her ground. In fact, she could even feel some sympathy for his emotional difficulties. There were no more depressions. Her treatment behavior grew calm, warm, and friendly, and if at times she talked of the impending end of therapy as if it were the end of a love affair, she did so with humor and wit. Her growing independence of me was expressed in one of her last interviews:

I got a revelation suddenly which explains much to me. A thing can happen and I cannot tell it to you, and that's all right too. You could have told me that but instead you waited for me to come to that idea.

Then followed a list of positive achievements with her children and friends. Describing a family gathering, she ended with, "Such happy chatter! But it's cheerful! It's good! and it's real, too, this time."

Let us now look more closely at the therapeutic process in the case just described:

The first step was to help the patient pour forth her impounded feelings about herself and other significant figures. Catharsis, especially when the impounded emotion is rage, invariably gives temporary relief —but it is only temporary. It relieves the tension of the suppressed affects and it also encourages the patient to see the therapist as an ally who understands her and does not judge her. But catharsis in this case had an even more important function. It provided a bridge for our patient to reach a critically important insight—the recognition that her own perceptions of herself and of others aroused inappropriate and exaggerated emotional reactions. The deeper reasons for the emotions, it is true, were still hidden from her. Adaptational theory agrees with Alexander and French (1946) in considering this an essential step toward a corrective emotional experience. As the patient achieved recognition of her true feelings, her relationship to me took on another meaning. Whenever an impounded impulse, angry or sexual, had to be faced, it tended to carry with it the guilty fears which had originally led to its repression. At such times, her relationship with me took on a critical quality. The transference reactions mirrored her earlier childhood pre-conceptions of a punitive parent. It was at this stage that I began the long and difficult task of altering her conviction of guilt and worth-lessness by avoiding criticism and by avoiding the trap of her maso-chistic self-punitive provocations. I was not always successful, but the ultimate outcome was a definite reduction of guilt, freer toleration of her angry feelings, and freedom from shame about "forbidden" sexual impulses.

The tactics I pursued were not analytical in the usual sense. I did not set the goal of a reconstructed personality but there is no question that the patient actually underwent some basic structural changes. Analysis would perhaps have accomplished no more. What were the interventions used to influence the patient? The magical omnipotence with which she endowed me was for a long time my most potent tool. Through it I tried to counteract the intense guilt stimulated originally by her mother and perpetuated by her husband. It made suggestion relatively easy to apply. It was not all, however. Interpretation helped her apply the understanding she gained about her motivation and per-ceptual distortions. The insight which she obtained in this way played a large part in altering her behavior.

Lack of time prevents a discussion of many fascinating bits of interplay between Mrs. B. and me. I wish only to emphasize again that her problem had been a life-long one. It reached the critical point that had forced her into therapy for two reasons. She had entered the involutional period, was losing her attractiveness, and the hope of enjoying the sexual pleasure she had been compelled to forego. At the same time her daughters and the youngest son were entering puberty and their youthful beauty reminded her more strongly of her own frustrations and aroused her competitive jealousy. Her husband's inability to respond to her needs for assurance, love, and respect invited a return of infantile phantasies of pleasure and aggression which had been repressed. As these began to press more and more strongly for admission into consciousness, the guilts of childhood returned with merciless intensity. Masochism and self-punishment became her most prominent defenses coupled with regressive dependent demands. What the therapeutic process meant to the patient herself she stated as follows:

I realize I must now learn again to keep things to myself. But with a difference. A good deal of the ache and panic are dissipated. Change, as you pointed out, happens slowly. But it happens. I remember how I felt a strong feeling of renunciation at the idea of stopping treatment and how I reproached you. I had attributed to you a fatherly and motherly interest in me and suddenly you seemed not to care what happened to me. Wanting to do things for you was pointless once you seemed indifferent whether I did or didn't do something. Today, I can put them both in proper perspective. Once I heard someone reviling a surgeon when her sister failed to recover quickly. At the time, the injustice of it struck me. No one should expect so much of anybody. That doesn't sound as I mean it to. There is only one respect in which I would have wished more from treatment—to help me understand the technical aspects of the process. The relationship of each session to the overall picture of change remains mysterious. I know it went in waves, a stormy, weepy, or confessional session followed by a couple of inane ones. Then a surprise revelation would come out that I had no previous intention of making. The mechanics of it would interest me though you would say it was not essential that I learn them.

So much for Mrs. B. In contrast, the second case that I shall review very briefly illustrates another type of depressive reaction. Whereas the first patient had always tended to be depressed, this patient's depression could be considered reactive. Mrs. M. was a 38-year-old married woman who had no children. She was an interior decorator, married to an attorney. My first knowledge of the problem came when her husband called to tell me that he intended to leave her and wanted me to "help her over the shock." He was in analysis and his therapist had recommended that he send his wife to me. I agreed to see her if she wished to come.

Mrs. M. proved to be an attractive woman who immediately assumed an air of superficial good humor and joked about the irony of *her* having to get psychiatric help. The facade quickly broke down, at least in part, and I could see a bitterly wounded and outraged woman whose brittle defense by denial of the truth about her marriage had suddenly been shattered. She faced a bleak and lonely middle age with fear and despair, but an even more important factor in her depression was the intense rage at her husband and the shame at having her failure in marriage exposed to the world.

During the first three interviews as she told me of herself there was a constant refrain: how could he do this to me, after all I've done for him; to me who sent him through law school and supported him for years; without me he couldn't even pick out the right clothes; I made his friends for him, etc. She wept frequently, then would try to smile bravely and assume a flippant cynicism, but in the end would return to her impotent angry blame and accusation.

The marriage had indeed been one in which she had "worn the pants," while the husband, a weak and passive man who was sexually impotent, leaned upon her until he had found another woman. Then all his resentment at her domination emerged with his decision to leave her.

Mrs. M. had always been strong, self-reliant, and independent. She was competent in her work, was well liked, and apparently made friends easily. Her childhood had been one of deprivation and tragedy which enforced an early self-sufficiency. Her father had deserted his wife and only child when she was one year old. Mrs. M.'s mother, in her words, promptly became a promiscuous alcoholic and when Mrs. M. was nine years old, killed herself at the doorstep of a rejecting lover. My patient felt no grief but only a guilty satisfaction at being rid of the mother of whom she was both afraid and ashamed. From then on an intense determination to make something of herself, and to be as different from her mother as she could, took over. She had suc-ceeded—until her marriage crashed around her ears.

It was during her third interview that I commented on the dis-crepancy between her continual smiling as she talked and the pain I knew she must be suffering. She broke down into a deeply touching outburst of grief which marked the first important emotional experi-ence in the therapy. From then on, she saw me as a friendly ally who understood her. She could now cry freely and reported that things no longer looked as black. This lasted for two weeks until her husband, whose vengeful hostility for his years of "castration" had not abated, entered their apartment in her absence and removed all the treasured furnishings she had collected. I learned of this the next day at the hospital to which she had been rushed after an impulsive attempt at suicide. The effort to kill herself fortunately failed, and, as it proved, was the turning point in her recovery from the depression. I visited her each day in her hospital room, encouraged her to describe her feelings, and carefully avoided showing any of the chagrin I felt at my failure to anticipate her suicidal gesture. Not long afterward she told me that she had never felt so close to anyone as she did to me during the week after her attempt to kill herself. She determined then that she would never again fail me—"it was an ungrateful thing to do."

I continued to see her for about six months during which time she obtained a divorce and a favorable settlement from her husband. Then, with my encouragement, she began dating other men. She even had a few satisfying sexual affairs and regained a sense of strength and attractiveness as a woman. She could now admit her part in the failure of the marriage and recognized her need to dominate and control a weaker man. The suicide represented, she thought, an identification with her mother and would, if successful, have killed two birds with one stone. She would have committed the ultimate aggression against the man who rejected her, and she would have expiated her guilt for her own destructiveness. The real fault, she felt, lay in her fear of any dependency and of being disappointed as she had been as a child, when no one seemed to care what became of her. As she admitted all this, she shyly told me that her relationship to me had taught her that she could depend upon another person without disappointment or betrayal. She wanted now to go off on her own and I agreed that she should.

The differences between the two cases I have described are striking. One was an hysterical personality, the other obsessive. The first lived with the relatively weak defense of excessive dependence, the second was strongly assertive and found security through dominance and control rather than through trusting love and affection. Mrs. M. had not wept so much because she had lost a love as because she had lost a husband who defined her status. Mrs. B. could have an emotional life that was richly varied, Mrs. M. was constricted and tended to limit her gratification to power politics.

In each case, however, the emotional consequences of the relationship to me was the critical factor in the improved function. In both cases, there was a salutary cathartic release of angry affect and a change in self-esteem. Mrs. B. had to undergo some fundamental change in character structure before she could improve her function; Mrs. M. needed only to be helped to regain her previous level of functional efficiency. Which result is likely to be longer lasting? I frankly do not know; chance will probably play a large part in deciding how each of these women will fare in the future.

A Survey of the
Development and Evolution of
Psychoanalytic Treatment

by Arthur A. Miller, M.D.

PSYCHOANALYSIS has contributed much to the development of various dynamic psychotherapies, that is, those therapies which are based on an understanding of dynamically interacting psychological forces. Concomitant with its contribution to other forms of psychotherapy, there has remained an area of psychotherapeutic endeavor, with its characteristic methods and goals, which has been called psychoanalysis and which has its own evolution and development. It has a past and a present, as well as more or less clearly defined lines indicating the course of its future development.

I do not intend to survey all of the developments in psychoanalytic therapy, but shall concentrate on the following:

1) A view of the development of psychoanalytic treatment from its beginning to the approach delineated in Freud's technical papers in the second decade of this century.

2) Remarks about the structural hypothesis and ego psychology which have contributed to refinements in psychoanalytic technique, enhanced our understanding of the psychoanalytic process, and facilitated the increasing scope of applicability of psychoanalytic technique.

3) Consideration of countertransference.

4) Remarks about the widening scope of indications for psychoanalysis.

5) Remarks about proposed modifications and variations of the standard psychoanalytic technique.

6) Something about psychoanalysis and dynamic psychotherapy, their similarities and differences.

I do not propose to be exhaustive in my remarks. My main purpose is to present a view of psychoanalysis as it is defined and has developed along what can be considered the direct line of "Freudian" psychoanalysis.

The term "psychoanalysis" has been used in three ways: to designate (1) a body of knowledge and a theory of human behavior; (2) a method of investigation whereby this knowledge is obtained and furthered; and (3) a method of therapy which, when systematically applied, can be used for the treatment of a variety of psychopathological conditions to effect personality reorganization. There is a close and reciprocal relationship between psychoanalytic therapy and psychoanalytic theory. Through the use of the method of therapy and the resulting clinical observations psychoanalytic theory has developed and expanded. Theoretical formulations have, in turn, influenced the development of the method and goal of psychoanalytic therapy. Therefore, in much of what follows, I shall indicate these interactions.

From Cathartic Hypnosis to Psychoanalytic Treatment

In 1893, Breuer and Freud published their paper, "On the Psychical Mechanism of Hysterical Phenomena." Their book, *Studies in Hysteria* (1936), appeared two years later. In these publications, they described how, through their use of "cathartic hypnosis," they attempted to recover the patient's earlier memories and feelings regarding a "traumatic" event. Hysterical symptoms were believed to be due to the existence, outside of consciousness, of such memories and feelings ("strangulated affects"). By hypnosis they could be recovered. The goal of therapy was to effect a catharsis—or abreaction—of the "repressed" feelings, and, thus, the source of symptoms from which the patient had been suffering would be removed. Hypnosis was used by Breuer and Freud to effect the recovery of memories and the abreaction of the related feelings. This differed from the previous therapeutic use of hypnosis aimed at the removal of symptoms by suggestion. Although cathartic hypnosis was rather short-lived as a form of therapy, it contributed to the development of a cornerstone of psychoanalysis—the knowledge of the existence, operation, and effect of unconscious mental processes.

Freud (1948a), at this early period, considered the question of why unconscious content was excluded from consciousness. He pointed to the conflict between opposing psychic forces and thus laid the foundation for the understanding of ego defense mechanisms. We shall see that this understanding flourished with the later development of ego psychology.

After his work with Breuer, Freud found hypnosis unsatisfactory and abandoned its use. The results of hypnosis were not lasting. Apparently the recovery by hypnosis of what was unconscious was not enough. While it was true that under hypnosis previously unconscious memories and feelings could be recovered, the removal or diminution of the defenses (what we would now call ego mechanisms of defense) by hypnosis did not allow for the investigation and analytic handling of such defenses against unacceptable feelings and ideas. Freud also found some patients to be refractory to hypnotism.

For a short period Freud used a "concentration" technique. The patient was encouraged, without hypnosis, to remember previous events related to his symptoms. This was soon abandoned and replaced by the method of "free association," which consists of the patient saying everything that comes without conscious reservation to his mind. This participation in the analytic process by free association has become known as the fundamental rule of psychoanalytic treatment. It was found that observations of the content and pattern of such associations could lead to knowledge of heretofore unconscious feelings, impulses, fantasies, and ideas.

It was observed that, despite the patient's conscious intent to free associate, there were obstructions to the associative process, to the uncovering of the unconscious, and to the recovery of the memories. These obstructions to analytic work became known as resistances. Consequently, an important component of the psychoanalytic effort became the recognition of resistances and the utilization of interpretation to remove their effect.

We shall now turn to a consideration of the concept of transference (Orr, 1954) and how transference (more accurately the transference neurosis), its development and resolution, has become the major distinguishing feature of that therapeutic method which is called psychoanalysis. The term, transference, at times has been applied loosely and taken to mean a rather general feature of the relationship between patient and therapist, essentially synonymous with the word, rapport. A phenomenon has been recognized which has been called a basic positive transference, the positive relationship which serves as a substrate for the analytic work. In psychoanalytic work, however, there is a more specific meaning to the concept of transference, namely the tendency for attitudes and impulses experienced in past relationships to repeat themselves in relation to the analyst.

In the report of the analysis of Dora (Freud, 1948j), which was published in 1905, Freud referred to transference, which he defined as "a special class of mental structures, for the most part unconscious. . . . They are new editions or facsimiles of the tendencies and fantasies which are aroused and made conscious during the process of the analysis; but they have this peculiarity, which is characteristic of their species, that they replace some earlier person by the person of the physician." Fenichel (1945) describes transference as follows: "The patient misunderstands the present in terms of the past; and then, instead of remembering the past, he strives, without recognizing the nature of his action, to relive the past and to relive it more satisfactorily than he did in childhood. He 'transfers' past attitudes to the present."

The analyst's efforts are directed toward the facilitation of the development and eventual resolution of the "transference neurosis." Gitelson (1951) describes transference neurosis as follows: "When the psychoanalytic technique is correctly applied, the events observed are relatively free from artifacts introduced by the activity of the observer. In this setting the phenomenon known as the transference neurosis develops. This is not created by the analyst. It appears under the pressure of the tendency of past attitudes and impulses to repeat themselves. It is permitted to establish itself and to evolve in its own terms and toward its own particular denouement. In the relationship to the analyst, there thus recur the significant emotional events of infancy and early childhood. These events do not present themselves as discrete transference episodes, but as part of a continuous process of recapitulation in the present of the continuous past, in the form of affects, fantasies, dreams, impulses, and somatic sets and tensions. It is this restoration of the past in the present that constitutes the microscopic field of psychoanalysis."

In the transference neurosis, there is directed toward the analyst a revival of emotional experiences from the past, an attributing to the therapist of the role of important persons from the patient's past life; a restoration of the past in the present; a replacing of some earlier person by the person of the physician; a misunderstanding of the present in terms of the past.

Having viewed the foregoing remarks regarding transference and resistance, let us consider a definition of psychoanalysis. The following remarks by Rangell (1954) offer a succinct statement of the basic ingredients. It is "a method of therapy whereby conditions are brought about favorable for the development of a transference neurosis in which the past is restored in the present, in order that, through a systematic interpretative attack on the resistances which oppose it, there appears a resolution of that neurosis (transference and infantile) to the end of bringing about structural changes in the mental apparatus of the patient, to make the latter capable of optimum adaptation to life." Thus, by interpreting resistances, there is a facilitation of the fullest possible development of the transference neurosis, i.e., the re-experiencing of the past in the present, which, in turn, is resolved by interpretation, which shows the patient how his misidentifications and distortions in the present relationship with the analyst have their origins in early life experiences.

I emphasize in this description of the standard psychoanalytic technique, the full development of the transference neurosis and the use of the technique of interpretation. We shall see, in relation to modifications of the standard technique, that suggestions are made according to which one does not strive for the full development of the transference neurosis, and in which techniques other than interpretation are used. Orr (1954) states that, "The development, interpretation and resolution of the transference neurosis in the analytic relationship is still the hallmark of psychoanalysis for perhaps a majority of analysts today; but for a considerable minority, this is by no means the case, or at least not without considerable attenuation and modification."

At the turn of the century and during the early decades of the 1900's, the nature and content of unconscious processes were explored, the libido theory was formulated, and the importance of infantile sexuality was emphasized. We shall not undertake detailed discussion of the libido theory and infantile sexuality. For our purposes, it is sufficient to note that exploration of the nature of the unconscious was a central aim of psychoanalytic effort in this early period.

Freud (1935) was aware that neurosis resulted from the effect of a combination of factors: (1) the predisposing effect of constitutional factors, (2) the precipitating effect of current life problems, and (3) the importance of early life experiences. The emphasis on early life experiences, of course, was a major contribution of psychoanalysis to the understanding of human behavior. In keeping with this theoretical formulation, the aim of psychoanalytic treatment at this time was to make the unconscious conscious, to recover memories of early childhood experiences, that is, to obliterate the infantile amnesia, to effect a reconstruction of the patient's early experiences. The phenomenon of transference was considered at first to present an obstacle to the task of making the unconscious conscious; it was seen as a block to the recovery of early memories and genetic reconstruction. Transference—the transference neurosis—has become the "dynamic axis of the curative process" (Alexander, 1956). As was described above, in the context of the transference tendency for the recurrence, in the relationship to the analyst, of significant past emotional events (which are elaborated in the transference neurosis), the old emotional conflicts can be resolved.

The tendency to repeat the past can be modified, by analysis, into a recollection of what is being carried over from the past, thus obviating the inclination for misidentifications and distortions in present relationships.

Although what has been described remains the basic core of psychoanalysis as a method of therapy, there have been subsequent developments of various facets of the psychoanalytic process. These developments were made possible by subsequent theoretical advances and clinical observations in addition to what was anticipated in remarks in Freud's series of technical papers.*

In 1920, Freud (1950) introduced the concept of the repetition compulsion and a revision of the theory of instincts to include more detailed knowledge of the aggressive drives. Transference was seen as an example of the repetition compulsion, manifested forcefully in the transference neurosis (Orr, 1954). The theory of aggressive drives represented an addition to previous emphasis on libidinal development and the role of psychosexuality, thus expanding our view of the instinctual drives. In addition, it contributed to subsequent theories about the development of the psychic apparatus, that is, the ego and the super-ego.

Thus far, our emphasis has been essentially on psychoanalysis as a method of treatment with the focus being mainly on such concepts as the unconscious, transference, transference neurosis, resistance, the fostering of the elaboration of the transference neurosis within the analytic relationship, and its resolution by interpretative efforts. I have not commented extensively on the psychoanalytic view of the nature of the content of the unconscious, the effect of psychosexual forces and their importance in the course of early development, and the central significance of the "Oedipus Complex." These, of course, have been among the distinguishing features of psychoanalytic theory, which have, in turn, determined the nature of psychoanalysis as a method of therapy. Psychoanalytic thinking about the nature of the unconscious and developmental experiences has determined the interpretation of the content of the transference.

There have been contributions during the past three decades regarding the early infantile phases of development, i.e., knowledge

---

*Freud stated and elaborated these principles in a series of papers on psychoanalytic technique, published between 1910 and 1919 (Freud, 1948b, c, d, e, f, g, h, i).

about the "pre-Oedipal" experiences and conflicts in the early mother-child relationship. These have influenced the content of our interpretation (Kris, 1951). In addition, our understanding of the nature of transference has been enhanced, e.g., when transference from early developmental periods occurs. There have been developments of knowledge of interpersonal and social factors. Depending on the author of such theoretical contributions, they have been offered in lieu of or as additions to the emphasis in psychoanalytic theory on intrapsychic factors—instinctual drives (Erikson, 1950; Fromm, 1947; Horney, 1939; Sullivan, 1953). From a technical point of view, the emphasis has remained in accordance with the established principles of dealing with resistance, fostering the development of the transference neurosis, the re-experiencing of early emotional conflicts within the analytic situation, the resolution of this transference neurosis by interpretative efforts, and the tracing of this to the past experiences of the individual and to his heretofore unresolved emotional conflicts.

Remarks about the Structural Hypothesis and Ego Psychology

Freud's *Ego and the Id* (1947) was first published in 1923. This book contained a statement of the structural hypothesis and a delineation of the components of the psychic apparatus into systems of function. In addition to the pre-existing predominance of psychoanalytic knowledge about unconscious "repressed" content and the id-unconscious instinctual drives, Freud crystallized and developed ideas regarding the nature, content, and functions of the ego and the super-ego. Briefly stated, the ego consists of those functions having to do with the harmonizing of subjective needs, the external environmental situation, and one's individual unconscious prohibitions and standards, in the form of a super-ego and ego-ideal. It includes such functions as perception, the ability to integrate external and internal perceptions, and control over motoric behavior. The super-ego, generally stated, includes the "regulators" of behavior in the form of unconscious prohibitions and standards.

There have been many and increasing contributions to the development and elaboration of ego psychology arising from the structural hypothesis (Gill, 1959). Ego psychology has included a view of the interrelationship among the various systems of function: of id, ego, and super-ego in relationship to the external environment. In addition, there have been studies of the "intrasystemic" functions of the ego, those functions related to what Hartmann (1958) has called the "conflict free sphere of the ego," the "autonomous" functions of the ego. Along with the theoretical developments, there have been increasing applications of ego psychology to psychoanalysis as a method of therapy (Hartmann, 1951; Kris, 1951, 1956).

In 1926 there appeared Freud's exceedingly important contribution, *The Problem of Anxiety* (1936), in which he revised the concept of anxiety consistent with the structural hypothesis. This has been of major significance in relation to the theory of psychic functioning and psychopathology. It has influenced the focus of psychoanalytic treatment. Anxiety was seen as a defensive warning signal which appeared in the face of intersystemic conflict. This warning stimulates defenses. The understanding of anxiety as a motive for defense has shed much light on the purpose and mechanism of ego functions in both pathological and non-pathological psychic functioning. The understanding of anxiety and derivative forms of motives for defense, namely guilt and shame, contributed to our understanding of what we see clinically and how and what we interpret to the patient.

Psychoanalysis can be said to have become concerned with "ego psychology," "psychology of the surface," "increased attention to the environment," and "introduction of cognitive and adaptive considerations" (Gill, 1959). These concerns have become increasingly and integrally synthesized with previous developments of the psychology of the id, *i.e.*, the nature of the unconscious instinctual forces, psychosexuality, and importance of infantile experiences.

Clinical problems have stimulated developments of theory. The development of the structural hypothesis can be seen to have received impetus from the necessity to answer questions arising during clinical observation. Kris (1951) points out that: an interest in psychoses led Freud to his formulation of narcissism and to approach the ego as a psychic organization rather than a series of isolated functions; clinical observations of patients with negative therapeutic reactions led to thinking about the unconscious sense of guilt, of self-punitive trends and self-reproaches, and to the recognition of important characteristics of the super-ego; observation of what today we call character neuroses led to consideration of the unconscious nature of resistances and defense and to formulations about the unconscious and preconscious functions of the ego.

To emphasize that the development of psychoanalytic treatment has been a continuous process, it should be noted that much of what is contained in the framework of ego psychology is not entirely new but represents elaboration of what was previously anticipated in psychoanalytic writings. Kris (1951) notes that Freud's papers on technique occupy a "pivotal position in psychoanalytic literature," and that many subsequent writings on technique, rather than modifying the precepts presented in these papers, have illustrated, confirmed, and elaborated them. For example, there is in one of these early papers, the advice that analysis should start from the surface and that resistance should be analyzed before interpreting content. This contains principles related to ego psychology which have been elaborated rather extensively in the past two or three decades. Changes in psychoanalytic technique have been not only the consequence of developments of psychoanalytic theory. Contributions have, of course, resulted from the process of increasing skill and improved ability in the course of clinical experience (Kris, 1951).

Significant effects that psychoanalytic ego psychology has had on the theory and practice of psychoanalytic technique include: (1) The enhancement of our understanding and ability to deal with resistance and defense. (2) The contribution to our understanding of what happens in the psychoanalytic process. (3) A widening of the scope of indications for psychoanalytic therapy.

Kris (1951) has pointed out that with better understanding and improvement in the handling of resistance and defense, there has been a change in the "climate" of analysis. There has been a gradual transformation of technique. We understand resistance as a part of the defensive activities of ego. It no longer has the connotation of a patient who "resists" the physician who is annoyed by the patient's opposition. It is no longer simply an obstacle of analysis, but part of the "psychic surface" which has to be explored. The understanding of resistance in the context of the defense activities of the ego brings it into focus as an integral part of the analytic interpretative effort.

Wilhelm Reich (1945) developed what has been called "resistance" and "layer analysis." His views represent a contribution to the analysis of character defense. Kaiser's proposed method, called "resistance analysis," was an extreme distortion of technique which emphasized the primacy of interpretation of resistance over content interpretation (Alexander, 1956). The real value of the understanding of resistance and defense mechanisms of the ego as a contribution to psychoanalytic technique results not from the emphasis on one component of the technical problem, but from the integration of the ego psychology emphasis, the exploration of the psychic surface, with the previously established knowledge of the operations of the unconscious content, i.e., the amalgamation of the analysis of the ego with the analysis of the id.

Ego psychology has offered us increased understanding of the process of psychoanalytic treatment. Alexander (1956) has summarized the essentials of some of the important contributions in this area: In

1924, Alexander (1925) considered how the analyst's interpretation helped the patient replace older, automatic super-ego functions with conscious judgment; that is, the super-ego functions were replaced by ego functions. In 1934, Strachey (1934) presented his ideas about the effect of the analyst's interpretations. He believed that the patient ascribes the functions of his super-ego to the analyst. In contrast to Alexander's view that the super-ego functions are replaced by ego functions, conscious judgment, Strachey saw the analytic effort resulting in the patient's having a more permissive super-ego in accordance with the modified image of the analyst. Sterba (1934), in his significant paper, "The Fate of the Ego in Analytic Therapy," delineated the capacity of the ego for "dissociation." During therapy there develops a "new point of view of intellectual contemplation" as well as "affective experience," i.e., while there is an automatic repetition of past feelings in the transference neurosis, there is the capacity to observe oneself and one's ego functions. Nunberg (1931), in writing about the "synthetic" functions of the ego, first emphasized that it is by an integrating act of the ego that unconscious content becomes conscious. He showed how analytic interpretations effected the breaking up of overgeneralized and primitive connections and the establishment of new connections. French's publications on learning in the course of psychoanalytic treatment (1936) and the integration of behavior (1952, 1954, 1959) offer us an understanding of psychological functioning, the therapeutic process, and psychoanalytic technique in terms of his development of psychoanalytic ego psychology.

Knowledge of ego functions and super-ego functions has increased with the delineation of the structural hypothesis and ego psychology. There has consequently resulted an increasing ability to deal with those cases wherein such functions are deficient; that is, where there are failures in ego-development, ego modifications, and ego distortions (Gitelson, 1958). Thus, the range of psychopathological conditions to which psychoanalytic treatment efforts can be applied, with more or less modification of the standard technique, has increased in scope.*

Countertransference

Freud (1948b) introduced the term countertransference in 1910, and, in recent years, there has been increasing interest in this subject (Orr, 1954). Freud said, "We have begun to consider the 'countertransference' which arises in the physician as a result of the patient's

---

*There will be further discussion of the widening scope of psychoanalytic treatment below.

influence on his unconscious feelings, and have nearly come to the point of requiring the physician to recognize and overcome this countertransference himself. . . . Anyone who cannot succeed in this self-analysis may without further ado, regard himself as unable to treat neurotics by analysis." In 1915 (Freud, 1948h), he referred again to this phenomenon, saying, "To the physician, it represents an invaluable explanation and a useful warning against any tendency to counter-transference which may be lurking in his mind. He must recognize that the patient's falling in love is induced by the analytic situation and is not to be ascribed to the charms of his person . . . and it is always well to be reminded of this."

It seems as if fuller understanding of the transference and trans-ference neurosis had to be developed before effective systematic atten-tion could be given to the analyst's emotional involvement in the treat-ment. In the past two decades there have been increased interest and fuller exploration regarding how the course of treatment is affected by the "analyst's unconscious and conscious, spontaneous and studied reac-tions toward the patients" (Alexander, 1956).

Theoretically, the analyst should represent a blank screen, a "mir-ror," in order that the transference neurosis can develop uninfluenced by the analyst's personality. With such avoidance of the intrusion of the analyst's personality, what is transferred to the analyst from sig-nificant persons in the patient's past can stand out clearly and more readily be recognized. The study of countertransference has involved the recognition of how there are deviations from this ideal model and considerations of how this can be handled.

In 1954, Orr (1954) published a valuable historical survey of trans-ference and countertransference.* He offered a catalogue of points of view about countertransference. The various definitions have included such ideas as countertransference being all the analyst's possible atti-tudes toward the patient, that there are conscious and unconscious countertransference, and that countertransference is a phenomenon paralleling transference in which the analyst repeats toward the patient emotional attitudes transferred from important figures in his earlier life. At present, I will not attempt to reproduce Orr's excellent review of ideas about countertransference. It is sufficient for our purposes to note that this important facet of the psychoanalytic therapy process has gained increasing attention and that future developments in this area will enhance psychoanalytic technique. It has been suggested by

---

*Orr (1954) states, "Although the concept of transference, from the point of view of definition, offers some semblance of evolutionary progression to some-thing commanding wide agreement among psychoanalysts, the same cannot be said of countertransference."

some that the analyst's understanding of his countertransference can be used to increase his understanding of the patient's transference reactions. In a recent paper, Tower (1956) stated that in truly deep analytic procedures, something in the nature of a "countertransference neurosis" develops and this may be of great significance, in the sense of a catalytic agent, for the course of the treatment. She states that "its uncovering, analysis, and resolution by the analyst may be useful to a deeper understanding by the analyst of the transference neurosis."

The present state of this problem is summarized by Orr (1954). He says, "During the past ten years, the psychoanalytic literature on the subject of countertransference—variously defined—has dealt with several possible themes; some old, some new: (1) the analyst as 'mirror' versus the analyst as 'human being'; (2) the question of whether the analyst stays out of the analysis as much as is humanly possible, except for the work of interpretation, in order to facilitate development of the transference neurosis; or whether he intervenes more actively in order to attenuate the transference, to manipulate it, or to assume attitudes or play roles designed to provide the patient with a more healthy interpersonal experience than he has known before; and finally, (3) when inevitable countertransference feelings or situations develop, whether or not to communicate those to the patient, together with a partial or complete analysis of them in order to mitigate or undo their effect." Current researches involving detailed observation of the analytic process will probably provide us with increased knowledge of the nature of the analyst's participation in the psychoanalytic treatment process.

Widening Scope of Indications for Psychoanalytic Therapy

With theoretical and clinical developments there has been a widening of the scope of indications for psychoanalysis (Freud, Anna 1954; Jacobson, 1954; Stone, 1954). (Stone's paper (1954) gives an excellent and comprehensive discussion of this topic). Psychoanalysis started with the treatment of hysteria, phobias, and obsessive compulsive neurosis. There was some early interest in character neurosis, but character analysis as such awaited the era of ego psychology, when Wilhelm Reich (1945) gave it impetus. Freud was conservative about the therapeutic application of psychoanalysis. He believed the true indications for psychoanalysis to be the transference psychoneuroses and equivalent character disturbances. "Transference psychoneuroses" were differentiated from "narcissistic neuroses." The former included hysteria, phobias, and obsessive-compulsive neurosis. The latter included such conditions as psychosis and depressive states. It was believed that in the narcissistic neuroses there was an incapacity for the development of the transference, which is necessary for the application of psychoanalytic technique aimed at mobilization and resolution of the transference neurosis.

In recent years, there has been an enthusiasm on the part of some to the point where "scarcely any human problems admits a solution other than psychoanalysis; by the same token, there is an almost magical expectation of help which does it grave injustice" (Stone, 1954). There has been, however, a real expansion of the indications for psychoanalysis. There were early applications to manic-depressives, psychoses, development of child analysis, and treatment of delinquents. Psychoanalysis (with more or less modification of the standard technique) has been applied to such conditions as depressions, perversions, schizophrenias, and psychosomatic disorders, and increasing interest has developed in what has been called the "borderline" states (Knight, 1953).

Facilitating this expansion, e.g., to include conditions which were formerly called "narcissistic neuroses," has been increasing knowledge and experience with transference phenomena, infantile developmental stages (pregenitality), knowledge of ego functions, including mechanisms of defense and early ego development and function, and the nature of the early mother-child relationships. For instance, it has been recognized that in "borderline" cases, the problem is not the absence of transference but its intensity and primitive nature. We are also in a better position now to deal with disorders in ego functions [e.g., in cases with ego modification (Eissler, 1953) and ego distortions (Gitelson, 1958)]. Necessary variations in technique can be employed without (or with as minimal as possible) interference with the goal of eventual mobilization of the transference neurosis and its resolution (or minimization) by interpretative means. Awareness of countertransference has also been important. For instance, the analyst has to be aware of feelings, fears, and anxiety aroused in him by the primitive nature and intensity of the transference.

Modifications and Variations of the Standard Psychoanalytic Technique

Variations from the standard technique have emphasized one or another of the following three therapeutic factors: (1) Emotional abreaction; (2) Intellectual insight; (3) Recovery of repressed infantile memories (Alexander, 1956). These are really closely interrelated and dependent upon one another. In Freud's technical papers, the importance of the emotional experience within the transference was emphasized. In the 1920's, Ferenczi and Rank (1925) emphasized the emotional experience within the transference neurosis, perhaps stimulated by the previous over-emphasis on psychoanalysis as an intellectual process. Alexander (1946, 1954, 1956) has offered a variation of traditional psychoanalytic technique aimed at fostering the emotional experience within the transference neurosis. He advocates that, after the establishment of the transference neurosis, the analyst should create an emotional climate to promote a "corrective emotional experience." He says, "The analyst attempts to replace his spontaneous countertransference reactions with attitudes which are consciously planned and adopted according to the dynamic exigencies of the therapeutic situation." For example, by taking an attitude toward the patient opposite to the parental attitude which had a pathogenic effect, a "corrective emotional experience" for the patient is fostered. This attitude assumed by the analyst is based on his knowledge of the interpersonal climate in the patient's early experiences. The interpersonal climate in the treatment situation challenges the patient's ego to find a new appropriate adjustment especially if the climate is in sharp contrast to the original interpersonal relationship in which the neurotic pattern was formed.

Regarding the transference neurosis, the emotional re-experiencing of the past, Alexander suggests techniques to keep it at an optimal intensity. Changing the frequency of interviews and temporary interruptions of the treatment are suggested to effect this, especially to avoid excessive regression and dependent transference.

Greenacre (1954) states that there are two points of view prevalent regarding the question of the development of the transference in psychoanalytic treatment. (1) There are those who advocate the full development of the transference neurosis, that is, to permit, even emphasize, the repetition of as full a transference reaction as is possible as a medium of re-experience and interpretation. (2) There is the other approach which uses the basic transference, avoids full transference neurosis development, interprets dynamic lines and relationships rather than specific past experiences. The advocates of the first approach emphasize that traditional formal arrangements, e.g., free association, the use of the couch, frequency of interviews, and the neutrality of the analyst, are important, insofar as they are conducive to the goal of the fullest possible development of transference neurosis (Greenacre, 1954). Flexibility of approach, however, has been suggested in psychoanalytic treatment which deals with resistances, the transference neurosis, and the countertransference (Weigert, 1954).

Variations from the standard psychoanalytic technique might be required on the basis of the nature of the patient's psychic structure and function. Intervention other than the basic model technique of interpretation in the context of the transference neurosis is required in cases where the structure of the patient's ego precludes the effective use of interpretation alone. Eissler (1953) has designated deviations from the basic model technique—using interpretation alone—as "parameters." He offers rules for the use of parameters within the framework of the basic model technique. It is required that the treatment does not end with the lasting effect of the parameter, but that the parameter itself should be brought into the transference situation and resolved by interpretation.

Psychoanalysis and Dynamic Psychotherapy: Their Similarities and Differences

Attention has been given to the question of the relationship between psychoanalysis and psychotherapy, and their similarities and differences (Alexander, 1956; Gill, 1954; Gitelson 1951; Rangell, 1954). Approaches other than psychoanalysis proper (as seen by those who maintain that there is a distinct difference) have been variously designated, e.g., "dynamic psychotherapy," "psychoanalytic psychotherapy," "psycho-analytically oriented psychotherapy," and "modified psychoanalysis." There are: (1) those who believe that there is a continuum with no discernible or practical line of demarcation; (2) those who hold that the two are separable and distinct entities and procedures (Rangell, 1954). These do not necessarily have to be mutually exclusive. We might consider that there is a continuum, but that activities, at the ends of the continuum are qualitatively as well as quantitatively different, thus separable and distinct.

Those who maintain the differentiation emphasize the differences in a) technique and b) goal (Gitelson, 1951). Without going into detail, it could be said that the technique and analytic attitude is that which favors the goal of the full development, understanding, and resolution of the transference neurosis. This is characterized by the following quotation from Gill (1954), that "Psychoanalysis is that technique, which employed by a neutral psychoanalyst, results in the development of a regressive transference neurosis and the ultimate resolution of this transference neurosis by interpretation alone."

Another point of view [e.g., Alexander (1956)] is that the only logical distinction is between approaches which employ supportive measures and those which use uncovering methods. Even differentiation of these is not always possible because supportive and uncovering elements are present in all treatment. Primarily supportive methods are indicated when the functional impairment of the ego is of a temporary nature caused by acute emotional distress. In chronic conditions where the ego's functional impairment is caused by unresolved emotional conflicts of childhood, there is required a treatment in which the ego is exposed to earlier pathogenic experiences. Alexander (1956) says, "Psychoanalytic principles are being applied in various forms. The only logical solution is to identify as similar a'l those related procedures which are based essentially on the same scientific concepts, observations, and technical principles and to differentiate them from intuitive psychotherapies and from those treatments which are based on different theoretical concepts and different therapeutic procedures."

Definitions of psychoanalysis as a treatment emphasize the importance of interpretation, i.e., the gaining of insight from interpretation and, ideally, by no other technique of interpersonal behavior on the part of the analyst. This is characteristic of the "standard" psychoanalytic technique [(cf. Alexander's proposed modification, 1946, 1954, 1956)] aimed at enhancing the emotional experience in the analytic process, the achievement of therapeutic effect by a "corrective emotional experience." The following brief remarks point to the nature of interpretation and its relationship to other technical activities.

Edward Bibring (1954) has proposed a conceptual scheme of psychotherapy that attempts to clarify this matter. He points out that interpretation means helping the patient become aware of the unconscious material, i.e., unconscious defensive operations (motives and mechanisms of defense), unconscious warded-off instinctual tendencies, the hidden meaning of the patient's behavior patterns, and their unconscious inter-connections. Interpretation is addressed to those unconscious processes that are assumed to determine the patient's manifest behavior.

Bibring outlined also the therapeutic principles and procedures that are applicable to psychotherapy, independent of ideologies or theoretical systems. The technical principles include: (1) suggestive, (2) abreactive, (3) manipulative, (4) clarifying, and (5) insight through interpretation. The therapeutic procedures include: (1) production of material, (2) utilization of the produced materials, (mainly) by the therapist and/or the patient, (3) assimilation by the patient of the results of such utilization (4) process of reorientation and readjustment. Bibring (1954) points out that "the dynamic psychotherapies (by which term we understand methods derived from psychoanalysis proper) are characterized by particular selections and combinations of the basic principles with their inherent goals and by certain modifications of the procedures." He then states that "In psychoanalysis proper, all of the therapeutic principles are employed to a varying degree, in a technical sense as well as in a curative sense, but they form a hierarchical structure in that insight through interpretation is the principal agent and all others are—theoretically and practically—subordinate to it."

I have tried to present a panoramic view of the field of psychoanalytic treatment as well as a closeup on some essential details. It seemed worthwhile, in the context of the consideration of various approaches, to get a view of the developments and evolution within the framework of psychoanalysis. We have seen how psychoanalytic treatment, originating from cathartic hypnosis, reached the point of development of its basic features, i.e., the central importance of the transference neurosis and its resolution by interpretative means; how it was augmented and enhanced by the structural hypothesis and ego psychology; that it became necessary to investigate the analyst's participation in the process (countertransference); that modifications of standard technique have been proposed; and that as a basic science, psychoanalysis has contributed so much to dynamic psychotherapies that there is the necessity to raise questions and to explore the relationship—make comparisons of the similarities and differences—between psychoanalysis and other psychotherapies.

A Demonstration of
Psychoanalytic Therapy

by Arthur A. Miller, M.D.

MY PURPOSE in this paper will be to demonstrate some of the essential features of the psychoanalytic process. I shall not present exhaustive case studies but enough of the patient's history to provide background information. I shall emphasize the transference reactions which occur, since the development of the transference neurosis and its resolution by interpretation is a critical feature of psychoanalytic therapy.

In my previous paper I pointed out the nature of transference, the transference neurosis, and how psychoanalytic therapy is characterized by these phenomena. The following three quotations offer a cogent summary view of this. Consequently, although they are cited in the previous paper, they bear repetition.

Fenichel (1945) defines transference as follows: "The patient misunderstands the present in terms of the past; and then, instead of remembering the past, he strives, without recognizing the nature of his action, to relive the past and to relive it more satisfactorily than he did in childhood. He 'transfers' past attitudes to the present."

Gitelson (1951) states: "When the psychoanalytic technique is correctly applied, the events observed are relatively free from artifacts introduced by the activity of the observer. In this setting the phenomenon known as the transference neurosis develops. This is not created by the analyst. It appears under the pressure of the tendency of past attitudes and impulses to repeat themselves. It is permitted to establish itself and to evolve in its own terms and toward its own particular denouement. In the relationship to the analyst, there thus recur the significant emotional events of infancy and early childhood. These events do not present themselves as discrete transference episodes, but as part of a continuous process of recapitulation in the present of the continuous past, in the form of affects, fantasies, dreams, impulses, and somatic sets and tensions. It is this restoration of the past in the present that constitutes the microscopic field of psychoanalysis."

Rangell (1954) presents the following definition of the essential ingredients of psychoanalysis: It is "a method of therapy whereby conditions are brought about favorable for the development of a transference neurosis in which the past is restored in the present, in order that, through a systematic interpretative attack on the resistances which oppose it, there appears a resolution of that neurosis (transference and infantile) to the end of bringing about structural changes in the mental apparatus of the patient, to make the latter capable of optimum adaptation to life."

In the face of the phenomenon of transference repetition, interpretative efforts are directed toward obviating the resistance to the development, elaboration, and concentration of this restoration of the past in the present relationship to the analyst and the analytic situation—the transference neurosis.

It should be noted that what is repeated in the transference neurosis can also be seen to occur in other relationships in the patient's current life; that both reactions within the analysis and in the patient's current life are characterized by transference misunderstandings, misidentifications, and distortions. In the analysis a substrate is provided, systematically, for viewing these transference repetitions. The analyst does not stop at the facilitations of these repetitions. He helps the patient observe what he is experiencing and to effect a recollection of its origins and relationship to the patient's past. The resolution of the transference neurosis requires repeated demonstration to the patient of the same thing in various connections. One interpretation does not suffice. This process of repeated demonstrations and gradual resolution of the transference neurosis is called "working through." (Freud 1948f).*

The following patient was a 32-year-old man of German Lutheran background, married and the father of a three-year-old daughter. He had a degree in electrical engineering from an outstanding university. He was in the midst of a promising career with a large corporation. At

---

*The foregoing description deals with the standard psychoanalytic technique. See my previous paper for a discussion of proposed modification and variations of the standard psychoanalytic technique.

the time he sought analysis, he had been advancing in his work and had recently been promoted to a junior executive position.

About a year before coming for analysis, when he knew he was being considered for promotion, he began to experience the symptoms which led him to seek help. He had begun to experience episodes of unexplained anxiety and periods of mild depression. He found that he had a disinclination to engage in sexual relations with his wife, although he was often preoccupied with fantasies of having an affair with another woman, and he had frequent episodes of sexual impotence when he did attempt sexual relations with his wife. He found that, although people with whom he worked considered him to be a very competent man, he had begun to have doubts as to whether he could do the work expected of him. There was an increasing tendency to procrastinate, e.g., when he had to prepare reports regarding his work which would come to the attention of senior executives in the corporation. On some mornings he found himself depressed on awakening and reluctant to go to the office. He had some recognition that this occurred on days when he had to attend an important business conference or when he was going to have lunch or play golf with the president of the corporation, who considered him an able young man on the brink of a promising career. With increasing frequency, he was bothered by the thought that he was in danger of having a heart attack and would thus become disabled.

The patient was the third of four siblings. He had two older brothers, three and five years older, and a sister five years younger. His father had migrated from Germany as a boy, started working during his early adolescent years and had managed to build a successful, medium-sized retail business. Although the father was capable of warmth and tenderness with his children, he always expected proper behavior, a high degree of academic performance, and that his sons be strong, masculine, competent, and successful. The patient's brothers were both in business with his father. There had recently been an increasing amount of conflict between his brothers regarding who was to be dominant in the business as the father was gradually going into semi-retirement. His sister, a registered nurse, had married a physician. The family, in general, appeared to be proud of the patient's success. There was, however, evidence of envy on the part of his brothers. At times, they would subtly depreciate the patient, his work, and his way of life. They were inclined to treat him as if he were still "little brother" and, much to his chagrin, he would find himself unable to free himself from that role in their presence.

His mother, whose family had come to the United States from Germany the year before she was born, was a hard-working, dutiful wife, whose life revolved around her husband, home, and her children. The patient was considered her favorite during his childhood. She had wanted a daughter when he was born. In his early years, she was over-protective of him and treated him as a "little prince." Although his mother's attitude toward him continued even after his sister's birth, he recalled responding to his sister's presence with a sense of disappointment and loss.

He was always a good student. Prior to his early teens he was looked upon by his family and his friends as being a little "sissyish." With the onset of adolescence, he made a strong effort to divest himself of any characteristics which could be called sissyish and put much effort into effecting the appearance of an independent, masculine person. He recalled that, during his adolescence, he was haunted by a fear that something would happen to his eyes and he would become blind. In high school and college, he was considered personable and very much "one of the boys." He dated a fair amount during his high school and college years, but he wondered whether this was not as much for the sake of appearance as from an interest in being with a female. He responded with most interest to women who seemed to be attracted to him, and who sought him out because of his rather charming, boyish quality and handsome, virile appearance. He recognized that in the relationship with the woman he eventually married, at 27 years, she, however subtly, had often taken the lead. In the course of their marriage, she had gradually come to expect more decisiveness on his part, a fact which at times led to arguments between them.

Early in the analysis, he presented an attitude of self-sufficiency. He expressed great pride in never having to ask for anything from anyone. He referred to his need to always be on the go and his difficulty in relaxing, even on week-ends and vacations. There were references in his associations to people he knew who were not as self-sufficient as he felt they ought to be and he considered their behavior shameful and a sign of weakness. I pointed out that he seemed to be ashamed of his own wish for help and his dependent longings and that he seemed to be exerting considerable effort in denying these wishes in himself. His associations led to a recollection of his father's pride in being a "self-made man" and his shaming, disdainful attitude toward men who could not solve their own problems. As he associated further, he came to the realization that he had expected that I would take the same attitude toward these wishes as his father had. During subsequent analytic sessions, his associations contained increasing references to wishes for attention, notice, and care. The flow of his speech became rather halting. There were intervals of silence and expressions of wishing me to give him a "road map." In his dreams and fantasies, he pictured me as a strict and suppressive person. I pointed out that he seemed to wish to see me in this way and was thus relinquishing his freedom of expression. There then appeared associations to the danger of freedom and the possibility of expressing angry demands. He recalled how, in his childhood, anger and what was considered selfishness were not tolerated by his parents, and that they would respond to his behavior with a firm expression of displeasure, scoldings, or spankings. In the course of the analysis, it became easier for him to express his demands and to venture to become more conscious of his anger when he felt it. He became less concerned about displeasing me and he became aware of how he had expected me to respond to his angry demands with the same critical, punitive, or rejecting attitude as his parents had. He became aware also of how this same concern had arisen in his relations with other people in his life.

At one analytic session, he was several minutes late. I ended the session at the usual time. When he returned the next time, he had difficulty in talking. He spoke at some length of his irritation with his wife and daughter on the previous evening. He realized that he had no real reason for this feeling toward them. In the course of his associations, he mentioned that he had been irritated by the heavy traffic as he drove to my office; that it was difficult to find a parking place today; that the elevator operator did not seem as friendly today as he usually was; that he did not like the color of the new drapes in my office. At times, he appeared to be scowling or pouting. I said that he might be feeling angry toward me. He then associated to the fact that I had not let him stay for the full period when he had been late for the previous session. He recalled that, earlier in the week, he had seen a young woman patient leave my office and that he had not seen her before. A recent newspaper account about a kidnapping and murder of a little girl came to his mind. I pointed out that he was angry about the new woman patient. This led to associations about whether I preferred her to him, his wish to be the only one, and fantasies that I did not care about him, but wanted to get rid of him.

He started the next hour by relating a dream. There was a woman in the dream who seemed to have features that were a combination of his mother and me. He was on a stage, in the spotlight, reciting or singing. There was a large audience. He tripped and hit his head on a table. A coat, or some discussion about a coat, also appeared in the dream. His associations led eventually to the new woman patient and a memory of feeling uncomfortable when he saw her for the first time. In connection with the coat, he thought of royal robes. The tripping and hitting his head brought to mind the time he had pushed his infant sister and her head had been hurt when it banged against the table. He became increasingly aware of his anger toward me because I had begun to see this new woman patient, whom he felt I might prefer to him. He then associated to memories of feeling angry toward his infant sister and toward his mother when she took care of the sister. He remembered how he had been treated like the "little prince" before his sister was born. He was the adored youngest child until then. He had received much attention because he was bright and had the ability to recite little poems. He then recalled how he had been somewhat depressed at times during his wife's pregnancy. He had a fear that something might happen to his daughter, whom he felt he loved, but, despite conscious feelings of love toward her, with whom he sometimes played a little too roughly. He thought of his irritation with his boss' new secretary. When with a group of people in social situations, he often experienced what he called "moods." He considered whether he might be feeling irritation at such times, e.g., when his wife was talking to someone else and he was not the center of attention.

A few months later, he started a session by saying that he had been to the theater on the previous evening and had thought he saw me there. He wondered what I do when I am not working; whether I enjoyed going to the theater. For several days, he had been feeling an irritation in his eyes and his vision at times was slightly blurred. He had been finding it difficult to read for more than a few minutes without feeling tired. He had read in the newspaper an article regarding the question of whether the city's movie censor board was too stringent in its standards. I pointed out that he seemed to be taking a rather stringent attitude toward his curiosity; that he seemed to feel guilty about it. He recalled with what trepidation he went to a burlesque show with his friends for the first time during his adolescence. He spoke of his anxious preoccupation, during his adolescent years, with the idea that he might go blind. During the next several analytic sessions, his associations revolved around the matter of curiosity. He gradually revealed more and more questions about me and my wife, e.g., when we were married, how many children we had, whether they were boys or girls, what my wife looked like, and what our sexual life was like. He felt that I would consider him a "snooper," that I would feel it was none of his business, and that I would chastise him for being so forward. He eventually associated to memories of his curiosity about his parents. A favorite childhood activity was looking at the family photo album. He was especially fond of looking at the photos of his mother and his father which were taken during their courtship and during the early years of their marriage. He remembered how, during his childhood, he would lie awake listening to the sounds coming from his parents' bedroom, which was adjacent to his. He would become frightened at his

inability to see anything in the darkness of his bedroom. A glimpse of
the light streaming in through the crack beneath the door of the room
would reassure him that he was not blind. He became aware of how he
had felt guilty and expected to be punished for his curiosity about his
parents' sexual activities and his rage about being excluded.

During a session a few months later, he remarked that he found
himself uncomfortable when standing next to me in the waiting room
or in my office. Being a very tall man, he would then see clearly that
he was taller than I. He remembered how, as a boy, he admired and
envied the physical stature of his father and his brothers. He had been
pleased when, during his adolescence, with a spurt of growth he became
the tallest one in his family. He then revealed, with some discomfort,
some recent recognition and advancement in his work. After speaking
with an air of confidence and pride in his ability at work, he began to
make some self-depreciating remarks in this connection. He then associated to how difficult it had been for him, even until recently, to completely divest himself of the feeling of being "young son" or "little
brother."

The following hour he reported a dream that referred to and led
to further associations about the second Joe Louis-Max Schmeling fight.
He remarked that in this fight Joe Louis won, having lost the first time.
He associated to Max Schmeling being a German and he wondered
whether my name was of German origin. He then mentioned the fact
that his father had been born in Germany. During the next several sessions, there were increasing references to his competitive feelings toward me. There appeared self-assertive remarks, depreciating thoughts
about me, at times followed by self-depreciating remarks and the tendency to present himself as being, after all, just a small son and brother.
He revealed a fantasy that, if he fully declared himself as a man, he
might hurt me or that I might hurt him in retaliation. He recalled,
with increasing clarity, fantasies he had had of this nature in the past
in regard to his father and brothers. During these sessions, I pointed
out to him such things as the following: his hesitant manner when he
began to make self-assertive and competitive remarks; how self-depreciating remarks and protestations of smallness defensively followed his
inclinations to self-assertion as they appeared in his associations and
dreams. In addition to seeing his pattern of defenses and the defended-
against impulses as they appeared in relation to me as well as, in the
past, in relation to his father and brothers, he recognized how he responded similarly in other situations in his current life. He, for example, noted that his anxiety about playing golf or having lunch with
senior executives with whom he worked caused him to be anxious and
to tend to shy away from such activities; that this was because if he

participated with them as an equal he was deprived of his previous defense of feeling himself as an underling, which helped him defend against his anxiety-provoking, guilt-laden competitive impulses toward men.

In the foregoing clinical excerpts, we can see how the analyst was identified variously in the patient's transference neurosis as his mother, father, or brothers, depending upon the state of his transference at any given time. Other persons in the analytic situation also became the carriers of transference from significant persons in the past. The central importance of transference in the therapeutic process may be seen from the fact that it was specifically the observation of what he experienced in the transference neurosis that led to an awareness of the connections of his responses with his past experiences. He also gained an understanding of how in other parts of his life—with his family, at work, and in social situations—he responded with misunderstandings, distortions and misidentifications based on transference repetitions from his past experiences.

Early in the analysis he presented an attitude of self-sufficiency, pride in not having to ask for help, and the feeling that seeking help was shameful and weak. I showed him his defenses against his dependent longings. It then became apparent to him that, in this connection, he evaluated himself in terms of his father's standards and expectations and that, at this time, he was misidentifying me—expecting me to take the same attitude as his father had.

When he was motivated by a wish for care and attention, together with anger over the frustration of such wishes, he pictured me as being strict and suppressive and wished me to give him a "road map." He wished me (ascribing to me a transferred parental role) to protect him against freedom of expression, which would place him in the danger of expressing his angry feelings. He unconsciously expected me to react toward such feelings as had his parents—with displeasure, scolding, or punishment. As he differentiated me from the transferred parental image he tended to ascribe to me, it became easier for him to express his demands and anger. As the difference between me and his parents became clearer, the seeming necessity for his previous defenses was removed and he could give expression to the previously warded-off ideas and feelings in increasingly less disguised form.

We have seen how a transference was made to the new woman patient. She was identified by him with a previous significant "newcomer," i.e. his sister at the time of her birth. His feelings toward me, at this time, were a repetition of feelings he had felt toward his mother when she took care of his sister. He was able to observe that he experienced similar transference elsewhere, e.g. when his wife or his boss represented his mother and his daughter or the boss' secretary represented his sister.

At the time the patient had the eye symptoms, he was experiencing a conflict over his curiosity, with a feeling of guilt about such wishes. As he realized that I, unlike his parents, would not oppose such interests on his part, he could express, with increasing clarity, his sexual curiosity. He saw that he was curious about my sexual life; that he, in the transference neurosis, ascribed to me the role of his father and to my wife the role of his mother; that, at this time, he was inclined to respond with the same anxiety, guilt, and defenses he had experienced in his childhood situation.

The patient's reaction to the fact that he was taller than I and his reactions in the subsequent hours were characterized by transference. His anxiety about surpassing me in this respect originated in his early relationships with his father and brothers. In the transference neurosis, he reacted toward me with the impulses, anxieties, and defenses which were at one time relevant to his relationship with them. His defensive self-depreciation and tendency to hold on to an image of himself as "younger son" or "little brother" in relation to me was to protect himself from his competitive impulses and fantasies of harming me or being harmed by me in retaliation. The defensive pattern of handling these impulses, fantasies, and anxieties was a repetition of what had developed in his childhood and adolescence in regard to his father and brothers. He was also able to see how the same conflict and defenses were transferred to other situations—e.g. in relation to men with whom he worked.

Certain features of the patient's transference may at times elicit responses from the analyst that would interfere with the analyst's understanding of the transference and his ability to make an effective interpretation. Responses of this kind on the part of the analyst would be included in what is called countertransference. An analyst with conflict about his own dependent, receptive longings and his shame over such longings, for example, might not be able to deal effectively with the patient's defenses against dependent and receptive wishes. If the analyst was inclined to defend himself by over-compensatory independence, he might not be able to see clearly the defensive nature of similar behavior on the part of the patient in the transference. Similarly, an analyst's anxiety about demands and expression of anger might interfere with his helping the patient to recognize the defensive wish to be controlled as being related to underlying hostile demanding impulses.

In the early hours of the above clinical material, for example, an analyst who had unresolved conflicts about dependent, receptive wishes, and about angry demands, could have interfered—because of his countertransference—with the expression of wishes and impulses which were defended against by over-compensatory independence and the defensive wish to be controlled.

Unresolved conflicts in the analyst about competition and rivalry, for example, with unresolved transferences in relation to his own father or brothers, might lead to activation of such conflict within the analyst when the patient's transference involves conflicts of this kind. This might interfere with the analyst's ability to help the patient express competitive strivings within the transference situation. As a result, the patient might repeat, but not resolve, a previous defensive pattern of considering himself a small person, little brother or small son. This could, for instance, have occurred in the later hours of the case presented above, when the patient was experiencing competitive feelings—and defenses against them—in relation to the analyst. The analyst might have communicated to the patient, more or less subtly, that he was not ready to accept the patient's expression of competition, but instead felt more comfortable with the patient's defensive protestations of smallness, being little brother, or young son. The analyst cannot expect to be completely free from the possibility of countertransference reactions. It is a part of his task to be aware of the possibility of such reactions, to be alert to their existence when they do occur, and to perform the necessary analytic work on himself in order to eliminate this potential impediment to the effective resolution of the patient's transference neurosis.

Here is another brief clinical illustration: This patient was a 27-year-old Jewish woman. When she sought analysis, she had been divorced for three years and was working as a registered nurse. She complained of concern about her difficulty in making a satisfactory relationship with a man, about periods of depression, and about increasing difficulty in performing her work.

Since her divorce, she had had four brief, tumultuous, unsuccessful relationships with men. She was an attractive woman and dates were readily available to her. She preferred men who were intellectual and who were pursuing an academic or professional career. As long as the relationship remained a companionable and intellectually stimulating one, she was relatively comfortable. Usually she shied away from any man who had romantic feelings toward her. In those instances when she did allow herself to become involved in a romantic relationship, it usually became stormy and complicated or was in some way untenable. When she found herself becoming fond of a man, she would, paradoxically, be provocative and act in such a way as to alienate him. At other times, she would find herself getting into a relationship with a man who was emotionally immature or who would mistreat her; or, she would find in a relationship that, for such reasons as geographic distance or social and religious differences, the likelihood of a successful outcome of the relationship was negligible.

She found herself drifting from one relationship of this sort to another. Her increasing awareness of this pattern began to cause her much concern and anxiety. She felt that there was something in her psychological makeup that brought this situation about and she had to understand herself and change. Her concern was augmented by the fact that she had had an unsuccessful marriage which had ended in divorce three years before, after lasting only one year. She had married a man who proved to be a dependent, ne'er-do-well, philandering, rather sadistic person. She felt that if she were ever going to marry again with the hope of having a successful, comfortable, enduring relationship, she would have to change.

With increasing frequency during recent months she had begun to experience periods of depression. The depressed mood would last two or three days, coming on with no clearly discernible precipitating cause. At such times, she would feel lonely and long to be home with her parents. She would react to her roommate and other women at work with both a feeling of irritation and a longing to be with them. Occasionally she would have dreams or fantasies which she felt were of a homosexual nature.

At work, she found it increasingly difficult to complete tasks. Her relationships with her supervisor, a woman 15 to 20 years older than she was, were tense and uncomfortable. She responded to this woman with an attitude of self-depreciation and seeming helplessness, but, at times, found herself to be rather tactless and openly critical of the woman.

In her relationship with women of her own age, she was inclined to foster their cause, either at work or in regard to men, and then she would resent having done so. She was working at the hospital where she had been a student. Despite the fact that she had been promoted and given increasing responsibility, she could not free herself from an often annoying sense of still being a student.

She was born and raised in a medium-sized midwestern city, where her father's family had been socially prominent for many years. She had a brother, seven years older, and a sister, five years older. Her father was a physician. He had achieved a fair degree of success and prominence as a physician, but mainly was recognized for his family background and affluence, having inherited a considerable sum of money from his father. Over the years, his business, political and intellectual aspirations increased. The patient, from an early age, manifested an interest in these things more than did her siblings and her mother. She became a sort of intellectual companion to her father.

She described her mother as a warm, contented, rather pretty woman, who, although she was not outstanding in any way, was adept at handling her role as a wife and mother in the social setting in which she found herself. When the patient was a child, the mother would spend a great deal of time dressing her up in pretty clothes. If the patient complained of any difficulty in getting along with her peers, the mother would comfort her and spend more time with her in order to ameliorate the patient's feeling of hurt. The mother was generally loving in her attitude toward the father, but at times would point out, subtly, what she considered his weaknesses and his lack of intensity of interest in sex.

Her sister and brother were married and had children. Her brother was a physicist, teaching at a large university in the East. Her sister had married a physician, after graduating college. Her relationship with her brother had always been casual, if not distant. During her childhood, she had been admiring of her sister, from whom she tended to seek advice and guidance. She recalled however, that early in her adolescence, she was jealous when boys paid attention to her sister. She recalled that when her sister married (when the patient was 16 years old), she felt depressed and felt an anger toward her sister, which she could not explain.

She noted that during her adolescence, although males were attracted to her, she would remain emotionally uninvolved. She would, however, become enamored of a male whom she would admire from afar and about whom she would weave elaborate romantic fantasies.

She appeared to be an attractive, young-looking, well-dressed, well-groomed, intelligent woman. Although she appeared somewhat anxious, she gave a coherent account of her difficulties, apparently the result of considerable thought. In the early hours, she manifested an air of composure and facility of speech. For several sessions, she presented historical information and made frequent attempts to engage me in conversations of a theoretical nature regarding the meanings of her experiences and behavior and human psychology in general. She raised questions and presented ideas about political matters then current in the news. This was all presented in a rather affable, conversational tone, but was generally devoid of any expression of feeling. She gradually became increasingly-frustrated by the fact that I did not engage in conversation with her.

In the light of her dreams and associations, I was able to point out to her that she had a wish to relate to me in the form of a chatty, conversational, intellectual, companionable exchange. This led to her associating to memories of the gratifying and comfortable relationship of this nature she had had with her father. She also noted that, with men in general, this was the form of relationship in which she felt most comfortable. It is to be noted that although this pattern of behavior, a compromise, offering a degree of gratification along with defense against heterosexual wishes, appeared and was recognized early in our contact, it had to be pointed out to her again and again at various times during the course of the analysis. When she experienced anxiety about the coming to consciousness of previously warded off ideas and affects, there was a tendency to return to this mode of defense—a repetition of the defense she had used in relation to her father.

Another mode of relating to me within the transference, which appeared rather early in the analysis, was as follows. She would appear as a rather frightened, uncertain little girl. She would ask for advice, direction and guidance, even when it was evident that she knew what to do. This was manifested not only in her verbalizations, but also in accompanying tone of voice, postures, and manner of dress. At such times, for example, she would wear low-heeled shoes, a skirt and sweater, whereas at other times, she would be dressed in a more mature, womanly fashion. I pointed out to her her apparent wish to have me see her as one who would be helpless and lost without advice, guidance and direction. She recognized the disparity between the manner in which she had, unconsciously, presented herself and her real ability. Further associations led to a recognition that this type of behavior occurred mainly with women, usually women older than herself or in positions of authority. She, through freely associating further, eventually recalled how she had behaved in this way with her mother, grandmother, and older sister, when she was a young girl and also during her adolescence. She recalled thinking that she would, in some way, be out of line if she showed them that she knew as much or more than they did about something. She remembered feeling that they would be hurt in some way or would be resentful of her if she did not appear to be apparently inferior and submissive to them in this way.

The patient had misidentified me, in the transference neurosis, as one of these significant women from her past. She was, unconsciously, inclined to repeat the past relationship, with me in the role of her mother, for example, and herself in the role of an uncertain, advice-needing girl. If I had responded to her in keeping with the role she unconsciously "assigned" to me in the transference, she would only have repeated the same defensive pattern, using this as a resistance against understanding the meaning of this behavior and against recalling its historical origin. In the course of an analysis, along with the patient's tendency to experience, in the transference neurosis, a repetition of past emotional relationships, there has to be an observation of this experience on the patient's part (cf. Sterba, 1934). This patient, in fact, later in the analysis, began to stop herself and observe what she had previously experienced repetitively in the transference manifestations delineated above.

She started one session by talking about a patient she had had to take care of during the previous evening, who had become delirious and uncontrolled. She associated to witnessing a child having a temper tantrum. As the hour proceeded, she began to talk about her lack of tact, her tendency to be critical and her fear at times of becoming uncontrolled. She then expressed having a fear that I would dislike her if she revealed feelings of jealousy and anger. Such feelings, she recalled, were not well tolerated by her parents.

In the following hours, she spoke of feeling more comfortable socially and said that she was trying to work out things rationally so that she would not have to be in analysis very much longer. At this point, the patient was experiencing a resistance to the developing transference neurosis and the likelihood of the coming to consciousness of previously warded-off ideas and feelings. I pointed out to her that she seemed to want to flee from the relationship with me and that this was probably a reaction to the feelings which were coming close to consciousness, as indicated by what she spoke about during the previous hour. She then spoke of her fear that she wanted more from a relationship than anyone could stand. During the next several hours, her associations and dreams indicated a preoccupation with a wish to have my exclusive interest and attention and her jealous anger toward my other patients and my family and regarding whatever activities in which I might be engaged, in which she was not included. She was angry at me for not being exclusively at her disposal and not indicating to her that she was first and foremost in my mind.

During one hour, there were indications from her associations that she had sexual wishes in relation to me. I pointed this out along with the fact that the hesitant expression of such wishes was accompanied by self-depreciating remarks. The next hour she associated to Henry Miller and pornography and to seeing me as being a delinquent, tampering with things which should not be tampered with and going into areas where one should not go. This was a manifestation of her unconscious resistance to the emergence of wishes and feelings in the transference neurosis. During the same hour, she associated to memories of accidentally breaking things and hurting people during her childhood. I pointed out to her that there seemed to be a link in her mind between having sexual desires and being destructive.

During the next several weeks, she found herself increasingly preoccupied with having thoughts of liking me and at times having sexual fantasies involving me. After some increase in the directness of expressions of affection for me and sexual wishes in relation to me, her anxiety increased and there was a change in the content of her associations. This reflected a defensive regression and avoidance of heterosexual interests and her father transference. She began to express wishes to have me respond to her as did her mother and the family maid in her childhood. The maid was always available to look after her and take care of her. The patient would clingingly follow her around the house. Her mother would take great pride in dressing her up and pampering her. She claimed that I did not help her enough with her day-to-day problems and was not supportive enough. She wanted me to respond with sympathy and solicitude. Dramatic and exhibitionistic inclinations appeared, which were a repetition of her childhood behavior with her parents, aunts, uncles and grandparents.

Whereas at other times, e.g. when she was preoccupied with heterosexual wishes, I was identified by her as her father, during such periods as the above, she responded to me as she once had to her mother and the family maid. Other patients were eventually seen to represent to her her siblings and she felt jealousy and anger toward them as she had felt toward her siblings during her childhood.

When heterosexual wishes appeared again, usually accompanied by associations to rivalry with other women, the ensuing anxiety and guilt would cause her to take one of the various defensive retreats—for example, the wish to establish the conversational companionable relationship, wishes of a homosexual nature in which she saw me as a woman instead of a man, the wish to be regarded as a favored, adored, pampered child, or the wish to be seen as a confused girl who needed advice and guidance from an older and wiser woman. These responses were pointed out to her and shown to be defenses against the heterosexual wishes, which aroused anxiety and guilt.

At times when she became aware of sexual wishes toward me and feelings of rivalry with other women, in the transference neurosis, she would have fantasies of being beaten and mishandled by me. She had the fantasy that I was disdainful of her and viewed her as an undesirable person. Her manner during the analytic sessions was provocative, eventually seen as an attempt to elicit a response of disdain from me. Her behavior was such, that, if one were not constantly mindful of the transference nature of this behavior, it would have been possible to respond, indeed, with irritation and disdain. This kind of response, of course, would have been inimical to the goal of analysis and would have fostered the transference repetition. Instead, what was necessary was to point out the behavior to the patient in order to explore its meaning and origins in the past. When I raised the question about this behavior and why it seemed necessary, she recognized that she did the same with other men. She eventually recalled that she had acted this way with her father, apparently to make him become irritated with her. She, in time, recognized this as a defense and a way of dealing with her guilt about the wish to be preferred and have other women excluded, just as she had felt a competition formerly with her mother and older sister.

Prior to my vacation, she had a fantasy that my wife and I were going away on a train trip and she feared that the train would be involved in a crash, that my wife would die and I would break a leg. She remembered similar thoughts and feelings from childhood when her parents went on vacations without her. She recognized that in her fantasy my wife, whom she had never seen, had been imagined as appearing similar to her mother.

The foregoing clinical excerpts and discussions have been presented to demonstrate some of the essential features of the psychoanalytic process. The "standard" psychoanalytic technique has been the model. It should be noted that important theoretical and technical questions, although relevant to psychoanalytic practice and the development of psychoanalysis as a method of therapy, have not been discussed. This includes such things as: variations in technique required by differences in psychopathology; proposed modifications in technique based on considerations as to what is the essential or predominant factor in the psychoanalytic process—e.g. emotional experience, intellectual insight, or recovery of repressed infantile memories; the question of the analyst as a "mirror" or "blank screen," the effect of the analyst's personality, countertransference.*

To summarize the view presented here: The patient's psychic functioning is characterized by the tendency for past attitudes and impulses to repeat themselves in the present. The present is misunderstood, and misidentifications and distortions are made as a result of this transference from the past. The patient is thus inclined to "relive" the past. The transference includes past emotional conflicts—the wishes, anxiety, guilt or shame, and the defenses—as they were experienced in relation to significant persons in the patient's infancy and childhood. In the patient's mind, the analyst is put in the place of significant persons from his past. There occurs a concentration, in regard to the analyst and the analytic situation, of the patient's transferences. The transference neurosis thus develops. The analyst addresses himself to the resolution of the transference neurosis, by means of interpretation of the

---

*See the preceding chapter for some discussion of these matters.

patient's resistances and transference, recognized by observation of the patient's free associations.

The patient tends to repeat the past, to "relive" it, in the transference neurosis. This repeated experience is an important component of the analytic process. The analyst however, must help the patient go beyond this. He must foster the patient's capacity to observe as well as experience, to view the nature and purpose of what he experiences and to see its infantile roots. Along with the transference, elaborated in the transference neurosis, which the patient observes as well as experiences, we must recognize the phenomenon called "working-through." It is only with repeated demonstration to the patient of resistance and transference in various connections that there is a gradual resolution of the transference neurosis.

References

Ackerman, N. W. *The psychodynamics of family life.* New York: Basic Books, 1958.

Adler, A. *The science of living.* New York: Greenberg Publ., 1929.

Adler, A. *Individual psychology and its results in the practice and theory of individual psychology.* New York: Harcourt Brace, 1932.

Adler, A. *Social interest: a challenge to mankind.* London: Faber & Faber, 1938.

Alexander, F. A metapsychological description of the process of cure. *Int. J. psychoanal.,* 1925, *6,* 13-34.

Alexander, F. Some quantitative aspects of psychoanalytic technique. *J. Amer. psychoanal. Ass.,* 1954, *2,* 685-701.

Alexander, F. *Psychoanalysis and psychotherapy.* New York: Norton, 1956.

Alexander, F. Psychoanalysis and psychotherapy. In J. H. Masserman (Ed.), *Science and psychoanalysis.* Vol. 3. *Psychoanalysis and human values.* New York: Grune & Stratton, 1960. Pp. 250-259.

Alexander, F., & French, T. M. & others. *Psychoanalytic therapy.* New York: Ronald Press, 1946.

Allport, G. W. *Becoming.* New Haven: Yale Univ. Press, 1955.

Ansbacher, H. L. & Ansbacher, Rowena R. *The individual psychology of Alfred Adler.* New York: Basic Books, 1956.

Baldwin, A. L., Kalhorn, J., & Breese, F. H. Patterns of parent behavior. *Psychol. Monogr.,* 1945, *58,* No. 3 (Whole No. 268).

Betz, Barbara J. & Whitehorn, J. C. The relationship of the therapist to the outcome of therapy in schizophrenics. *Psychiat. res. Rep.,* 1956, No. 5, 89-117.

Bibring, E. Psychoanalysis and the dynamic psychotherapies. *J. Amer. psychoanal. Ass.,* 1954, *2,* 745-770.

Binswanger, L. *Sigmund Freud: reminiscenses of a friendship.* (Trans. by N. Guterman.) New York: Grune & Stratton, 1957.

Bloch, B. Über die Heilung der Warzen durch Suggestion. *Klin. Wochenschr.,* 1927, *6,* 2271-2325.

Breuer, J. & Freud, S. *Studies in hysteria.* New York & Washington: Nerv. & Ment. Dis. Publ., 1936.

Buber, M. Guilt and guilt feelings. *Psychiatry*, 1957, *20*, 114-129.

Buber, M. & Rogers, C. Transcription of dialogue held April 18, 1957. Ann Arbor, Mich. Unpublished manuscript.

Burgess, E. W. The dilemma of family relations in a changing society. Paper presented at the Amer. Orthopsychiat. Ass. meetings, Chicago, March, 1957.

Cantril, H. *The psychology of social movements.* New York: Wiley, 1941.

Chappell, M. N., Stefano, J. J., Rogerson, J. S., & Pike, F. H. The value of group psychological procedures in the treatment of peptic ulcer. *Amer. J. Digestive Dis. & Nutrition*, 1936, *3*, 813-817.

Deutsch, F. & Murphy, W. F. *The clinical interview.* Vol. 2. *Therapy.* New York: Int. Universities Press, 1955.

Deutsch, L. *Guided sight-reading.* New York: Crown Publ., 1951.

Dewey, J. & Bentley, A. F. *Knowing and the known.* Boston: Beacon Press, 1949.

Diethelm, O. *Treatment in psychiatry.* (2nd ed.) Springfield, Ill.: C. C. Thomas, 1950.

Dittes, J. E. Galvanic skin response as a measure of patient's reaction to therapist's permissiveness. *J. abnorm. soc. Psychol.*, 1957, *55*, 295-303.

Dollard, J., Auld, F., Jr., & White, Alice M. *Steps in psychotherapy.* New York: Macmillan, 1953.

Dollard, J. & Miller, N. E. *Personality and psychotherapy; an analysis in terms of learning, thinking, and culture.* New York: McGraw-Hill, 1950.

Dreikurs, R. *Fundamentals of Adlerian psychology.* New York: Greenberg Publ., 1950.

Dreikurs, R. The unique social climate experienced in group psychotherapy. *Group Psychotherapy*, 1951, *3*, 292-299.

Dreikurs, R. The psychological interview in medicine. *Amer. J. Ind. Psychol.*, 1954, *10*, 99-122.

Dreikurs, R. *Psychology in the classroom.* New York: Harper Bros., 1957.

Eissler, K. R. The effect of the structure of the ego on psychoanalytic technique. *J. Amer. psychoanal. Ass.*, 1953, *1*, 104-143.

Ends, E. J. & Page, C. W. A study of three types of group psychotherapy with hospitalized male inebriates. *Quart. J. Stud. Alcohol.*, 1957, *18*, 263-277.

Erikson, E. H. *Childhood and society.* New York: Norton, 1950.

Fairbairn, W. R. D. On the nature and aims of psychoanalytical treatment. *Int. J. Psychoanal.*, 1958, *39*, 374-385.

Farson, R. E. Introjection in the psychotherapeutic relationship. Unpublished doctoral dissertation, Univer. of Chicago, 1955.

Fenichel, O. *The psychoanalytic theory of neurosis.* New York: Norton, 1945.

Ferenczi, S. Stages in the development of sense of reality. Vol. 1. *Selected papers.* New York: Basic Books, 1955. (a)

Ferenczi, S. *The problems and methods of psychoanalysis.* (M. Balint, Ed.) New York: Basic Books, 1955. (b)

Ferenczi, S. & Rank, O. *The development of psychoanalysis.* New York & Washington: Nerv. & Ment. Dis. Publ., 1925.

Fiedler, F. E. Quantitative studies on the role of therapists' feelings toward their patients. In O. H. Mowrer (Ed.), *Psychotherapy: theory and research*. New York: Ronald Press, 1953. Pp. 296-315.

Fortin, J. N. & Abse, D. W. Group psychotherapy with peptic ulcer. *Int. J. Group Psychother.*, 1956, *6*, 383-391.

Frank, J. D. *Persuasion and healing: a comparative study of psychotherapy*. Baltimore: Johns Hopkins Press, 1961.

Frank, J. D., Gliedman, L. H., Imber, S. D., Nash, E. H., & Stone, A. R. Why patients leave psychotherapy. *Amer. Med. Ass. Arch. Neu. & Psychiat.*, 1957, 77, 283-299.

Frank, L. K. Teleological mechanisms. *New York Acad. of Sciences Ann.*, 1948-1949, *50*, 189-196.

French, T. M. A clinical study of learning in the course of a psychoanalytic treatment. *Psychoanal. Quart.*, 1936, *5*, 148-194.

French, T. M. *The integration of behavior*. Vols. 1-3. Chicago: Univer. of Chicago Press, 1952-1954-1959.

Freud, Anna. *The ego and the mechanisms of defence*. New York: Int. Universities Press, 1946.

Freud, Anna. The widening scope of indications for psychoanalysis: discussion. *J. Amer. psychoanal. Ass.*, 1954, 2, 607-620.

Freud, S. *A general introduction to psychoanalysis*. New York: Liveright Publ., 1935.

Freud, S. *The problem of anxiety*. New York: Norton, 1936.

Freud, S. *The ego and the id*. London: Hogarth Press, 1947.

Freud, S. The defence neuro-psychoses. Vol. 1. *Collected papers*. London: Hogarth Press, 1948. Pp. 59-75. (a)

Freud, S. The future prospects of psycho-analytic therapy. Vol. 2. *Collected papers*. London: Hogarth Press, 1948. Pp. 285-296. (b)

Freud, S. Observations on "wild" psycho-analysis. Vol. 2. *Collected papers*. London: Hogarth Press, 1948. Pp. 297-304. (c)

Freud, S. The dynamics of the transference. Vol. 2. *Collected papers*. London: Hogarth Press, 1948. Pp. 312-322. (d)

Freud, S. Recommendations for physicians on the psycho-analytic method of treatment. Vol. 2. *Collected papers*. London: Hogarth Press, 1948. Pp. 323-333. (e)

Freud, S. Further recommendations in the technique of psycho-analysis. On beginning the treatment. The question of the first communications. The dynamics of the cure. Vol. 2. *Collected papers*. London: Hogarth Press, 1948. Pp. 342-365. (f)

Freud, S. Further recommendations in the technique of psycho-analysis. Recollection, repetition and working through. Vol. 2. *Collected papers*. London: Hogarth Press, 1948. Pp. 366-376. (g)

Freud, S. Further recommendations in the technique of psycho-analysis. Observations on transference-love. Vol. 2. *Collected papers*. London: Hogarth Press, 1948. Pp. 377-391. (h)

Freud, S. Turnings in the ways of psycho-analytic therapy. Vol. 2. *Collected papers*. London: Hogarth Press, 1948. Pp. 392-402. (i)

Freud, S. Fragment of an analysis of a case of hysteria. Vol. 3. *Collected papers*. London: Hogarth Press, 1948. Pp. 13-146. (j)

Freud, S. On narcissism: an introduction. Vol. 4. *Collected papers*. London: Hogarth Press, 1948. Pp. 30-59. (k)

Freud, S. Repression. Vol. 4. *Collected papers*. London: Hogarth Press, 1948. Pp. 84-97. (1)

Freud, S. The unconscious. Vol. 4. *Collected papers*. London: Hogarth Press, 1948. Pp. 98-136. (m)

Freud, S. *Beyond the pleasure principle*. New York: Liveright Publ., 1950.

Freud, S. Interpretation of dreams. Vols. 4 & 5. *The complete psychological works of Sigmund Freud*. (Standard ed.) London: Hogarth Press, 1953.

Fromm, E. *Escape from freedom*. New York: Farrar & Rinehart, 1941.

Fromm, E. *Man for himself*. New York: Rinehart, 1947.

Fromm-Reichmann, Frieda. *Principles of intensive psychotherapy*. Chicago: Univer. of Chicago Press, 1950.

Gendlin, E. The function of experiencing in symbolization. Unpublished doctoral dissertation. Univer. of Chicago, 1958.

Gill, M. M. Psychoanalysis and exploratory psychotherapy. *J. Amer. psychoanal. Ass.*, 1954, *2*, 771-797.

Gill, M. M. The present state of psychoanalytic theory. *J. abnorm. soc. Psychol.*, 1959, *58*, 1-8.

Gill, M. M., Newman, R., Redlich, F. C., & Sommers, Margaret. *The initial interview in psychiatric practice*. New York: Int. Universities Press, 1954.

Ginsburg, S. W., & Arrington, Winifred. Aspects of psychiatric clinic practice. *Amer. J. Orthopsychiat.*, 1948, *18*, 322-333.

Gitelson, M. Psychoanalysis and dynamic psychiatry. *Amer. Med. Ass. Arch. Neurol. & Psychiat.*, 1951, *66*, 280-288.

Gitelson, M. On ego distortions. *Int. J. Psychoanal.*, 1958, *39*, 245-257.

Gleidman, L. H., Nash, E. H. Jr., Imber, S. D., Stone, A. R., & Frank, J. D. Reduction of symptoms by pharmacologically inert substances and by short term psychotherapy. *Amer. Med. Ass. Arch. Neurol. & Psychiat.*, 1958, *79*, 345-351.

Goldman, G. S. Reparative psychotherapy. In S. Rado & G. E. Daniels (Eds.), *Changing concepts of psychoanalytic medicine*. New York: Grune & Stratton, 1956.

Goldstein, K. *The organism*. New York: Amer. Book Co., 1939.

Greenacre, Phyllis. The role of transference: practical considerations in relation to psychoanalytic therapy. *J. Amer. psychoanal. Ass.*, 1954, *2*, 671-684.

Greenspoon, J. The reinforcing effect of two spoken sounds on the frequency of two responses. *Amer. J. Psychol.*, 1955, *68*, 409-416.

Grinker, R. R. On identification. *Int. J. Psychoanal.*, 1957, *38*, 379-390.

Group processes. Transactions of the Third Conference. New York: Josiah Macy Jr. Found., 1957.

Haley, J. *Control in psychotherapy*. (To be published).

Halkides, G. An experimental study of four conditions necessary for therapeutic change. Unpublished doctoral dissertation, Univer. of Chicago, 1958.

Harlow, H. F. The nature of love. *Amer. Psychologist*, 1958, *13*, 673-685.

Harrower, M. R. *Personality change and development*. New York: Grune & Stratton, 1958.

Hartmann, H. Technical implications of ego psychology. *Psychoanal. Quart.*, 1951, *20*, 31-43.

Hartmann, H. *Ego psychology and the problem of adaptation.* (Trans. by D. Rapaport) New York: Int. Universities Press, 1958.

Heine, R. W. A comparison of patients' reports on psychotherapeutic experience with psychoanalytic, nondirective and Adlerian therapists. *Amer. J. Psychother.,* 1953, 7, 16-23.

Hilgard, E. R. *Theories of learning.* New York: Appleton-Century Crofts, 1948.

Horney, K. *New ways in psychoanalysis.* New York: Norton, 1939.

Hughes, E. C. Psychology: science and/or profession. *Amer. Psychologist,* 1952, 7, 441-443.

Ingham, H. V., & Love, L. R. *The process of psychotherapy.* New York: McGraw-Hill, 1954.

Jackson, D. D. Guilt and the control of pleasure in schizoid personalities. *Brit. J. Med. Psychol.,* 1958, *31,* 124-130.

Jackson, D. D. Family interaction, family homeostasis and some implications for conjoint family psychotherapy. In J. H. Masserman (Ed.), *Science and psychoanalysis.* Vol. 2. *Individual and family dynamics.* New York: Grune & Stratton, 1959.

Jacobson, Edith. Transference problems in the psychoanalytic treatment of severely depressed patients. *J. Amer. psychoanal. Ass.,* 1954, *2,* 595-606.

Jahoda, Marie. *Current concepts of positive mental health.* New York: Basic Books, 1958.

James, W. *The principles of psychology.* Vol. 1. London: Macmillan, 1901.

James, W. *The varieties of religious experience.* New York: Modern Library, 1936.

Janet, P. Miraculous healing. In *Psychological healing.* Vol. 1. New York: Macmillan, 1925. Pp. 21-53.

Kallmann, F. J. The genetic theory of schizophrenia; an analysis of 691 schizophrenic twin index families. *Amer. J. Psychiatry,* 1946, *103,* 309-322.

Kardiner, A., Linton, R., DuBois, C., & West, J. *The psychological frontiers of society.* New York: Columbia Univer. Press, 1945.

Kardiner, A. & Spiegel, H. *War stress and neurotic illness.* (2nd ed., rev.) New York: Paul B. Hoeber, 1947.

Kelly, G. A. *The psychology of personal constructs.* Vol. 1. *A theory of personality.* New York: Norton, 1955.

Kirtner, W., & Cartwright, D. Success and failure in client-centered therapy as a function of initial in-therapy behavior. *J. consult. Psychol.,* 1958, 22, 329-333.

Knight, R. P. Borderline states. *Bull. Menninger Clin.,* 1953, *17,* 1-12.

Kris, E. Ego psychology and interpretation in psychoanalytic therapy. *Psycholanal. Quart.,* 1951, *20,* 15-30.

Kris, E. On some vicissitudes of insight in psycho-analysis. *Int. J. Psychoanal.,* 1956, *37,* 445-455.

Kubie, L. S. *Practical aspects of psychoanalysis.* New York: Norton, 1936.

Kuenkel, F. *Einführung in die Charakterkunde.* Leipzig: S. Hirzel, 1928.

Levy, D. Development of psychodynamic aspects of oppositional behavior. In S. Rado & G. E. Daniels (Eds.), *Changing concepts of psychoanalytic medicine.* New York: Grune & Stratton, 1956.

Lindsley, O. R. Operant conditioning methods applied to research in chronic schizophrenia. *Psychiat. res. Rep.,* 1956, No. 5, 118-153.

Maskin, M. Adaptations of psychoanalytic technique to specific disorders. In J. H. Masserman (Ed.), *Science and psychoanalysis.* Vol. 3. *Psychoanalysis and human values.* New York: Grune & Stratton, 1960. Pp. 321-352.

Menninger, K. *Theory of psychoanalytic technique.* New York: Basic Books, 1958.

Modell, W. *The relief of symptoms.* Philadelphia: W. B. Saunders Co., 1955.

Moreno, J. L. Philosophy of the third psychiatric revolution with special emphasis on group psychotherapy and psychodrama. In Frieda Fromm-Reichmann & J. L. Moreno (Eds.), *Progress in psychotherapy.* New York: Grune & Stratton, 1951.

Mowrer, O. H. *Psychotherapy: theory and research.* New York: Ronald Press, 1953.

Muncie, W. *Psychobiology and psychiatry.* (2nd ed.) St. Louis: Mosby, 1943.

Murphy, G. & Cattell, Elizabeth S. Sullivan and field theory. In P. Mullahy (Ed.), *The contributions of Harry Stack Sullivan.* New York: Hermitage House, 1952.

Murray, E. J. A content-analysis method for studying psychotherapy. *Psychol. Monogr.,* 1956, *70,* No. 13 (Whole No. 420).

Neufeld, I. Holistic medicine versus psychosomatic medicine. *Amer. J. Ind. Psychol.,* 1954, *10,* 140-168.

Nunberg, H. The synthetic function of the ego. *Int. J. Psychoanal.,* 1931, *12,* 123-140.

Orr, D. W. Transference and countertransference. A historical survey. *J. Amer. psychoanal. Ass.,* 1954, *2,* 621-670.

Page, C. W. & Ends, E. J. A review and synthesis of the literature suggesting a psychotherapeutic technique based on two-factor learning theory. Unpublished manuscript.

Parloff, M. B., Goldstein, N. & Iflund, B. Communication of values and therapeutic change. *Amer. Med. Ass. Arch. Gen. Psychiat.,* 1960, *2,* 300-304.

Parsons, T. & Shils, E. A. *Toward a general theory of action.* Cambridge: Harvard Univer. Press, 1951.

Quinn, R. D. Psychotherapists' expressions as an index to the quality of early therapeutic relationships. Unpublished doctoral dissertation, Univer. of Chicago, 1950.

Rado, S. *Psychoanalysis of behavior; collected papers.* New York: Grune & Stratton, 1956.

Rangell, L. Similarities and differences between psychoanalysis and dynamic psychotherapy. *J. Amer. psychoanal. Ass.,* 1954, *2,* 734-744.

Raskin, N. J. An analysis of six parallel studies of the therapeutic process. *J. consult. Psychol.,* 1949, *13,* 206-220.

Redlich, F. Social aspects of psychotherapy. *Amer. J. Psychiat.,* 1958, *114,* 800-804.

Rehder, H. Wunderheilungen, ein Experiment. *Hippokrates,* 1955, *26,* 577-580.

Reich, W. *Character analysis.* New York: Orgone Inst. Press, 1945.

Reider, N. A type of transference to institutions. *J. Hillside Hosp.,* 1953, *2,* 23-29.

Rioch, D. Theories of psychotherapy. In W. Dennis (Ed.), *Current trends in psychological theory*. Pittsburgh: Univer. of Pittsburgh Press, 1957.

Rogers, C. R. *Counseling and psychotherapy*. Boston: Houghton Mifflin, 1942.

Rogers, C. R. A research program in client-centered therapy. In *Psychiatric treatment*. Research Publ. Ass. for Res. in Nerv. & Ment. Dis., 1951, *31*, 106-113.

Rogers, C. R. The necessary and sufficient conditions of therapeutic personality change. *J. consult. Psychol.*, 1957, *21*, 95-103.

Rogers, C. R. A process conception of psychotherapy. *Amer. Psychol.*, 1958, *13*, 142-149.

Rogers, C. R. A theory of therapy, personality, and interpersonal relationships as developed in the client-centered framework. In S. Koch (Ed.), *Psychology: a study of a science*. Vol. 3. New York: McGraw-Hill, 1959. Pp. 184-256.

Rogers, C. R. & Dymond, Rosalind F. (Eds.) *Psychotherapy and personality change*. Chicago: Univer. of Chicago Press, 1954.

Rosen, J. M. *Direct analysis*. New York: Grune & Stratton, 1953.

Rosenthal, D. Changes in some moral values following psychotherapy. *J. consult. Psychol.*, 1955, *19*, 431-436.

Ruesch, J. *Disturbed communication*. New York: Norton, 1957.

Ruesch, J. & Bateson, G. *Communication, the social matrix of psychiatry*. New York: Norton, 1951.

Salzinger, K. & Pisoni, S. Reinforcement of affect responses of schizophrenics during the clinical interview. *J. abnorm. soc. Psychol.*, 1958, *57*, 84-90.

Schaffer, L. & Myers, J. K. Psychotherapy and social stratification. *Psychiatry*, 1954, *17*, 83-93.

Schein, E. H. The Chinese indoctrination program for prisoners of war. *Psychiatry*, 1956, *19*, 149-172.

Seeman, J. Counselor judgments of therapeutic process and outcome. In C. R. Rogers and Rosalind F. Dymond (Eds.), *Psychotherapy and personality change*. Chicago: Univer. of Chicago Press, 1954. Pp. 99-108.

Seeman, J. & Raskin, N. J. Research perspectives in client-centered therapy. In O. H. Mowrer (Ed.), *Psychotherapy: theory and research*. New York: Ronald Press, 1953. Pp. 205-234.

Shlien, J. M. An experimental investigation of time limited, client centered therapy. *Counseling Center Discussion Papers*, Univer. of Chicago, 1956.

Skinner, B. F. *Science and human behavior*. New York: Macmillan, 1953.

Smuts, J. C. *Holism and evolution*. New York: Macmillan, 1926.

Spiegel, J. P. The social roles of doctor and patient in psychoanalysis and psychotherapy. *Psychiatry*, 1954, *17*, 369-376.

Sterba, R. The fate of the ego in analytic therapy. *Int. J. Psychoanal.*, 1934, *15*, 117-126.

Stone, L. The widening scope of indications for psychoanalysis. *J. Amer. Psychoanal. Ass.*, 1954, *2*, 567-594.

Strachey, J. The nature of the therapeutic action of psychoanalysis. *Int. J. Psychoanal.*, 1934, *15*, 69-74.

Strupp, H. H. A multidimensional analysis of technique in brief psychotherapy. *Psychiatry*, 1957, *20*, 387-397.

Strupp, H. H. The psychotherapist's contribution to the treatment process. *Behav. Sci.*, 1958, *3*, 34-67.

Sullivan, H. S. The study of psychiatry. *Psychiatry*, 1947, *10*, 355-371.

Sullivan, H. S. *Contributions of Harry Stack Sullivan.* (P. Mullahy, Ed.) New York: Hermitage House, 1952.

Sullivan, H. S. *The interpersonal theory of psychiatry.* (Helen S. Perry & Mary L. Gawel, Eds.) New York: Norton, 1953.

Sullivan, H. S. Basic concepts in the psychiatric interview. In Helen S. Perry & Mary L. Gawel (Eds.), *The psychiatric interview.* New York: Norton, 1954. Pp. 3-27.

Tillich, P. *The courage to be.* New Haven: Yale Univer. Press, 1952.

Tower, Lucia E. Countertransference. *J. Amer. psychoanal. Ass.*, 1956, *4*, 224-255.

Verplanck, W. S. The control of the content of conversation: reinforcement of statements of opinion. *J. abnorm. soc. Psychol.*, 1955, *51*, 668-676.

Volgyesi, F. A. "School for patients," hypnosis-therapy and psychoprophylaxis. *Brit. J. Med. Hypnotism*, 1954, *5*, 8-17.

Walker, A., Rablen, R. A., & Rogers, C. R. Development of a scale to measure process changes in psychotherapy. *J. clin. Psychol.*, 1960, *16*, 79-85.

Way, L. M. *Adler's place in psychology.* London: Allen & Unwin, 1950.

Weigert, Edith. The importance of flexibility in psychoanalytic technique. *J. Amer. psychoanal. Ass.*, 1954, 2, 702-710.

Whitaker, C. A. & Malone, T. P. *The roots of psychotherapy.* New York: Blakiston, 1953.

Whitehorn, J. C. Understanding psychotherapy. *Amer. J. Psychiat.*, 1955, *121*, 328-333.

Whitehorn, J. C. Goals of psychotherapy. In E. A. Rubinstein & M. B. Parloff (Eds.), *Research in psychotherapy.* Washington, D. C.: Amer. Psychol. Ass., 1959.

Whitehorn, J. C. & Betz, Barbara J. A study of the psychotherapeutic relationships between physicians and schizophrenic patients. *Amer. J. Psychiat.*, 1954, *111*, 321-331.

Whorf, B. L. Language, thought, and reality. In J. B. Carrol (Ed), *Selected writings of B. L. Whorf.* New York: Wiley & Sons, 1956.

Wolff, W. Fact and value in psychotherapy. *Amer. J. Psychother.*, 1954, *8*, 466-486.

Zilboorg, G. *A history of medical psychology.* New York: Norton, 1941.

Index